Civil Engineering
for the
Plant Engineer

Civil Engineering for the Plant Engineer

Max Schwartz

Civil and Mechanical Engineer

McGRAW-HILL BOOK COMPANY

New York   St. Louis   San Francisco   Düsseldorf   Johannesburg
Kuala Lumpur   London   Mexico   Montreal   New Delhi
Panama   Rio de Janeiro   Singapore   Sydney   Toronto

Library of Congress Cataloging in Publication Data

Schwartz, Max, 1922–
   Civil engineering for the plant engineer.

   Bibliography: p.
   1. Civil engineering. 2. Plant engineering.
I. Title.
TA153.S43   624   72-177374
ISBN 0-07-055710-1

CIVIL ENGINEERING FOR THE PLANT ENGINEER

1234567890 KPKP 765432

   The editors for this book were William G. Salo, Jr., Linda B. Hander, and Don A. Douglas, the designer was Naomi Auerbach, and its production was supervised by George E. Oechsner. It was set in Caledonia by The Maple Press Company.
   It was printed and bound by Kingsport Press.

To my daughter Nina, to whom I owe so much
for the completion of this book

Contents

Foreword

THE PLANT ENGINEER comes from all walks of professional engineering. He may be a mechanical, electrical, civil, chemical, or petroleum engineer, an architect, or a general or industrial engineer. Regardless of the field of professionalism in which he was initially educated and employed, it is necessary that he develop and broaden his knowledge of all fields of engineering to successfully perform his responsibilities.

This book is therefore aimed toward the plant engineer who comes from areas other than civil engineering, although it certainly will whet the appetite of the civil engineer who finds that his talents are keyed to the plant engineering profession and the goal of a plant engineer. In relating civil engineering to plant engineering, this is a book that is a must for all professional engineers who are involved in plant engineering.

For years the author has been directly concerned with many and varied aspects of civil engineering and specifically associated with the functional responsibilities of plant engineering. He speaks out in this book on the many facets of civil engineering directly involved in the vast field of plant engineering and shows how the plant engineer, regardless of his professional training and experience, must become knowledgeable in civil engineering practices as they relate to plant engineering.

Plant engineering—what does it encompass functionally, and what types of organization does this profession serve? Plant engineering takes over at the time of a plant's conception. It includes the responsibility for planning, layout, and budgeting, provides for design and estimating, accomplishes contracting, inspection, and construction, requires direct association with purchasing, and then encompasses the overall plant maintenance and its associated operations. Add to these responsibilities the continual modification and expansion of plant facilities to meet the day-to-day tenant requirements, and you can easily visualize the magnitude of this multidisciplined engineering profession.

Whether the plant be an industrial facility, hospital, institutional complex, hotel, stadium, depot, airport, entertainment center, or convention hall—plant engineering definitely becomes a major part of its development, construction, and maintenance.

How does the plant engineer become involved in the civil engineering aspects of a plant's growth and operations? He does not need to read this book to know that he becomes responsible for site planning and the design and construction of plant facilities, including their continued operations and maintenance, and to know that he must become familiar with building codes, utility and site drainage requirements, types of materials used in plant construction, transportation, and pollutant control. Yet, if he does read this book, he will become more knowledgeable in all of these aspects of plant engineering.

How is a plant engineer involved in his company's profit picture? Regardless of his professional discipline, an engineer involved in the plant engineering function must of necessity realize that his performance on the job—whether as a planner or designer, an estimator or construction inspector, a supervisor of construction or maintenance, a works planner or administrator—relates directly to the profit status of his organization. His layouts, designs, purchases, construction methods, and maintenance techniques, plus his analytical budgeting and his managerial expertise, all relate to his company's profits or its losses. He must therefore keep up with new developments in plant engineering; he must be effective in each and every function he performs as a plant engineer so that his service to his organization is rendered in a most effective and least costly manner. To accomplish this, a plant engineer must constantly keep abreast of current plant engineering trends; he must school himself in the techniques of all phases of plant engineering materials, procedures, design, etc.—and he must wisely associate himself with the professional organization which is related directly to plant engineering, the American Institute of Plant Engineers. The members of this professional society of engineers are all bound by their professional interests and responsibilities in plant engineering.

The Institute offers many intangible benefits to its members. It provides a meeting ground where one may exchange his plant engineering problems with others and obtain solutions, exchange up-to-date plant engineering know-how, learn of revolutionary engineering, maintenance, and managerial techniques, tour varied plant facilities, participate in committee action for developing specific facets of the profession, prepare and present papers at chapter meetings and seminars, participate in round-table discussions, and, in general, may elevate his plant engineering stature in the eyes of industry, his management and associates, and in the community.

As a graduate civil engineer—one who has been involved for many years in the planning, design, and construction of architectural, civil, electrical, chemical, and mechanical projects involving military installations, institutional complexes, commercial, industrial, and research facilities, in the construction, maintenance, and operation of many of these types of facilities, and as the plant engineer for many years for a large research and development corporation, together with being a Fellow member of ASCE, a Fellow member of the Institute for the Advancement of Professional Education, and a member and past International President of the American Institute of Plant Engineers—I highly recommend that all professional engineers involved in plant engineering read and absorb the contents of this book.

Bernard R. Costales
Past International President
American Institute of Plant Engineers
Manager of Plant Engineering
Hughes Aircraft Co.
Culver City, California

Preface

THE COMPLEXITIES OF MODERN SOCIETY have produced another professional—the plant engineer. He is the individual responsible for the efficient operation of his manufacturing facilities.

But today's industrial plant is a community itself. The plant engineer must design, approve, and supervise all aspects of construction just as a city engineer must. The plant engineer's responsibilities include the design and construction of new structures, streets, and drainage systems, installation and maintenance of utilities, concurrence with local ordinances, and location and maintenance of legal boundaries.

To function properly in this interdisciplinary field, the plant engineer must be equipped to handle the civil, mechanical, electrical, and administrative aspects of plant life.

Civil Engineering for the Plant Engineer has been created to help the plant engineer better understand how the discipline of civil engineering applies to his plant. Only those areas directly relating to industry have been included.

With a firm foundation in civil engineering the plant engineer will be able to make decisions that result in economy in both the construction and the maintenance of his plant facility.

Max Schwartz

CHAPTER ONE

Civil Engineering Responsibilities of the Plant Engineer

A GREAT DEAL of the plant engineer's daily activity is related to the field of civil engineering, including the design of new facilities, modifications and major repairs of existing buildings, development of criteria for new projects, and the supervision of maintenance and repair of plant structures.

In designing new industrial facilities, the plant engineer becomes involved with surveying the property, the acquisition of new plant sites, and investigation of soil and flooding conditions. He also becomes closely concerned with all new plant structures—whether steel, wood, concrete, or masonry. These are among the many items related to the field of civil engineering with which the plant engineer must become familiar so that he can understand and supervise the design and construction within his responsibility.

Throughout the planning and engineering of new facilities, the important objective is to "design out" maintenance problems while giving close consideration to initial and long-term costs. A larger area of responsibility for the plant engineer is planning and implementing modifications and major repairs of existing facilities whenever new equipment is installed or existing equipment is relocated. Most cases of plant modification call for an understanding of foundations, framing, connections, building codes, and the design loading requirements. The plant engineer must also be aware of the properties of the structural and architectural materials used in framing, foundations, roofing, siding, flooring, ceilings, and insulation. He must become familiar with relative costs, durability, ease of repair, and other properties of the various materials which house the plant's operations. The plant engineer must understand the different mixes and strengths of concrete, the various types of structural steel and other building materials, including masonry, aluminum, and wood. He should be aware that each of these materials has specific advantages and disadvantages with respect to maintenance, alteration, and fire resistance.

Another area of responsibility for the plant engineer is developing design criteria for new projects. Although he may never be called upon to design a foundation, a steel structure, or a building, he is often required to set up the criteria according to which others are to design.

In preparing preliminary building specifications, he must be aware of the limitations, advantages, and relative costs of the construction materials he specifies. Also, he should be aware of the most efficient sequence of construction in order to complete a project economically and on schedule. Occasionally the plant engineer acts as his company's superintendent and hires the contractors to perform their work under his control. He, in fact, serves as his own general contractor. He then must plan the entire work to include the drawings, building permit, demolition, field layout, excavation, foundations, steel structures, equipment setting, and finally the enclosure of a structure. When this occurs, the plant engineer must be fully aware of the interface and potential interferences of the various trades. To achieve his awareness he must think in terms of the civil engineer and the general contractor who plan and construct the project.

The final and most important phase of responsibility of the plant engineer is not shared by either the civil engineer or the general contractor. This is the area of maintenance and repairs over the lifetime of the plant. The plant engineer normally writes up the work order for the repair of roofs, repainting of buildings, waterproofing and replacement of insulation, revision of drainage systems, reinforcement of structures, and much more day-to-day maintenance and alteration work.

The problems that confront the plant engineer are different from those facing the design engineer, who starts with a relatively clean job on a blank sheet of paper. The plant engineer, on the other hand, has an existing structure or facility he must work with. His understanding of the strengths and other properties of structural materials is thus quite different from that of the design engineer.

The plant engineer should be familiar with the design principles, construction procedures, and cost factors involved with the civil engineering phase of site development and construction. The operations of the existing facility, the repair of supporting equipment for maintenance and its necessary overhead, and the supervision and record keeping for efficient operation of a plant engineering department are also vital to the plant engineer.

Every site-development project involves some aspects of the civil engineering fields of surveying, soil analysis, foundation design, road and railroad design, and drainage and the legal aspects of real estate and of property acquisition. In construction, the civil engineering areas include the design and erection of steel, concrete, masonry, and wood structures and the closely related fields of building codes, fire codes, zoning laws, and the recommended practices of the material organizations. The most notable organizations which publish are the American Institute of Steel Construction, the American Welding Society, and the Portland Cement Association. In the field of maintenance operations, the civil engineering principles and cost factors regarding types of paints, waterproofing, insulation, paving, and general preventive-maintenance procedures should be familiar to the plant engineer. If the plant engineer is to run an efficient and professional department, he will require certain tools, including drafting and surveying instruments, mobile cranes, air compressors, electric generators, jackhammers, drills, and other light construction tools. He must also follow proper engineering office and maintenance management procedures and insist upon correct filing and recording techniques of drawings, specifications, and catalogs of all plant buildings, facilities, and machines. He must operate his plant engineering department like a city engineer's office, responsible for public facilities.

Although the plant engineer's duties do not include complete structural design or drafting of working drawings, he must be able to review completed plans and specifications to evaluate calculations and proposals. He must also coordinate the appearance, costs, performance, and other details necessary for the complete job as required by plant operations. The plant engineer thus finds himself as industry's agent in the control of the interdependence of design, construction, and maintenance from the initial phase of the project to the maintenance of the completed facility.

The various stages of evolution of a plant project are generally as follows:

1. In the planning phase, the plant engineer guides management in recognizing the dollar implications of site-acquisition problems, which may involve soil conditions, drainage problems, topographic

characteristics, and the direct cost of the property. All must be taken into consideration to establish true value.

2. The second phase, acquisition, includes the purchase of real estate or an existing plant or the addition of new buildings to existing facilities. Here the plant engineer should be familiar with the governing zoning codes and legal restrictions, such as easements, rights of way, setbacks, and protective covenants, which may limit or hamper future plant development.

3. The third phase can be called a conceptual stage. It is during this period that everything from the specific setting and orientation of the facilities in relation to the real estate to the modifications of existing buildings or addition to present facilities is made. Also developed are the determination of building areas, the type of construction, the height of the building, the group occupancy, the flow of materials, the traffic, and all the general aspects of plant layout and design. The plant engineer must be familiar with the local building codes as related to the maximum area, group occupancy, and type of construction permitted for the various buildings of the property. It goes without saying that a carelessly planned addition to an existing building can nullify its original use. This is a critical phase of design since the entire concept must be kept in accordance with all governing regulations. The legality of the proposed project must be determined by the plant engineer.

4. The fourth phase, called the design stage, is where specific design criteria are established through the coordination of the design engineers and the operating personnel in setting up specific criteria. The plant engineer is usually the coordinator who passes the requirements of his own operating department on to the design engineers and continually supervises their effort.

5. The fifth phase continues the design stage, but during this period the plans and specifications are actually prepared. The plant engineer should set up and use checklists to be certain that all criteria are being adhered to by the design engineers.

6. The sixth phase, the final design stage, is when the plant engineer acts as the plan checker. He must establish procedures to ensure adequate review approval and control of the final design by all concerned. He is the liaison between the project manager, the operating personnel, and all interested parties of his company to be sure that everything necessary is in the design plans.

7. In the seventh or construction stage the plant engineer must insist on good contract administration and inspection. He uses checklists and "punch lists" to be certain that all important items are properly inspected and approved.

8. The final phase is the conclusion of design and construction, but it is also the beginning of maintenance and repair responsibilities for the plant engineer for years to come. This is the test period of quality of design and construction. Obviously a design decision that does not consider maintenance factors will inevitably result in a costly facility.

Throughout the various stages of design and construction the plant engineer must always be aware of the maintenance implications of all the many design elements of the project. He should realize that not only must a foundation be sound but that the anticipated settlement must be controlled so as to limit differential settlement, which cracks walls and floors. He should check that the roofs are properly designed, installed, and inspected so that they are watertight at all joints, penetrations, and edges. The plant engineer should stress economy within the framework of aesthetic acceptance of all exterior surfaces. In any case, all surfaces should be made watertight and provide proper insulating features. Site work, roads, and landscaping should be properly designed for snow removal, trimming, mowing, cleaning, grading, and servicing of drainage structures. Access should be provided for maintenance of all craneways, hydraulic and pneumatic lifting devices, elevators, and other mechanical equipment used in plant operation. Partitions and the walls of the buildings should be constructed with a consideration of air conditioning, soundproofing, dust control, and the corrosive effect of chemicals and humidity. Natural light should be planned wherever possible.

The plant engineer should check that finishes are easily and readily painted or treated so they can withstand chemical spillage and dust caused by plant operations. Floor surface designs should consider dust and floor tempering, equipment loading, frequency of moving of machines and equipment, amount of heavy traffic, spillage control, cleanliness requirements, and protection against fire hazards. In the design of ceilings, the plant engineer must be certain that consideration is given to sound insulation, fire resistance, ease of repainting, access to air-conditioning equipment, and reflectivity for lighting.

These items constitute many of the critical features related to civil engineering design of plant facilities; many others will be covered in detail in the following chapters, which contain checklists, case studies, and references to existing handbooks for tables and formulas as they apply to specific plant engineering problems.

The chapters have been organized in accordance with specific areas of the field of civil engineering design and construction, namely, surveying, background and legal aspects of plant property acquisition, construction codes relating to industry, the interrelationships of soil and foundation, analysis of structural materials, mechanics of stress and strain, design of steel, timber, concrete, and masonry structures, and industrial roofing and insulation. This is intended as a practical book for the plant engineer. By providing him with guidance in the civil engineering discipline it will enable him to communicate better with the civil engineer.

CHECKLIST FOR DESIGN CRITERIA

Whether a job is designed in-house by the plant engineering department or by an outside firm, certain preliminary structural data are required. It is usually the duty of the plant engineer assigned to the new project to provide the required information for general design. A suggested outline for preliminary job information follows.

Loads and General Design

Unless otherwise noted, use the recommendations shown in parentheses.

1. Live loads
    a. Roof live loads (Uniform Building Code)
    b. Check for snow load in addition to live load
2. Platforms in structures (75 lb/sq ft)
3. Circular platforms, walkways, and stairways (75 lb/sq ft)
4. Special landings (50 lb/sq ft)
5. Trench covers not for vehicular traffic (100 lb/sq ft)
6. Lateral loads
    a. Wind load (Uniform Building Code)
    b. Seismic load (Uniform Building Code)
    c. Crane and trolley beams (AISC recommendations)
    d. Impact loads for crane, rotary equipment, reciprocating equipment, and vibrating equipment
    e. Self-supporting equipment foundations and conditions for design
        (1) Empty (equipment empty plus wind or seismic)
        (2) Operating (equipment operating plus wind or seismic)
        (3) Test (equipment full of water)

CHECKLIST FOR A NEW PROJECT

When the plant engineer is involved with the design of new facilities, it is useful to prepare a checklist or an outline of the major architectural, civil and structural, electrical and mechanical requirements for the new project. The preliminary data he will require for any new project are outlined in the following suggested form.

1. Location of job
2. Preliminary design data

a. Weather
  (1) Prevailing wind direction
  (2) Maximum wind velocity
  (3) Maximum and minimum atmospheric temperature
  (4) Relative humidity (ranged by day, month, and season)
  (5) Rainfall (maximum yearly and seasonly average)
  (6) Snow conditions
  (7) Frost line
b. Earthquake conditions
c. Local flood and tide conditions
d. Plant terrain
  (1) Soil test for load-bearing characteristics, water table, excavation and compaction conditions
  (2) Contour maps, natural drainage, and existing bench marks
e. Water requirements, supply, and treatment
  (1) Processed water
  (2) Process cooling water
  (3) Sanitary water
  (4) Utility water for washing operation
  (5) Boiler feedwater
  (6) Fire-protection water
  (7) Construction-use water
  (8) Water tests
  (9) Turbidity
  (10) Sedimentation
  (11) pH
  (12) Bacteriological analysis
  (13) Chemical analysis
f. Source of water
  (1) River, lake (high and low waterline, quality of water)
  (2) Deep well (depth of water table, drawdown, flow)
  (3) Public water supply (name of water company, location of supply line, size and pressure of supply line)
g. Plant wastes (storage and handling facilities)
h. Waste disposal
  (1) Industrial waste (treatment and disposal)
  (2) Sanitary waste (treatment, septic tanks, cesspools, sewage plant, disposal, leaching pit or leaching field, and public sewer line)
i. Plant buildings other than process structures
  (1) Offices
  (2) Laboratories
  (3) Garages
  (4) Gas stations
  (5) Change houses
  (6) Housing
  (7) Commissary

      (8) Warehouses
      (9) Shop buildings
      (10) First-aid building
   j. Plant roads
      (1) Surfacing
      (2) Width
   k. Plant railroad facilities
   l. Plant security
      (1) Fencing
      (2) Gatehouse
  m. Governmental agencies and regulations
      (1) Building and safety codes
      (2) Electrical code
      (3) Plumbing code
      (4) Insurance regulations
      (5) Industrial-waste regulations
      (6) Air-pollution regulations
      (7) Fire-prevention codes

CHECKLIST FOR DESIGN PHASE

1. Flow diagram
   a. Chemical engineering: selection of tanks, vessels, process equipment, controls, pumps, and equipment material
   b. Industrial engineering: selection of main production machinery and equipment
2. Preparation of equipment layout or plot plan, including accessory buildings, laboratories, offices, shops, etc.
3. Preparation of preliminary specifications covering equipment, piping, electrical, structural, and controls
4. Mechanical engineering
   a. Piping and pumps
   b. Vessels and tanks
   c. Hoppers and bins
   d. Conveyors and chutes
5. Civil and structural engineering
   a. Equipment supports and foundations
   b. Enclosures
   c. Buildings, warehousing, shops, change rooms, and control rooms
   d. Site work, grading, roads, railroad, drainage, and sewerage
6. Electrical engineering
   a. Power distribution
   b. Lighting
   c. Motor controls
   d. Main substation
7. Receipt of vendor's equipment proposal and certified drawings
8. Determination of critical working points and centerlines

9. Obtain weights of all equipment
10. Obtain anchor-bolt data on all equipment
11. Check code for type of construction
    a. Group occupancy
    b. Allowable area
    c. Exterior walls
    d. Fire-resistive construction
    e. Required exits
    f. Soil test
    g. Loading: snow, roof, and floor live load; seismic and wind loads
    h. Fire code
12. Select structural materials for frame, walls, floors, roofs, stairs, and platforms
13. Prepare preliminary plan, elevations, and specifications
14. Distribute preliminary plans for group approval
15. Complete plans and specifications

CHECKLIST FOR PROCUREMENT ON A NEW PROJECT

When the plant engineer becomes involved with the construction purchasing and subcontracting for a new project, the following data for soliciting bids are recommended. This is also a useful outline to help in realistic estimating.

1. Preliminary procurement data (When can materials be received at job site?)
2. Types of construction materials available in the area
3. Industrial equipment in the area
4. Connecting railroads and motor trucklines
5. Main highway locations
6. Preliminary construction data
7. Area wage rates, trade-union contracts in force, and expiration dates
8. Availability of local skilled craftsmen
9. Trade/union representation
10. Work permits if workers must be imported
11. Personnel housing, food, and recreational facilities
12. Medical facilities and climatic conditions
13. Area practices
14. Transportation requirements
15. Personnel parking facilities
16. Change and sanitary facilities
17. Personnel identification
18. Construction materials, storage facilities
19. Operating-plant labor union
20. Construction interferences

  a. Overhead and underground electric power lines
  b. Overhead and underground piping and sewers
21. Plant hazards
  a. Obnoxious or hazardous vapor or fumes
  b. Inflammable fumes
22. Receiving and handling plant equipment
23. Communication facilities (name the telephone company)
24. Telephone service
  a. Availability
  b. Capacity
25. Airport facilities

CHECKLIST FOR PURCHASING AND CONTRACTING

1. Specifications, descriptions, performance, definition of item purchased, and list of drawings
2. Price
3. Freight f.o.b. and location of delivery
4. Use tax
5. Delivery date and penalty if any
6. Spare parts and special tools
7. Painting, shop or finish
8. Installation supervision, engineering service, and amount furnished and cost
9. Methods of payments and address where invoice is sent
10. Discount terms
11. Warranty
12. Method of shipping
13. Vendor's drawings, shop drawing, type of schedule
14. Affiliation, small vendors
15. Job and purchase-order number
16. Account distribution
17. Vendor's correct legal name, address, phone number, name of representative
18. Package marking, item or mark number
19. Check for omissions (What other material and labor are necessary for complete installation?)
20. Check vendors' financial and performance reputation
21. Inspection test necessary
22. Samples to be submitted
23. Method of computing extra work
24. Method of computing escalations
25. Acceptance and approval by regulating agencies
26. Control and appurtenances (Who furnishes?)
27. Has bid abstract been made for comparison between vendors?
28. Approval by owner and engineer

CHECKLIST FOR SUPERINTENDING A PROJECT

When the plant engineer must act as a job superintendent, the following checklist is recommended.

1. Study drawings and specifications
2. Inspect job site
3. Decide with purchasing agent which items are to be subcontracted
4. Review preliminary schedule and recommend changes if necessary
5. Study labor and material budget prepared by estimating department
6. Prepare organization chart for field forces
7. Arrange for key foremen
8. Make out hiring schedule by crafts
9. Make out bill of material for temporary buildings and requirements for light, power, water, and petroleum supply list to purchasing agent
10. Obtain all city and county permits
11. Arrange for survey and have site staked out
12. Contact union halls and line up labor supplies
13. Arrange for temporary buildings
14. Have cost-control supervisor set up field office
15. Prepare detailed construction schedule
16. Schedule construction equipment
17. Order small tools
18. Contact local building inspectors

PRELIMINARY JOB INFORMATION
ENGINEERING DATA

HEAT EXCHANGERS AND PROCESS EQUIPMENT STRUCTURES

1. Type of structure
   a. Steel, with or without fireproofing _____
   b. Reinforced concrete _____
2. Stairs or ladders _____
3. Platforms _____
4. Clearances   Channel end _____ Body end _____
5. Removal equipment
   a. Bundle removal and handling _____
   b. Pull beams and posts _____
   c. Crane, gantry, monorail, or bridge _____
   d. Type of hoist _____
6. Body cover removal
   a. Davits on exchangers _____
   b. Monorail or crane _____
   c. Type of hoist _____

PAVEMENTS

1. Type   Gravel _____ Oil _____ Asphalt _____
              Concrete _____
2. Location _____
3. Loading _____

FOUNDATIONS

1. General
   a. Soil report
   b. Existing and final contours
   c. Fills: character and extent
   d. Underground obstructions
   e. Corrosive character of soil
   f. Frost line
   g. Water table
   h. Elevations
      (1) Finish grade
      (2) High point of paving
      (3) Major equipment foundations
      (4) Pump pads
      (5) Pipe-support foundations
      (6) Building floors
2. Spread footings
   a. Maximum gross soil bearing at what depth for major structures?
   b. Maximum gross soil bearing at what depth for minor structures?
   c. May soil bearing be increased for lateral loads?
   d. Minimum depth of footing below natural grade
   e. Minimum depth of footing below finish grade
3. Pile foundations
   a. Pile type
      (1) Wood, treated or untreated
      (2) Precast concrete
      (3) Metal shell, poured in place
      (4) Poured in place in drilled holes
      (5) Steel
      (6) Composite
   b. Pile loading
      (1) Vertical loads, point bearing, friction; may allowable load be increased for effect of lateral loads? Is there a drag-down effect of fill on piles?
      (2) Lateral loads: Are batter piles necessary for lateral loads? What lateral load is permissible for vertical piles?
      (3) Pile groups: Must pile loading be reduced where used in groups?

(4) Pile spacing (Uniform Building Code)

(5) Pile elevations: minimum depth of pile cap below finish grade

4. Caissons
   a. Minimum diameter of shaft
   b. Depth of footing
5. Retaining walls
   a. Type of material retained, density, equivalent fluid pressure (earth $W_r = 100$ lb/cu ft; $W_h = 30$ lb/sq ft per foot of depth)
   b. Surcharge: sloping, traffic, structural
   c. Drainage
6. Special foundations
   a. Compressors and building will be placed on a single mat-type foundation
   b. Ratio of weight of compressor to weight of concrete and building (1:5)
   c. Crusher foundations (ratio of weight 1:3)

PRELIMINARY JOB INFORMATION
ARCHITECTURAL DATA
FOR BUILDINGS

1. Item number and name _____
2. Sketches, layouts, or specifications available _____
3. Length _____ Width _____ Clear height _____
   Provision for extension _____
4. Frame: Steel _____ Concrete _____
   Wood _____ Load-bearing walls _____
5. Exterior walls: Poured concrete _____
   Precast concrete _____ Brick _____
   Concrete block _____ Metal panel _____
   Corrugated metal _____ Corrugated cement asbestos _____
   _____ Wood _____ Stucco _____
6. Parapets: Height _____ Coping _____
7. Roof: Poured concrete _____ Precast concrete _____
   Metal panel _____ Corrugated metal _____
   Corrugated cement asbestos (pitch 4:12) _____
   Gypsum _____ Wood sheathing _____ Roofing _____
8. Door schedule: Number _____ Size _____ Type _____
9. Window schedule: Number _____ Size _____ Type _____
10. Room-finish schedule
    Floors: Type _____ Finish _____
    Walls: Type _____ Finish _____
    Ceiling: Height _____ Type _____ Finish _____
11. Crane or trolley: Capacity _____ Type _____ Height _____
12. Toilet and change room:
    Floor and base _____
    Wainscot _____

Toilet partitions ————————————————————————

Toilet-room accessories ————————————————————

13. Plumbing:

Toilet	No. ——————	Type ——————
Lavatory	No. ——————	Type ——————
Urinal	No. ——————	Type ——————
Service sink	No. ——————	Type ——————
Shower	No. ——————	Type ——————
Water heater	No. ——————	Type ——————
Sink	No. ——————	Type ——————
Floor drain	No. ——————	Type ——————
Drinking fountain	No. ——————	Type ——————
Fire hose	No. ——————	Type ——————
Laboratory sink	No. ——————	Type ——————
Cup sink	No. ——————	Type ——————
Emergency shower	No. ——————	Type ——————
Eyewash	No. ——————	Type ——————
Still	No. ——————	Type ——————
Distilled-water outlet	No. ——————	Type ——————
Gas cock	No. ——————	Type ——————
Vacuum pump	No. ——————	Type ——————
Vacuum cock	No. ——————	Type ——————
Air compressor	No. ——————	Type ——————
Compressed-air outlet	No. ——————	Type ——————

14. Roof ventilator:　　　Size ————— Type —————

15. Exhaust fan:　　　　　Size ————— Type —————

16. Laboratory hood:　　　Size ————— Type —————

17. Heating and ventilating:　Size ————— Type —————

18. Air conditioning:　　　Size ————— Type —————

19. Lockers:　　　　　　　No. ————— Size ——— Type ———

20. Hardware:

　　　Exterior doors ————————————————————

　　　Interior doors ————————————————————

　　　Windows ——————————————————————

21. Door frames: Pressed metal ———— Channel ———— Wood ————

22. Thresholds: Brass ———— G.I. ———— Wood ————

23. Glass: Doors ———————— Windows ————————

24. Plaster: Interior ———————— Exterior ————————

　　　Lath: Gypsum lath ———— Expanded metal ———— Wire ————

25. Studs: Wood ———————— Steel ————————

26. Gutters: G.I. ———————— Transite ————————

27. Downspouts and roof drains: ————————————————

28. Stairs: Grating ———— Checker plate ———— Wood ————

29. Trench covers: Grating ———— Checker plate ———— Other ————

CHAPTER TWO

Property Acquisition

THE PLANT ENGINEER is responsible for the physical status of his company's facility. In a dynamic company methods of production are constantly being replaced by other, more economical methods. A company that previously bought its packaging containers may decide to manufacture its own in a warehouse on its own property. Will the zoning of that property permit such manufacturing? That question is put to the plant engineer.

Perhaps this building is too small. Management may decide to build one that will meet the present needs and yet be able to expand to accommodate future packaging demands. This type of plant-expansion program falls in the domain of the plant engineer. He must be familiar enough with his plant's property to know the laws involved with proposed building on the selected site (Fig. 2-1). He must also be aware of the easements for present and future utilities which may affect the land upon which the structure is to be built. He should also be familiar with the locations of survey monuments so that the site of the new building can be correctly located.

A frequent problem in plant expansion is encroachment upon property lines; the plant engineer should therefore keep an eye on the boundaries of his property when his company begins to talk of addition. He may

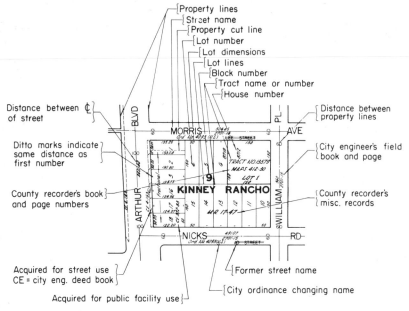

Fig. 2-1.   Explanation of data shown on plat maps.   (*Brewster Map Co.*)

discover that a neighboring company has already erected a fence or even a building on his company's property, or his own company may have built on its neighbor's land.   Occasionally both companies have encroached simultaneously.   Whatever the case, the plant engineer must be able to supply documents to support his findings so that the company's legal staff can act.

THE RIGHT OF EMINENT DOMAIN

Eminent domain is the inherent right of a state to force a property owner to sell his property when it is needed for public use.   The local government may exercise its right of eminent domain to build a storm-drain channel or freeway access ramp or to widen a street at the expense of private industrial property.   The plant engineer should understand the major legal aspects of transactions with local or state government so that his company will be equitably compensated for the inconvenience and loss of land it suffers.

The local government, after exercising eminent domain, may purchase the piece of land or may be granted an easement to the land.   The purchase is a clear transfer of title and is not easily forgotten, but an easement may be granted long before construction is to begin.   For this reason, the plant engineer should search the records relating to his company's property to determine whether any easements were granted before he assumed his role as plant engineer. Frequently, when a building permit on new construction is granted, the local city or county government acquires easement for future street widening if this is part of their master plan.

When the government engineers prepare plans for construction of public facilities through private industrial property, they will issue a set of plans to the company affected. It is then the responsibility of each company's plant engineer to examine these plans closely. Anything that might affect his plant adversely should be noted on these drawings and the desired alternative suggested. The marked drawings and letter are then returned to the local government engineers for their review.

The plans of the public project are often revised as far as possible to the satisfaction of the companies affected if their wishes are compatible with the master plan provided that the governmental agency is informed of these wishes before the final plans have been completed. Typical public facilities affecting industrial property are freeways, street widening, major storm-water and sanitary trunk sewers, and airport expansion.

Years ago a southern California refinery was constructed in an undeveloped area on both sides of a natural creek. All plant storm-water drainage and industrial waste discharged into the creek. As the surrounding community developed, the county storm-drain district found it necessary to expand its facilities to include the area, and this creek was selected as the best location for a major storm drain.

The refinery management received preliminary plans for the storm drain, which would divide its property into two parts. The management was invited to appear at the county engineer's office to discuss any objections it had to the project. The plant engineer was requested by management to represent the company's position.

In preparation for this meeting, the plant engineer reviewed and studied all alignment, grades, and easement lines and all aspects of the plants to achieve a full understanding of the effect the drain and its lengthy construction period could have on company facilities. He also considered the future plans of the refinery, which included new tank farms. As a result of his study, he reported to management that the following problems had to be met and solved before construction began:

1. Access across excavation during construction
2. Coordination of plant drainage system with new storm drain
3. Separation of industrial waste from storm water
4. Dedication of easement to county

5. Relocation of piping due to construction
6. Preventing undermining of adjacent foundations

Thanks to this report, the county revised their plans to accommodate the refinery so that construction caused the minimum interference to plant operation.

Another case history concerns a western chemical company constructed in open, undeveloped land. The company thrived and expanded through the years, but as it expanded, so did the surrounding residential community. The company eventually found itself sharing a property line with a score of private homes constructed by a developer.

As families moved in, complaints were filed about odors, noise, and floodlights from the plant. The local city government sent official letters to the company about the property owners' protests. Management turned the letters over to the plant engineer for a solution. He reviewed the history of the development of the land, the zoning, subsequent subdivision, recorded tract restrictions, and all other aspects affecting the plant's existence and operations. His findings were as follows:

1. The residential property in question was initially zoned for agricultural use.
2. The prior owner, a major oil company, obtained a special permit for the installation of oil storage facilities on agricultural-zoned land.
3. A tank farm had been in operation for 20 years but had just been phased out 2 years ago.
4. The land was then sold to a housing developer, who applied for a zone change from agricultural use to residential use.
5. A public hearing was held on the zone change.
6. In spite of the strong opposition of the chemical plant's previous management, who wanted the land zoned for industrial use, the planning commission ruled in favor of housing.
7. The housing development was constructed and sold to individual families.
8. Concurrently, the chemical plant continued to expand its facilities.
9. Soon after moving in, the new homeowners became more intolerant of the nuisances of the chemical operations and filed protests.

Once the facts were uncovered, the plant engineer and the present management became aware that industrial operation and expansion cannot be isolated from the community. The voice of the people has become more potent and must always be considered by industry. Management saw that it must satisfy its neighbors.

To offset the protests and protect its public image, the chemical plant installed dust collectors, scrubbers, and sound-absorption equipment, relocated floodlighting, and planted tall trees to screen its operations. This was a temporary solution.

This situation might have been avoided if the plant engineer had recognized the implications of a neighboring residential area when his plant was expanding. Consideration for the public during plant expansion clearly pays off in today's public-oriented society.

PROPERTY DOCUMENTS

The most critical phase of the plant engineer's role as his company's land expert comes when the management decides to acquire new property. It is then the plant engineer's responsibility to review all aspects of the land being considered and advise management of the benefits and disadvantages of such an acquisition.

To handle all land problems, the plant engineer must not only have copies of all necessary legal documents but also a general knowledge of the background of the subdivision of his plant's property.

Plant management must check many documents relating to land acquisition when they expand facilities (Figs. 2-2 and 2-3). The law permits any proceeding that affects real estate to be recorded as a notice to the public and therefore available to the plant engineer, although a deed delivered by a grantor to a grantee is effective between the parties even if that deed is not recorded. A title policy lists the information that has been recorded but does not list litigation claims and unrecorded liens. The plant engineer should bear in mind the possibility of unrecorded liens.

If a manufacturing company buys property for a new plant, the plant engineer makes use of the title reports and the title policies available from a title-insurance company to determine the legal restrictions on the new land.

When loaning money to industry, banks and other lending institutions often use the land as security. The lender naturally requires information about the title of the landowner and therefore relies upon the findings of the title-insurance company. The government also depends on the title company to ascertain the legality of the ownership of the land when it seeks to condemn or purchase industrially owned land. Therefore, any transaction or potential transaction regarding lands involves the title-insurance policy. The beneficiary of the policy is usually either the land purchaser or the lender who has loaned the money with the land as security.

(b)

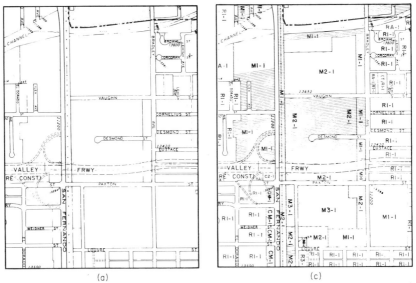

(a)   (c)

Fig. 2-2. Portion of a typical (*a*) base map, (*b*) aerial photograph, and (*c*) zone map. (*Metrex Aerial Surveys.*)

The plant engineer should be familiar with the various types of title services available from the title companies, some of which are:

1. Preliminary Report of Title, which provides only information from county assessor's records
2. Mechanic's lien report, which shows all recorded mechanic's liens against the land
3. Restriction report, which is a copy of building or tract restrictions
4. Tax report, which provides a list of taxes, bonds, and assessments that are liens against the property
5. Lot book report, which is a simple and limited but informative report on the apparent owner

The title-policy company can also search the records and issue a report on all recorded instruments in the chain of title of a particular parcel of land, all judgment liens against the property, the apparent owner and the title he holds, and all recorded easements.

The title-insurance policy is at the disposal of the plant engineer as well as all land purchasers. It is a written guarantee that at a certain moment in time no title defects other than those stated exist; it is usually limited to title facts of records, not matters of location or unrecorded documents.

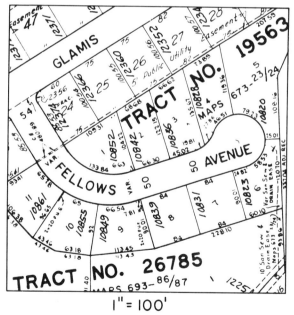

Fig. 2-3. Portion of a typical tract map. (*Brewster Map. Co.*)

In summary, title-insurance policies usually report the following items: taxes, bonds, assessments, trust deeds, mortgages, easements, and liens. However, they do not cover bankruptcy, eminent domain, ordinances, or regulations limiting the use of the property such as zoning, building ordinances, or unrecorded mechanic's liens.

HISTORY OF LAND SUBDIVISION

For the plant engineer in rural areas, a general understanding of land subdivision is invaluable. On May 20, 1785, the United States government authorized the U.S. Rectangular System for surveying public lands. This congressional authorization was henceforth known as the Land Ordinance of 1785. The system established townships, 6 miles square, each township being divided into 36 one-mile-square sections. The north-south axis was called the "principal meridian," and the east-west axis was called the "base line." These were established as reference lines throughout the United States. As an example, in California the three principal meridians and base lines are Humboldt in the north, Mt. Diablo in the center, and San Bernardino in the south (Fig. 2-4).

As people purchased smaller areas of land, sections were further subdivided, most commonly by fractions of a section. This division was done in direct proportion to the true area of the section. A section measured to an exact mile square contains 640 acres. A quarter of a section can be described as the west half of the west half of a section and is written W½ of W½ of section, which contains 160 acres. The area can be further divided to equal ¼ acre as follows: N½ of the SE¼ of the SE¼ of the SE¼ of a section.

When the land came into the hands of the private land developers, civil engineers were retained to make careful subdivisions of the land into tracts by preparing tract maps. The tract maps then legally subdivided the land within its boundaries into blocks, lots, streets, and easements. This division of the property was then recorded onto maps and permanently marked on the land by monuments set by surveyors.

PROCEDURE FOR AN INDUSTRIAL TRACT SUBDIVISION

The procedure the present-day industrial-land developer follows to subdivide his property is complex, but it is necessary for orderly community development in today's fast-expanding cities. Subdivision usually follows the trail shown in Fig. 2-5 and briefly explained below.

The landowner (who may or may not also be the subdivider) and the subdivider confer with the regional planning commission to agree on the best use of the land in conformity with the master plan of the area. The tract is given a number from the office of the county surveyor, and a civil engineer is retained to prepare a tract layout and statement of conditions to be submitted to the regional planning commission. The tentative layout must be approved by the planning commission.

The planning commission distributes copies of the tentative tract map to other county departments, including the survey, road, building and safety, sanitation, fire, and health departments and the real estate com-

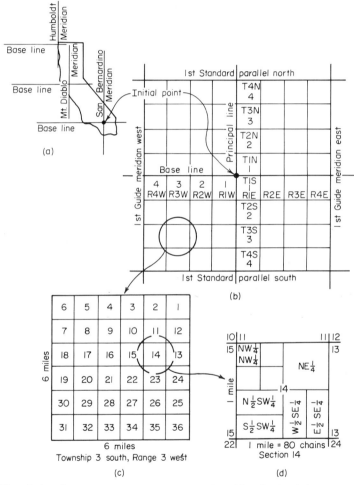

Fig. 2-4. Government survey system of public land; (*a*) starting points of land surveys in California; (*b*) standard parallels and guide meridians; (*c*) typical township subdivided into 36 sections; (*d*) typical section showing fractional sections.

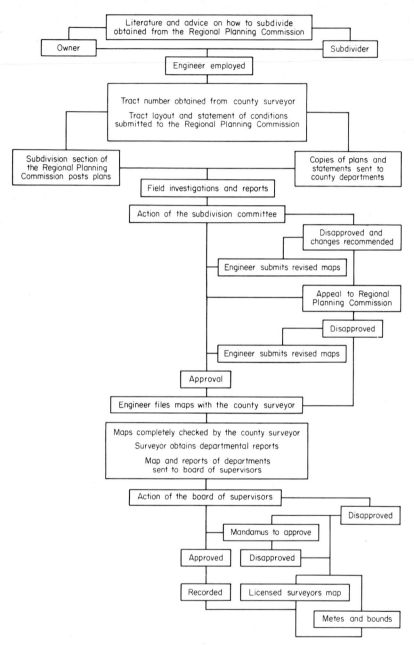

Fig. 2-5. Subdivision trail. (*Association of Land Surveyors of Los Angeles County, The Subdividers Guide.*)

mission.   All departments review and comment on the proposed tract and return the map to the subdivider and his civil engineer.   If the basic plan has been approved by all the necessary departments, the civil engineer, in conjunction with the subdivider, completes the final tract maps, street plans, water and sewage plans, and survey of the site.   The work is then rechecked by each concerned department and submitted to the board of supervisors for final approval.   If approval is granted, the information is recorded and the land is considered legally subdivided.   The names of departments vary with the community, but the process is similar throughout the country.

Along with the preparation of the tract map, the subdivider may create his own set of restrictions to protect and control the character of the tract, especially for industrial property.   The declaration of restrictions is executed and recorded when the subdivision map is recorded.   These restrictions or covenants usually run for at least 25 years and provide for:

1. Regulation of land use
2. Architectural control
3. Side-yard and setback regulations
4. Regulation of lot sizes
5. Restriction of temporary dwellings
6. Limitation of minimum cost and area of building
7. Reservation of utility easements
8. Suitable enforcement of provisions
9. Regulation of nuisance

Future purchasers of portions of the subdivided land, such as the plant engineer's company, must be aware of the restrictions of the tract, as they may limit plant operation.   Also important is the placement of the monuments, because subsequent surveys within this tract are always based upon the original survey and its monuments.

LOT SUBDIVISION

Regardless of the original intent of the industrial subdividers, various plant owners may later wish to sell portions or combinations of the recorded lots.   When a company wishes to purchase land at this stage of its subdivision, it is important that the plant engineer be able to follow the entire history of the subdivision of the land under consideration.   In these land sales or long-term leases the lots may be divided by fractions, for example, the $W\frac{1}{2}$ of lot 3, or the portion may be irregular, in which case it is described by metes and bounds.

Metes and bounds is a term that incorporates monuments, distances, and bearings and is based on the principle that any irregular polygon closes. That is, if one records the length of the various sides and angles at the vertices of these sides and ties the readings to monuments (either found on the property or placed there by the present surveyor) a complete self-contained area will be described. A typical metes and bounds description begins as follows:

> All that certain parcel or tract of land in Los Angeles County, California, said tract being the same land described in deed from John Smith to Arthur Adams dated March 14, 1956 and recorded in Volume 3, page 122 of the Los Angeles County Deed Records, said tract called to contain 18 acres but found by resurvey to contain 18.21 acres. The tract herein conveyed is described by metes and bounds as follows: beginning at a 3-inch iron pipe at the southwest corner of the said tract as recorded in Volume 3, page 122 of the book of records of the County of Los Angeles. Thence from the point of beginning with the west line of said tract 1245.67 feet at a bearing of N10-31-16W, thence in an easterly direction 857.21 feet at a bearing of N73-21-12E, thence in a southerly direction 1167.22 feet at a bearing of S10-31-16E. . . .

PROBLEMS OF BOUNDARY SURVEYS

The official U.S. Public Land Survey became one of the finest systems in the world for describing and marking land, but there was one serious flaw. There was no provision requiring the perpetuation of monuments or for recording that perpetuation publicly. Therefore, some of the early monuments were lost. The deeds were still in the possession of the owners of the land and changed hands with every sale. This caused difficulties because new owners could not accurately determine the boundaries of their land according to the deed. People eventually began to protect their survey monuments, and the boundary question for the time being stabilized.

At the turn of the twentieth century, the science of measuring became even more accurate, as it became easier to make precise measurement of angles and distance. Landowners again became careless with their monuments, thinking that a written description was sufficient to determine the exact boundaries of their land. The courts did not hold this view, because all surveys must be tied to some type of monument. No survey can be accurately tied to a monument that is 10 miles away. The courts ruled that a fixed monument locating the boundary of a piece of property takes precedence over recorded courses and distances.

Nevertheless, if a plant engineer finds himself involved with property that does not have a definite boundary monument, or if he is unable to locate one, he will find it necessary to have a search made of the records and of the land itself for ancient boundaries that can be tied to. Perhaps some almost obliterated boundary monuments actually represent the latest survey made on the property.

A surveyor can provide the plant engineer with various types of evidence to prove the location of the property line, such as monuments, stakes, and lead and tack markers. Trees or other relatively stable objects can also be used as reference points.

An experienced property surveyor usually begins his survey by obtaining written evidence of the title in the form of a deed or an abstract. Maps, field notes, county, city, state, and public agency records of surveys and title are searched for any reference to the land to be surveyed. The surveyor must be careful to choose valid sources, for he is absolutely responsible for the records he uses. After researching the documents, the surveyor goes onto the land and seeks physical evidence of existing corners, surveyor's stakes, trees, or anything mentioned in the documents he used.

The surveyor accumulates all evidence of possession, but this evidence alone does not necessarily provide proof of possession or ownership. It must be ascertained whether any changes in boundaries have occurred by the operation of law, such as estoppel, prescription, agreement, or adverse possession. He may be required to seek testimonial evidence about the location of old monuments and about ownership rights on the property. Finally, after this research and field survey, the surveyor can prepare the plat.

When the plant engineer receives the surveyor's plat, it should be a complete document that ties the property to adequate recorded monuments so that there is no question of its clarity. A complete surveyor's plat of an industrial property should include the following:

1. Records of all monuments referred to
2. Mention of all physical monuments found along with a full description of them
3. Basis of bearings used
4. Measurement of all lines, including direction, distance, coordinate, and curve data
5. All new monuments set by surveyor
6. Oath or witness evidence
7. Date of survey
8. Client's name
9. Surveyor's signature and seal
10. Easements located
11. Encroachments on all property lines
12. Reference to zoning laws

13. Reference to tract restrictions
14. Reference to recorded tract map

Many plant engineers believe that a legal knowledge of property boundaries is not essential for a property surveyor. This attitude is misguided since there are so many laws and changes in the laws which vitally concern property boundaries that they cannot be ignored.

The plant engineer should realize that boundaries of land are shown and created both by physical measurements on the ground and by legal documents. The most important consideration in determining the position of the line is the intent of the parties who established the boundary. Determination of property boundaries is therefore more a matter of law than a science of measurement. The property surveyor must understand the principles of property law and the rules of evidence if he is to perform his function competently. When surveying is done without an appreciation of the law, the surveyor becomes merely a measuring technician; he can cause increased litigation arising from boundary disputes. The plant engineer should understand how serious this can be, because he will act as his company's representative.

Boundaries of property are tied to the time and conditions of their creation. The principles originated in England in 1676 when Parliament passed the Statute of Frauds, which required that transfers of real property be in writing. It soon became apparent that legal descriptions were capable of being interpreted in more than one way. From a set of precedents a common law of boundaries evolved. The Statute of Frauds and that body of common law were later adopted by practically every state in America.

Many of the property surveys and legal descriptions made today do not measure up to the requirements of the law. Some of these incorrect surveys will become legal boundaries with the passage of time or by agreement; others will be challenged successfully because it is still generally held that an incorrect survey is not binding on the landowner and especially not binding on an injured adjoiner. It is therefore the plant engineer's responsibility to follow the surveys made on the land to be acquired and to ascertain and/or establish the correct boundaries of his company's land, thus avoiding conflicts with neighbors or governing agencies.

GOVERNMENTAL AGENCIES' EFFECT ON INDUSTRIAL USE OF LAND

Because the plant is part of a social community with common regulations and laws, the plant engineer must be aware of the interests and wishes of the surrounding community.   Good public relations is becoming in-creasingly important today.   If the community dislikes the presence of a dirty, foul-smelling, unsightly manufacturing plant, it is the plant engi-neer's responsibility to get the plant into a more acceptable condition. In a country where the majority can and does change the laws, an unsightly, unhealthy plant may be voted out of existence by a simple change in the zoning regulations of the area.   In order to protect them-selves, most communities have created regulatory departments to control all aspects of development.

The various departments which closely affect plant operations are shown in Table 2-1.

TABLE 2-1

Department	Jurisdiction
Building and safety	Buildings, tanks, structures, fences, electricity, plumbing
Planning	Parking, zoning, building lines, occupancy (use of land)
Grading	Landfill, excavation
Public works	Streets, underground structures, curbs, gutters, storm drains
Sanitation	Sewers, manholes, lift stations
Air-pollution control	Exhaust from process units, dust
Industrial waste	Nonsanitary waste, acid, oil, caustic waste, pipelines, neutralization of industrial waste
Fire department	Fire hydrants, tank dikes, hazardous liquids, fire water, storage tanks
Storm drain	Catch basins, manholes, culverts, pipelines, channels
Health	Food handling, septic tanks, sewage disposal
Electric power	Overhead and underground power
Fuel gas	Gas main, pressure reducers, meters
Water	Water main, pressure, meters, backflow preventers, fire water
Telephone	Overhead or underground cables
State industrial safety	Walkways, ladders, railroad spur tracks

EXAMPLE

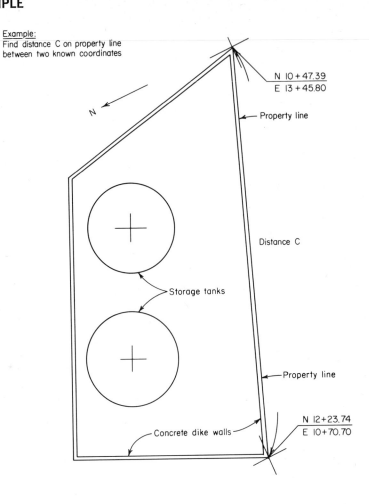

Example:
Find distance C on property line
between two known coordinates

N

N 10 + 47.39
E 13 + 45.80

Property line

Distance C

Storage tanks

Property line

N 12 + 23.74
E 10 + 70.70

Concrete dike walls

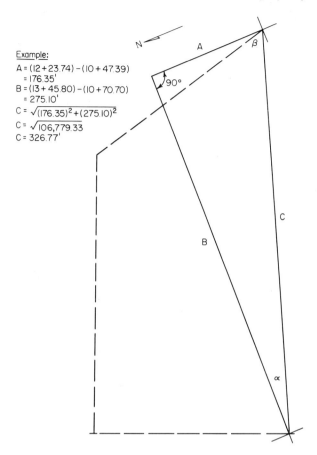

Example:

$A = (12 + 23.74) - (10 + 47.39)$
   $= 176.35'$
$B = (13 + 45.80) - (10 + 70.70)$
   $= 275.10'$
$C = \sqrt{(176.35)^2 + (275.10)^2}$
$C = \sqrt{106,779.33}$
$C = 326.77'$

SUMMARY

Before any serious planning can be made for new plant facilities a thorough understanding of the legal limits and boundaries of the land is necessary. These limits can be in the form of property lines, easements, and right-of-way. Other limitations may be in the form of zoning regulations, tract restrictions, approved street widening, and public drain and sewer projects.

The best sources for plant-related information are title-insurance policies, maps on file in city or county engineers' offices, and the local city planning department.

CHECKLIST FOR PROPERTY ACQUISITION

1. Survey plot
2. Metes and bounds
3. Legal descriptions: lot, block, tract, book of records

4. Title policy
   a. Mechanic's liens
   b. Taxes
5. Tract restrictions
6. Owner
7. Easements
8. Rights-of-way
9. Location of all corner monuments
10. Zoning
11. Encroachments

BIBLIOGRAPHY

Bowman, Arthur G.: *Real Estate Law in California,* Prentice-Hall, Inc., Englewood Cliffs, N.J., 1965.

Brown, Curtis Maitland, and Winfield H. Eldridge: *Evidence and Procedures for Boundary Location,* John Wiley & Sons, Inc., New York, 1962.

City of Los Angeles: *Zoning Code,* Building News, Inc., Los Angeles, 1967.

Clement, Donald B.: *Restoration of Lost or Obliterated Corners and Subdivision of Sections,* Government Printing Office, Washington, 1960.

Kissam, Philip: *Surveying for Civil Engineers,* 2d ed., McGraw-Hill Book Company, New York, 1956.

Los Angeles County Regional Planning Commission: *Los Angeles County Zoning Ordinance,* Los Angeles, 1966.

Searles, William H., Howard Chapin Ives, and Philip Kissam: *Field Engineering,* John Wiley & Sons, Inc., New York, 1950.

Seelye, Elwyn E.: *Data Book for Civil Engineers, Vol. I, Design,* 3d ed., John Wiley & Sons, Inc., New York, 1960.

State of California Printing Division: *Laws Relating to Subdivided Lands,* Sacramento, Calif., 1961.

Tillotson, Ira M., and Charles E. Snyder: *Current Problems in Property Location,* Title Insurance and Trust Company, Los Angeles, 1965.

Title Insurance and Trust Company: *When You Subdivide,* Los Angeles, 1963.

————: *Title Services,* Los Angeles, 1963.

CHAPTER THREE

Industrial Surveying

THE SCIENCE OF SURVEYING is as old as civilization itself. Originally, using only trigonometry and the North Star, the ancients mapped out their lands after each flood. Today geophysics has been added to trigonometry and astronomy, but surveying remains basically the same. It is a scientific system that determines the form, contour, shape, dimensions, and location of any part of the earth's surface.

Surveying is important to the plant engineer because by the use of two-dimensional maps, profiles, plans, and cross sections he is able to "see" his property. Only after land is accurately described and visualized can a plan to develop the industrial facilities for the property be made.

TYPES OF SURVEYING

There are generally two main categories of surveying, geodetic and planar. Geodesy, with which the plant engineer is seldom concerned, takes into account the earth's curvature and is used to survey whole countries or continents. The other method of surveying, which most directly involves the plant engineer, plane surveying, assumes, for all practical purposes, that the earth is flat. This assumption causes no appreciable error within a 100-mile square area.

Plane surveying can again be subdivided according to the specific purpose for which it is done: railroad, mine, hydrographic (bodies of water), photogrammetric (high-speed camera photographs of aerial work), and land surveys. The plant engineer may be involved with several of these surveying techniques depending on the size, type, and location of his facilities.

The land may be the property upon which the engineer's plant is presently located or it may be under consideration as the site for a new plant expansion program. Because it is so important to determine the nature of the land upon which structures are to be erected, a careful study of the land must be made. The plant engineer may decide to order a resurvey of the land previously surveyed. To better understand a plant survey, he must at least be familiar with the tools and methods used by the land surveyor in determining the plant property lines and the topography.

SURVEYING EQUIPMENT

The instruments the surveyor or surveying plant engineer uses are simple but invaluable. The chief instruments required in surveying are the level, rod, theodolite or transit, and tape. The level, or Dumpy level (Fig. 3-1), is simply a telescope mounted on a hardwood tripod (Fig. 3-2). Attached to the telescope is a horizontal spirit level. Adjusting

Fig. 3-1. Model 45 Dumpy level, which, because of its sturdiness, convenience, and stability, has superseded the Y level. The telescope is provided with stadia hairs. (*Brunson.*)

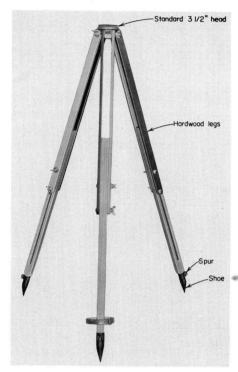

Standard 3 1/2" head

Hardwood legs

Spur

Shoe

Fig. 3-2. Tripod used to support either a transit or Dumpy level. (*Kueffel & Esser.*)

screws make it possible to be sure that the telescope is in a perfectly level position. Professional surveyors often use automatic leveling instruments, which cost more than adjustable levels, to save time on major surveys. The Abney level is used to determine the approximate angle of a slope for distances measured on a slope which must later be corrected for horizontal distance. The common hand level (Fig. 3-3) is also used to ensure that the tape is level when horizontal distances are measured.

Fig. 3-3. Hand level used for leveling the tape in chaining and preliminary topographic surveying. (*Buez.*)

The rod (Fig. 3-4), a narrow pole or board graduated in feet and decimals of a foot, is used for determining elevations. The stadia rod is a highly visible calibrated board used in conjunction with pairs of cross hairs in the telescope for determining distances by reading the interval between the horizontal cross hairs.

The theodolite (Fig. 3-5) consists of a telescope, a compass, vertical and horizontal scales, three spirit levels, and adjusting screws. The most common theodolite is the transit, which can be revolved completely in a vertical plane. The transit has a plumb bob (Fig. 3-6) which allows it to be located directly over a particular point on the ground. The transit is a useful tool because it can measure horizontal and vertical angles and distances by the stadia rod and can also be used for leveling. All angles are read by use of calibrated verniers, which are graduated into degrees and minutes.

The surveyor's basic tool is the tape (Fig. 3-7), which may be fabric, metal, or invar steel. Invar steel is an alloy which eliminates the excessive error caused by the thermal expansion and contraction of ordinary steel. For very accurate work a steel tape can be calibrated and checked by the U.S. Bureau of Standards at a known temperature and tension for 100 ft of length. The tape accessories include clamps, spring balance, and repair kits. The spring balance, when used, is attached to one end of the tape so that the chainman is always aware of the tension on the tape when measurements are being made. With proper tension kept constant, the error caused by excessive sag is reduced.

The plant engineer should take pride in the condition of his survey equipment, handle it properly, and keep it immaculate.

A transit mounted on a tripod may be carried over the shoulder as long as the survey party is in the field, but when entering a building or passing through a gate, the instrument should be carried ahead of the person holding it to avoid hitting it against the frame of the door or gate. In an automobile the transit or level should never be placed in the trunk but rather on the floor of the back seat to limit the amount of shifting and sliding.

All survey equipment should be cleaned after each day's work. Mud and dirt should be removed from

Fig. 3-4. Philadelphia leveling rod with target, used for topographic surveying and establishing grades of foundations, pavements, and pipelines. (*Kueffel & Esser.*)

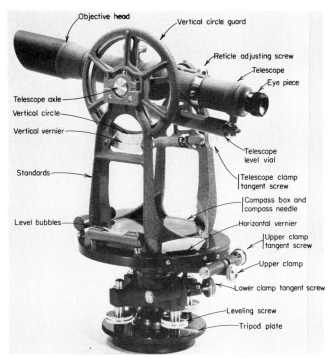

Objective head

Vertical circle guard

Reticle adjusting screw

Telescope

Eye piece

Telescope axle

Vertical circle

Vertical vernier

Telescope
level vial

Standards

Telescope clamp
tangent screw

Compass box and
compass needle

Level bubbles

Horizontal vernier

Upper clamp
tangent screw

Upper clamp

Lower clamp tangent screw

Leveling screw

Tripod plate

Fig. 3-5. Engineer's transit, consisting of telescope attached to vertical and horizontal verniers. (*Kueffel & Esser.*)

Fig. 3-6. Plumb bob, used for centering a transit accurately over a point and for chaining distances in conjunction with a steel tape. (*Kueffel & Esser.*)

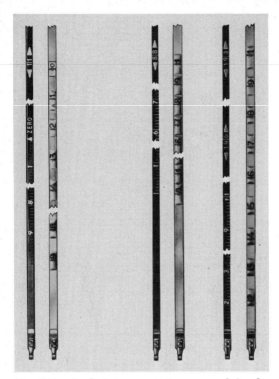

Fig. 3-7. Band chains or steel tapes used for determining distances between points. Tapes can be equipped with reels, spring balance, leather thongs, and holding clamp. (*Kueffel & Esser.*)

the steel chain, which should then be lightly wiped with an oily rag to prevent corrosion. All lenses on equipment should be dusted and all adjusting screws set lightly.

When the transit is stored, it should first be screwed onto the threaded metal stud attached to a sliding board which holds the transit in an upright position. It is then fitted into a hardwood instrument case, in which are stored the sunshade, wrench, screwdriver, plumb bob, magnifying glass, and adjusting pins. An aluminum cap is also provided to protect the threads of the tripod head. The case containing the transit should be stored in a place that does not experience extremes of temperature or unusually heavy traffic that would jar it.

UNITS OF MEASUREMENT

Only with an understanding of the units of measurement used in land surveying can the plant engineer take advantage of the survey information he has at his disposal.

In the United States most surveys measure distance in feet and decimals of a foot. In measurements of townships the term "chain" is also used. A Gunter's chain is 66 ft long and contains 100 links. Areas are expressed in acres, square miles, sections, square yards, or square feet. The length of a chain is such that 80 chains constitutes 1 mile, 1 sq chain equals 1 acre, and one section is 80 by 80 chains.

Angles are measured in degrees, minutes, and seconds. It is usually not possible to determine fractions of a minute visually with ordinary instruments. The direction or heading of a line is identified by its bearing. The bearing is determined by the angle the line makes with a line running north and south. A bearing 30 degrees and 20 minutes west of north is written N30°20′W. The direction based as north is either that of the previously recorded north or true astronomical north. All surveys should state the reference basis of north used to determine bearings.

The azimuth of a line is similar to the bearing. It is the direction of a line stated in terms of its angle as measured clockwise from reference north. Azimuth can vary from 0 to 359°. Azimuths are not commonly used in land surveying but are used in navigation.

Topographic surveys record the relative elevation of a portion of land, elevations being given in feet above or below sea level. Mean sea level is an arbitrary elevation determined by U.S. Geodetic Survey upon which most topographic surveys are based. Throughout the United States spot elevations are indicated with government bench marks. The name, location, and elevation of these permanent markers, also known as monuments, have been recorded and are at the disposal of any private surveyor or plant surveyor.

In surveys requiring measurement of curves, the term "degree of curvature" is used. In highway work, the degree of curvature (D) is the angle subtended at the center of a circle by a 100-ft chord, but in railroad work the degree of curvature is the angle subtended at the center of the circle by a 100-ft arc.

Plant roads and railroads as well as pipeline installations often require measurement of a slope. The slope of a grade line with respect to the horizontal is the ratio of the vertical rise or fall in feet per 100 ft of horizontal distance and is expressed as a percentage. A fall of 3 ft in 100 is written as minus 3 percent or (—)3% grade. In pipeline grades, a slope is expressed as a decimal. A 0.3 foot rise in 100 ft is called a 0.003 gradient. The slope of drain lines is sometimes expressed in fractions of an inch per 1 ft of horizontal distance such as $\frac{1}{4}$ in./ft.

To locate positions along a centerline of a road, railroad, or pipeline, the line is broken into 100-ft increments starting at some arbitrary point. A single 100-ft interval is called "one station." Points between stations are decimal parts of a station and are noted with a plus mark, such as station $3 + 72.12$, which is 372.12 ft from the beginning point.

MEASUREMENT OF HORIZONTAL DISTANCES

Measuring the distance between two points is the most common form of field surveying. This measurement can be done in many ways, all differing in degree of accuracy. In the most basic form of measurement, called "pacing," the plant engineer can predetermine the length of his stride by practice over a measured length. Another method is the use of steel tape, which is held taut and horizontal between points by holding a plumb bob and string over the two points being measured.

Distances can also be measured by the stadia method, which uses the instrument telescope equipped with cross hairs and a stadia rod. The interval distance shown on the rod between the horizontal cross hairs of the telescope represents the distance between the transit and the rod. A 1-ft interval on the rod equals a 100-ft distance. Other distances are proportionate to this rod interval.

Without exception, the most important method for surveying and land measuring is triangulation. With this method, a minimum of distance has to be measured and the maximum use is made of angular measurement. Measurement by triangulation is based upon the use of triangles and their properties. In surveying, distances often cannot be measured directly by chaining due to inaccessibility caused by a building, hill, or gully. Triangulation is therefore the best method of bypassing the obstacle.

MEASUREMENT OF VERTICAL DISTANCES

Leveling is used to determine the topography of an area of land. Leveling is a system of determining first the height of the instrument (HI), then subtracting from this elevation all subsequent rod readings.

To obtain an accurate rod reading the following sequence of operations is recommended to the plant surveyor:

1. Focus on the rod to see figures clearly.
2. Adjust vertical hair to coincide with rod.
3. Center outer bubble in tube between two graduations.
4. Read rod to nearest $\frac{1}{100}$ ft.
5. Check bubble again to see that it is still centered.
6. Record reading.

The height of the instrument is determined by placing the rod vertically upon a known point or bench mark. The reading is made where the center horizontal cross hair intercepts the rod. The calibration on the rod is recorded and added to the elevation of the bench mark. The sum of two values is the height of instrument. All subsequent rod readings to unknown points from this HI are subtracted from the HI, producing the elevation of the unknown point. The procedure continues until the distance between instrument and rod becomes too great for accurate reading. Then a new bench mark must be set. This new point is called a turning point (TP). The instrument can then be relocated beyond the turning point, and the procedure continues.

By keeping the distance between the instrument and the backsight equal to the foresight, instrument error is minimized.

For quick and rough topographic surveying, a hand level and a level rod can be used. The hand level is equipped with a spirit-level bubble and lenses with cross hairs. The bubble can be seen through the eyepiece when the instrument is held level. When the instrument is held at eye level with the bubble split by the cross hairs, any object seen at the hairline is at the same elevation as the viewer's eye. Rod setups must be close, as there is no magnification in the lenses.

MEASUREMENT OF ANGLES

To determine the angle between two lines, the surveyor uses only the transit and a plumb bob. The instrument is carefully set up so that the plumb bob attached to the center of the transit hangs directly over the marker. Sighting is done to as small a target as possible for the most precise results. The target may be another plumb bob suspended over the other points. The telescope is then moved so that the vertical cross hair of the transit coincides with the string of the target plumb bob.

The angle on the horizontal verniers of the transit is read after the telescope is sighted to a point on one line. The telescope is rotated to sight upon a point on the second line. The angle is again read from the vernier. The angular distance between the two readings represents the angle between the two lines.

When points are to be set on lines at a given angle, the following sequence should be followed. The instrument is leveled, and both table and telescope level bubbles should be centered. Both the outer and inner verniers are turned to zero. The outer vernier is then locked. The telescope is carefully turned to the angle desired. This movement is done manually until the desired angle is almost reached. The final angle is attained by the use of the adjustment screw.

Depending on the type of transit used, the vernier is read to the nearest minute or fraction of a minute. If greater accuracy is required, the telescope is turned a number of times and the average of all readings is taken.

Vertical angles can be determined by the use of the vertical dial attached to the telescope. A vernier on this dial indicates all angles above and below the horizontal plane of the telescope.

PROPERTY SURVEYING

For plant property located in urban areas, the surveyor usually begins his survey at city-recorded points. These recorded points are normally located at the intersection of the centerlines of streets. By referring to the recorded map of the block, distances between the recorded points and the property in question can be determined.

The surveyor sets up the transit over the recorded point and sights to the other recorded point at the next street intersection.

The surveyor now has a true visual line along the centerline of the street. Once this line is known, chaining the distance from either point at the street intersection to lines intersecting the corners of the property is easy.

Sometimes in order to avoid traffic in the street, an offset line is made in the parkway parallel to the centerline of the street. Property-line intersection points are marked after chaining is completed.

Property corners are permanently marked by chipping a hole in the concrete surface, filling the hole with lead, and then driving a small copper tack into the lead. Markers are also made by driving a hardwood hub into the ground until it is flush with the surface; then a steel nail is driven into the top of the hub. Sometimes a steel pipe is set in the ground and filled with concrete, a steel nail being driven into the concrete to mark the point.

For plant property located in rural areas, the surveyor may have to start his survey from the nearest recorded section corner monument which had been set by the federal government.

The procedure for locating plant property in rural areas is similar to that of a street survey. The transit is set up over a monument and sighted to an adjacent monument. Once a line has been established, distances can then be measured by chain.

In all property-location surveys it is customary to start the survey at markers established by city, county, or state surveyors. In this way the descriptions of the points are properly recorded and legally recognized.

PIPELINE SURVEYING

The plant surveyor is sometimes called upon to stake out a new sewer line on plant property. The first requirement in staking out the line is to run a transit line parallel to the centerline of the sewer where it will not be disturbed by construction or excavated soil.

Hubs are driven at intervals along this line flush with the ground. Profile levels are then run along the transit line, and the elevations are noted to the nearest hundredth foot. A grade sheet is then prepared that lists the distances from the top of each hub to the bottom of the pipe trench or the top of the pipe at a point adjacent to each hub. Excavation and pipe placement are then controlled.

CONSTRUCTION SURVEYING

Every building to be constructed must first be staked out (Fig. 3-8). Usually three stakes are placed at all corners of the building far enough back so that they will not be disturbed during construction. Batter boards are nailed to these stakes with their tops horizontal and set at a definite elevation. Nails are driven into the tops of the boards on the projected line of the building. Strings stretched between nails at opposite ends of the lines provide both the line and the grade of the building. With these established reference points, the building can be constructed exactly as designed.

SURVEY DOCUMENTS

All survey field records must be kept in the prescribed field notebooks. The name of the recorder, the project, and type of field work are usually marked on the cover. The book contains the date, weather, temperature, and names of all the men in the survey party. It is written in pencil and recorded daily.

Since an entire survey may be made worthless if notes are incomplete or ambiguous, notes must be neat, accurate, and orderly and be clarified whenever possible with sketches. All notes and sketches are recorded with a hard pencil which does not smear. Incorrect figures are usually crossed through and rewritten above, rather than erased. The notes, including sketches and numerical values, give a written description of everything that has been done.

A fieldbook can contain many tables. Level notes are a list of rod readings, description of rod locations, and the computed elevation at each rod location. Cross-section notes are simply a list of rod readings and the distance of each rod location 90° to the transit line.

A profile is a drawing showing the contour of a line over the ground

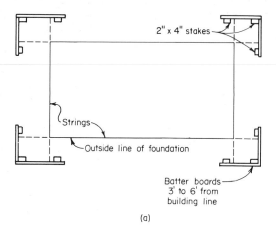

(a)

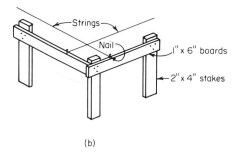

(b)

Fig. 3-8. Construction batter boards, used as a guide for excavation, forming foundation walls, and establishing grade to top of wall. (*a*) Plan showing arrangement of batter boards and string lines; (*b*) detail of corner of batter boards.

surface. In order to exaggerate changes of elevation, the vertical scale is usually drawn 10 times larger than the horizontal scale.

A grading sheet is a tabulation showing the amount of cut or fill necessary to bring the land to the level indicated on the grade stake.

Traverse notes describe the distance measured between points and the angular difference between lines.

A topographic map can be produced from the elevation statistics found in the fieldbook. Such a map illustrates on paper the surface characteristics of the land being mapped. The main feature shown by contour lines is variation in elevation. A contour line is an imaginary line of constant elevation along the ground. As an example, the shoreline of a body of water appears as a contour line which is equal to the elevation of the water surface.

Contour lines show up close together on steep slopes and far apart on relatively flat land. The spacing and general arrangement of the lines give the plant engineer a picture of the actual topographic condition of the land, from which he can design drainage systems, roadways, excavation and fill requirements, and a general layout of plant facilities best suited to the topography.

SUMMARY

Every new plant project must start with an accurately drawn plot plan based upon field measurements made by surveying. Since the tools and methods used by the plant engineer for field measurement are similar to those of the private land surveyor, he must follow the same techniques used by the professional. Most surveying instruments are a valuable asset to a plant engineer's office.

Equally important is the ability to understand and use the technical language of the surveyor. Terms often used in plant site work are bearings, elevations, acres, degree of curvature, and gradients.

The ability to read topographic maps is an absolute necessity for planning drainage, roads, parking areas, and railroads.

CHECKLIST FOR PLANT SURVEYING

1. Property survey
2. Property corners
3. Bearings of property lines
4. Distances of property lines
5. Basis of bearing
6. Lot number
7. Block number
8. Tract number or name, where recorded
9. Building setback requirement
10. Side-yard requirement
11. Rear-yard requirement
12. Utility easements
    a. Electricity
    b. Water
    c. Gas
    d. Storm drain
13. Railroad right-of-way
14. Topographic survey
    a. Bench mark or reference of elevations
    b. Elevation at all corners of property
    c. Elevation of curb and gutter
    d. Elevation of finish floor of each building

    e. Elevation of top rail of plant railroad
    f. Elevation of plant sewer at property line
    g. Elevation of invert of all drains at each manhole
    h. Finish elevation at edges of all paved areas
    i. Exterior dimension of each plant building and structure
    j. Orientation of all buildings
    k. Width of all roads
    l. Centerline of all roads
    m. Centerline of all railroads

CHECKLIST FOR RAILROAD SURVEY

1. Location of centerline of railroad track
2. Tie-in to property line
3. Location of PIs (Points of Intersection)
4. Length of tangents between PIs
5. Angle of all PIs (in degrees)
6. Radius of all curves
7. Degree of curvature of all curves
8. Length of arc at each curve
9. Length of semitangent at each curve
10. Grade of top of rail (percent)
11. Switches and frog number of switch
12. Clearances, width, and height

BIBLIOGRAPHY

Bouchard, Harry: *Surveying,* International Textbook Company, Scranton, Pa., 1946.
Brown, Curtis Maitland, and Winfield H. Eldridge: *Evidence and Procedures for Boundary Location,* John Wiley & Sons, Inc., New York, 1962.
Clement, Donald B.: *Restoration of Lost or Obliterated Corners and Subdivision of Sections,* Government Printing Office, Washington, 1960.
Hosmer, George L.: *Geodesy,* John Wiley & Sons, Inc., New York, 1930.
Kissam, Philip: *Surveying for Civil Engineers,* 2d ed., McGraw-Hill Book Company, New York, 1956.
Los Angeles City School Districts: *School Planning Manual,* Los Angeles, 1963.
Merriman, Thaddeus, and Thomas H. Wiggin: *American Civil Engineers' Handbook,* John Wiley & Sons, Inc., New York, 1947.
Merritt, Frederick S.: *Standard Handbook for Civil Engineers,* McGraw-Hill Book Company, New York, 1968.
Searles, William H., Howard Chapin Ives, and Philip Kissam: *Field Engineering,* John Wiley & Sons, Inc., New York, 1950.
Seelye, Elwyn E: *Data Book for Civil Engineers, Vol. I, Design,* 3d ed., John Wiley & Sons, Inc., New York, 1960.
State of California Printing Division: *Laws Relating to Subdivided Lands,* Sacramento, Calif., 1961.
Tillotson, Ira M., and Charles E. Snyder: *Current Problems in Property Location,* Title Insurance and Trust Company, Los Angeles, 1965.

Title Insurance and Trust Company: *When You Subdivide,* Los Angeles, 1963.

———: *Title Services,* Los Angeles, 1963.

Urquhart, Leonard Church: *Civil Engineering Handbook,* 4th ed., McGraw-Hill Book Company, New York, 1959.

War Department: *Technical Manual of Surveying,* Government Printing Office, Washington, 1943.

Wattles, W. C.: *Land Survey Descriptions,* Title Insurance and Trust Company, Los Angeles, 1960.

CHAPTER FOUR

Soils and Foundations

THE HISTORY AND CHARACTERISTICS of the soil conditions of a plant site are as important to the plant engineer as the legal definitions of the site. The type of soil can greatly affect the cost of all structures to be built on the site.

In order to understand the soil condition, the plant engineer must look at not only the site itself but also at adjoining areas and the community to obtain a proper perspective of the situation. The plant property may be located in an alluvial plain, at a river's edge, in an excavated section of a hill, on a man-made fill, or in the gravel wash of an old riverbed. The plant may be on or adjacent to a man-made flood-control device such as a levee or dike. All these facts will greatly affect the initial cost, the operating cost of the plant, and its future expansion possibilities.

A knowledge of the surface soil alone is not sufficient. The history of the soil beneath the surface is in many cases more important than the exposed material. The real strength is in the subsoil. For a better understanding of the classification of the composition of soil, the following brief geological summary should help the plant engineer.

All soil material comes from original igneous rock. Over the centuries particles of rock have been broken free from the original material by freezing, chemical reactions, or contact with other rocks. They were washed down by wind, rain, or the force of gravity. Layer upon layer of the decomposed rock formed what is now known as soil.

The term "soil" as used by soil engineers usually implies the earth material lying in its original, undisturbed state. The soil is usually found in layers. The surface material is called the "topsoil," which contains, in addition to its mineral composition, organic material derived from decomposed vegetation. Beneath the topsoil lies another layer commonly known as "subsoil." Below the subsoil is found the "substratum," where the water table is usually found. This stratification was caused by the continual erosion from higher ground.

Most industrial plants are on level sites and are therefore founded on deep beds of mineral and organic sediment which have been transported over long periods of time by wind and rain.

In general, the strength of soil is determined by the age of the sedimentation, the history of freezing and thawing, the degrees of chemical cementation of the particles, the water content, and the density of the particles.

CLASSIFICATION OF SOIL

As rock is disintegrated into smaller particles, the particles are classified according to their size and chemistry. In order to identify a soil, the soil engineer informs the plant engineer of its grain size, gradation, chemical composition, density, and moisture content. As an example, the Los Angeles City Building Code divides soil into these eight major groups:

1. *Rock:* rock can be a single mass of igneous material, crystalline bedrock (as in granite), foliated rock (as in slate), sedimentary rock (as in sandstone), or soft or broken bedrock. Some common names for rock soils are shale, slate, and schist.
2. *Gravel:* gravel can be well graded (the voids are filled by smaller grains of gravel), poorly graded (all the grains are the same size, and there are many voids), silty (the voids are filled with silt), or clayey (the voids are filled with clay), with a grain size of $\frac{1}{4}$ in. or more in diameter. Gravel lacks both cohesion and plasticity but has a high friction value.
3. *Sand:* sand may also be either well graded, gravelly, poorly graded, silty, or clay. When dry, sand has practically no cohesion. It also has no plasticity. Grains of sand are smaller than $\frac{1}{4}$ in. in diameter.

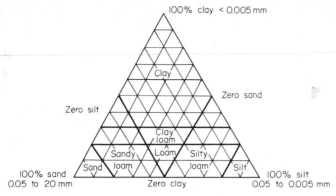

Fig. 4-1. Graphic description of soil types based upon U.S. Department of Agriculture textural classification chart.

4. *Silt:* silt is inorganic, organic, or elastic. It has no cohesion and very little plasticity; its elasticity is a measure of its ability to return to its original shape after a load has been removed.
5. *Clay:* clay can be fat (containing oil), lean (without oil), compressible, expansive organic with high plasticity, or organic. Clay is very cohesive.
6. *Muck:* muck is decomposed organic material. Ordinarily black, it is found in swamps.
7. *Peat:* peat consists of partly decayed plants. It is organic and still fibrous.
8. *Man-made fill:* fill may be compacted or uncompacted and of unknown composition.

Another method for accurate classification of granular soil is by its grain size and the percentage of each grain size to the mixture, as illustrated in the textural-classification chart shown in Fig. 4-1.

Generally, the grain size of the particles defines the soil. Grains of sand, for example, are between 2.0 and 0.05 mm in diameter while silt is between 0.05 and 0.002 mm in diameter. Clay is soil with grains under 0.002 mm in diameter. A variety of laboratory testing procedures have been developed to determine specific gravity, grain size and shape, liquid limit, water content, ratio of voids, unconfined compressibility of soil, and other important soil properties.

SOIL TESTING

To assist in evaluating the soil condition of a prospective site for plant expansion, the plant engineer should obtain a soils report before he makes his final recommendations to management. The report obtained from a soil test should contain the following basic information:

1. Site description, topography, existing vegetation, drainage, general geology
2. Soil condition, moisture content, water table

LOG OF BORINGS   BORING NUMBER   1

Sample depth	Blows per foot	Moisture content, %	Dry unit weight, lb/cu ft	Depth, ft		DESCRIPTION Surface conditions: Level asphaltic concrete parking
				0	SM– SP	Sand: Brown-gray, fine to medium, silty, damp, moderately dense
2	Push	9	98			
4	11	7	95			grades dense
				5		
8	44	5	98			grades very dense
				10		
12	3	4	99		- - - -	grades no silt and fine to coarse
				15		grades gravel
17	2	8	104		ML– SM - - - - - - - -	Silt: Gray-brown, sandy, damp to moist, firm (8" sand layer) (cobble)
22	2	11	108	20	ML– SM	
						End of boring at 25 1/2', no water

No caving, much caving at 4' to 8'

Fig. 4-2. Typical boring log report showing (*a*) boring number, (*b*) depth at which undisturbed samples are taken, (*c*) strength of soil at various depths as indicated by the number of blows per foot of penetration, (*d*) moisture content of soil at various depths, (*e*) dry density of various samples taken, (*f*) depth of boring, (*g*) description of soil type at various depths. (*R. T. Frankian & Associates.*)

3. Graphs showing cross sections of borings taken, listing various depths of color, moisture content, and density of soils (Fig. 4-2)
4. Recommendations for method of backfill for structural excavations and trenches
5. Suitability of local soil for use as compact fill

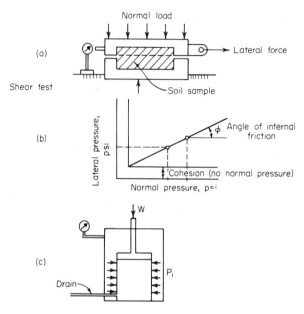

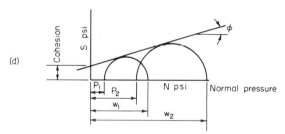

Fig. 4-3. Testing devices for determining shearing strength of soil samples. (*a*) Unconfined shear-test apparatus. (*b*) Shear-test curve plotted from (*a*). (*c*) Triaxial test apparatus. (*d*) Mohr's circle diagram plotted from shear test results. (*From Elwyn E. Seelye, Data Book for Civil Engineers, Vol. I: Design, Third Edition. Copyright, 1945 by Elwyn E. Seelye. Copyright, 1951 © 1960 by Jane Seelye West, Elwyn Seelye, 2nd, Elizabeth Seelye Williams, and Edward E. Seelye. Reprinted by permission of John Wiley & Sons, Inc.*)

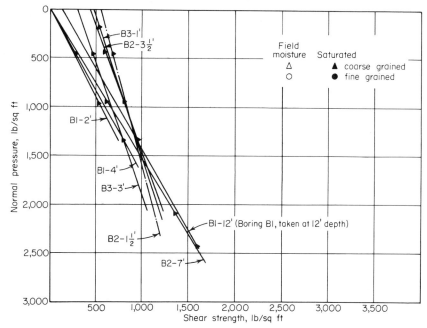

Fig. 4-4. Typical shear-test curves made from tests of eight soil samples. Samples are identified as B1-12', or boring no. 1 taken at 12 ft depth. (*R. T. Frankian & Associates.*)

6. Charts showing results of shearing tests and expected settlements under various loads and at various moisture contents (Figs. 4-3 and 4-4)
7. Treatment of soils under roads and paved areas
8. Statement of anticipated plant structures and the types and amount of loadings
9. Recommendations for types of footings or foundation, sizes, depths, allowable loading, and expected settlement (Fig. 4-5)
10. Recommendations for the treatment of soil including reworking, rolling, compacting, and removal

STRUCTURAL CHARACTERISTICS OF SOIL

The strength of any soil is based on its primary properties, which are internal friction (or resistance to sliding), cohesion (or mutual attraction of its particles), compressibility (reduction of volume under pressure), capillarity (attraction of moisture), elasticity (or ability to rebound), and permeability (the property that permits water to flow through a material). The internal resistance, which is a combination of internal

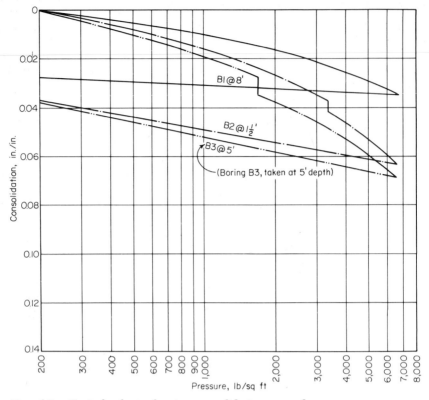

Fig. 4-5. Typical chart showing consolidation test data illustrating pressure in pounds per square foot versus consolidation in inches per inch. Three samples are charted (B1, B2, and B3) which were taken at 1½, 5, and 8 ft depth. (*R. T. Frankian & Associates, Inc.*)

friction and cohesion, is the most important of all soil properties. Internal friction is characteristic of granular soil, and cohesion is typical of clay. Granular-soil classifications include gravel, sand, coarse sand, compact gravel, compact sand, loose gravel, and loose sand.

Cohesive soil consists of hardpan, which is a compact mixture of clay with sand, hard clay, medium clay, soft clay, and inorganic soil. Granular soils are very low in cohesion but high in internal friction; they have a high shearing strength that increases with pressure. Clay soils are highly cohesive because of molecular attraction but are very low in internal friction. The shearing strength of clay soil depends only upon its cohesion and is independent of the pressure, but the strength of clay soils is greatly reduced by water.

It is therefore apparent that an ideal soil is a mixture of both granular and cohesive soils.   Such a foundation soil would possess the good properties of each type of soil because the weaknesses of one are canceled out by the strengths of the other.   The measure of good soil is its degree of shearing strength and resistance to settlement.   The ability of the soil to support heavy foundations or to remain stable on a steep slope is directly proportional to its shearing strength.   Friction is a resistance that exists independently of the area loaded; it is a function of the intensity of the load and the surface of contact.

Other important properties of soil which the plant engineer should be aware of are its capillarity, plasticity, liquid limit, and permeability. In the case of clays which become highly plastic with the addition of moisture, excessive settlement or plastic flow could be a danger to a structure. High permeability is dangerous when there is water with the soil.   Water changing to ice will tend to expand and raise the surface of the soil and, with it, foundations or paved surfaces.   This is known as "frost heave."

Capillary action by the soil causes water to be drawn into a building through the basement walls and floor slabs.   The moisture can damage the interior finishes of the building.   Another term used by the soil engineer is the "plastic limit," defined as the least amount of moisture a soil sample can hold and still be rolled into an $\frac{1}{8}$-in. diameter thread. This is an indication of the type of plasticity the soil has.   The liquid limit is the maximum amount of liquid a soil can absorb before it fails in shear.

SOILS AND FOUNDATION AS A UNIT

The foundation engineer looks upon the structure and the soil supporting it as a working unit.   In the design of any structural foundation, two questions arise: (1) Will the natural earth mass or soil under the proposed building support the structure and the superimposed loads? (2) How great is the resulting settlement?   These two questions constitute the two major parts of soils mechanics., The first question deals with the stability of the soil and the second with its elasticity.

TYPES OF FOUNDATION

In most cases the plant engineer must work with the existing site of his company.   He then must make the best of existing soil conditions. One way to improve the bearing capacity of the soil is by designing deep footings which bear on a better stratum.   Wide footings also resolve the problem of poor soil bearing by distributing the load over a

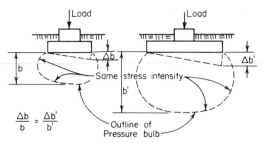

Fig. 4-6. Settlement of a foundation is proportional to size of footing and intensity of load.

larger area. Both these methods are commonly used with weak soil conditions where piles are not economical.

The best foundation for any particular situation depends upon three factors: (1) the loading conditions, (2) the area available, and (3) the soil condition. Assuming that the load is moderate, the two most common types of foundations are the "isolated spread footing" and the "continuous spread footing." Both types are usually near the surface of the soil and are relatively shallow foundations. They are used in clay and better-grade soil.

For deep foundations, a belled caisson is used. Often this consists of a drilled hole flared out at the bottom in which the shaft and bell have been filled with concrete. Stiff clay soils underlying a stratum of uncompacted fill call for the use of belled caissons.

There are many types of piles. Some are friction types and others are end-bearing. The friction types include the caisson without the bell bottom, the precast concrete pile, the steel pile, the wood pile, and the concrete cast-in-place pile. All these piles develop their strength through the fricton upon the surface of the shaft of the pile, which resists downward force of the structure. When a substantially hard stratum could be reached at the lower level, the use of end-bearing piles is recommended. These are of steel pipe or structural shapes or precast concrete.

A floating or raft foundation is generally a large concrete pad rigid enough actually to float by distributing the load upon a low-bearing-value soil.

Smaller pads, called "spread footings," can be square, rectangular, round, or any polygonal shape. They must bear on relatively good soil, which must be protected from intrusion of water. This type of footing is relatively shallow and therefore the least costly.

As a rule of thumb for soil which has good bearing value at an excessive depth, belled caissons are recommended, as spread footings would require too much excavation. But when loose topsoil or a high water table exists, the belled caissons become impractical and a pile foundation is indicated. Where bedrock underlies a very loose and frictionless soil, the end-bearing pile must be used, but when the overlying soil has a high friction value, the friction pile is recommended.

The design engineer therefore has a multitude of choices which include friction, end-bearing, and spread foundations. Each has its place, depending upon the soil conditions encountered.

SOIL FAILURES

All plant engineers have probably seen foundation failures, although they may not have recognized them (see Figs. 4-6 and 4-7). The simplest failure is a settlement of a rigid structure, such as a concrete-block wall, in which a settlement of one end of the foundation causes diagonal

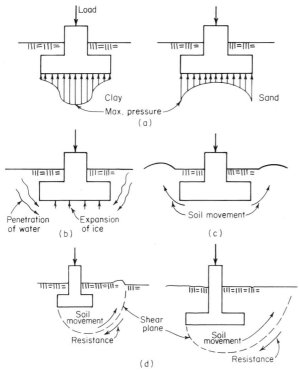

Fig. 4-7. Various properties and failures of a foundation. (a) Pressure isobars in clay and sand. (b) Failure by frost heave. (c) Failure by moisture-caused soil displacement. (d) Shear failure decreased by making footing deeper and wider.

cracking in the wall. Settlement in any type of rigid structure usually results in obvious cracks in the building. Unfortunately, settlement in steel structures is not as apparent because the deformation occurs throughout the structure. However, excessive settlement can overstress connections, causing them to fail when a heavy live load, as from a bridge crane, is applied.

Failures of high retaining walls are obvious when the wall starts to tip. Railroad tracks have been known to settle because of an intrusion of water under the track. Floor covering may become loose or plastered walls disintegrate from the intrusion of water due to capillary action. Corrections made to inadequately designed foundations are usually very costly and can interrupt production seriously.

EFFECT OF WATER ON SOILS

Moisture in soil will freeze and expand if the temperature drops below freezing. This can cause frost heave, which raises foundations or pavements. To prevent frost heave, foundations should be extended below the frost line, and the subgrade below roadway pavement should be kept drained. Another danger is that surplus water in clay soils will reduce the shearing strength of soil, causing failure by lessening the bearing power.

It is good practice to grade soil away from all building foundations to prevent water from standing next to the foundation. For basement construction, it is recommended that drainpipes be installed with open joints laid parallel to the footings to intercept subsurface water. This subterranean water should be drained away from the foundations.

GENERAL NOTES

The following notes should appear, when applicable, on earthwork construction drawings and can also serve as a punch list for the plant engineer.

1. All open excavations shall be completely surrounded at all times with sturdy barricades. All excavations and trenches left open at night shall be surrounded by flashing lights at intervals not to exceed 10 ft.
2. All backfills and fills to be used as subgrade shall be compacted to a relative density of 90 percent unless otherwise specified.
3. All excavation shall be done with care to see that no existing footings are disturbed.

4. Any overexcavation shall be filled with concrete up to the bottom of the footing elevations indicated on the drawing.

5. Excavations shall be neat lines and of sufficient size to permit installation and removal of formwork.

6. The bottoms of excavations shall be on firm undisturbed soil thoroughly compacted with a vibrating roller if required.

7. All underground pipelines shall be bedded on compacted bank-run sand. The first layer shall be bank-run sand with thickness of loose material to the center of the pipe. Subsequent layers shall be bank-run sand and shall not exceed 9-in. thickness of loose material to a minimum depth of 12 in. below the exposed surface. Fill shall be placed in loose layers not greater than 6 to 8 in. thick and compacted to 90 percent of maximum density.

8. Soils beneath all slabs shall be wetted sufficiently to obtain a moisture content in excess of optimum (as related to compaction) to a depth of 8 in. below the subbase. Moisture content is to be verified by soils engineer prior to placing slab.

9. Backfill adjacent to all walls shall be clean sand providing a separation of not less than 12 in. from soils native to site.

10. A 6-in.-thick layer of free-draining gravel (¾ in. maximum size) shall be placed beneath concrete floor slabs to act as a capillary break.

11. All layers shall be compacted with pneumatic hammer-type tampers to 95 percent minimum compaction.

12. Site clearing, stripping, surface preparation, compaction of soils, and foundation excavations shall be inspected and approved by a soils engineer.

13. The site shall be stripped to remove all trash, debris, asphalt paving, concrete, and other deleterious materials. These materials shall be removed from the site.

14. Surface of the cleared site in building or paved areas and in areas to receive fill shall have all exposed surfaces scarified, wetted, or dried to optimum moisture content and compacted to a minimum condition of 90 percent of maximum density.

15. The contractor is required to take due precautionary measures to protect the utility lines not of record or not shown on this drawing.

EXAMPLE

Specifications for Recompacted Fill
Under Storage Tanks

1. *Scope of work.* The work shall include all labor, material, and appliances required to complete all excavating, backfilling, filling, and grading necessary to properly complete the work indicated on the drawings and herein specified.

2. *Soil borings.* Log of soil boring, as indicated on the drawings and the soil report, does not constitute a guarantee of the uniformity of soil conditions over the entire site.

3. *Excavation.* The area designated as bottom of excavated plane (BEP) shall be excavated to the depths indicated. After the earth excavations have been made, the surfaces shall be scarified to a depth of 6 in., moistened to optimum moisture as specified under "filling." The areas shall then be filled and graded to the indicated finish grades and to the proper elevations to receive granular base and surfacing material. The earth excavated from the BEP area may be used for fill provided it conforms to the specifications and is approved by the soil engineer. Any earth required to complete the filling of the BEP area shall be provided by the contractor. All earth imported for this purpose shall be as specified under "filling."

4. *Backfilling and filling.* Required fills shall be made of materials free from debris, large clods, or stones and shall be deposited in layers, each layer being moistened and thoroughly compacted by rolling or tamping to avoid future settlement. The actual thickness of each layer of fill shall be held within such limits as to produce the degree of compaction specified and will depend upon the nature of the soil and the type and size of compacting equipment used. The amount of water used shall be rigidly controlled to ensure optimum moisture conditions for the type of fill materials used. Using the following modification of the AASHO method of testing (10-lb hammer, 18-in. drop, 25 blows on each of three layers, $\frac{1}{30}$ cu ft sample), the degree of compaction shall be at least 90 percent of maximum possible unless otherwise noted on drawings and/or specified by soil engineer.

5. *Imported fill material.* Any additional material required to complete the fills shall be clean, free from debris, large clods, stones, vegetable growth, or foreign materials, and may consist of fine gravel or crushed rock sand or earth of a sandy nature suitable for compaction as specified under "filling."

6. *Grading.* Upon completion of filling and backfilling, all areas to receive granular base or surfacing shall be uniformly graded to levels indicated on the drawings and/or required by base and surfacing thicknesses. Earth to receive granular base or surfacing shall be wetted down, and all loose material shall be compacted by rolling or tamping to create a smooth surface.

7. *Excess material.* All excess earth resulting from the excavating and backfilling not used in site grading work shall be removed from job site.

8. *Stockpile of excavated material.* Location of stockpile shall be as directed by the owner.

9. *Soil engineer.* All recommendations by soil engineering report shall be considered part of these specifications. All compaction of earthwork shall be approved by soil engineer.

EXAMPLE

Recompaction of Uncontrolled Fill Under Storage Tank

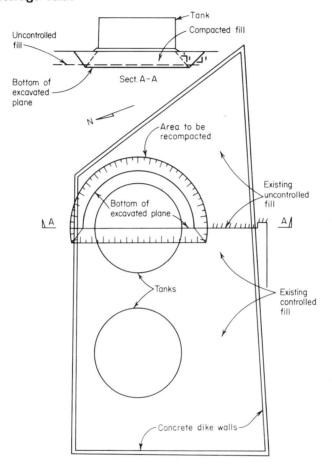

Tank

Compacted fill

Uncontrolled fill

Bottom of excavated plane

Sect. A-A

N

Area to be recompacted

Bottom of excavated plane

Existing uncontrolled fill

A

A

Tanks

Existing controlled fill

Concrete dike walls

Example:
Recompaction of uncontrolled fill under storage tank

SUMMARY

One of the hidden costs of most plant projects is the building foundation. Surface conditions often have very little relationship to the soil condition under the proposed foundations. Because of this, a soils investigation and report by a reputable soil engineer is recommended.

With the cost of plants continually rising, the difference in cost between a shallow spread-footing system and a deep pile-supported foundation may be the difference between an economic structure and an expensive one. To determine the most economic foundation for the situation, the plant engineer should have a basic knowledge of soils and geology in order to understand the soil report. Following the analysis of the soil, the plant engineer often must work with the designer of the foundations. For this reason, his familiarity with the various types of foundations must be adequate to enable him to choose the most economic combination of soil and foundation.

CHECKLIST FOR SOIL CONDITIONS

1. Classification of soil at various levels
2. Water table
3. Location of borings
4. Percent moisture in soil samples
5. Density of soil samples
6. Consolidation curve
7. Stability in excavation
8. Bearing value of soil

BIBLIOGRAPHY

American Institute of Architects and Charles George Ramsey, and Harold Reeve Sleeper: *Architectural Graphic Standards*, 6th ed., John Wiley & Sons, Inc., New York, 1970.

Chellis, Robert D.: *Pile Foundations*, 2d ed., McGraw-Hill Book Company, New York, 1961.

Department of Building and Safety Grading Division: *City of Los Angeles Official Grading Regulations*, Building News, Inc., Los Angeles, 1963.

Holmes, Arthur: *Principles of Physical Geology*, The Ronald Press Company, New York, 1946.

Krynine, Dimitri P.: *Soil Mechanics*, McGraw-Hill Book Company, New York, 1947.

Los Angeles City School Districts: *School Planning Manual*, Los Angeles, 1963.

Merriman, Thaddeus, and T. H. Wiggin: *American Civil Engineers' Handbook*, John Wiley & Sons, Inc., New York, 1947.

Merritt, Frederick S.: *Standard Handbook for Civil Engineers*, McGraw-Hill Book Company, New York, 1968.

Portland Cement Association: *PCA Soil Primer*, Skokie, Illinois, 1956.

Urquhart, Leonard Church: *Civil Engineering Handbook*, 4th ed., McGraw-Hill Book Company, New York, 1959.

CHAPTER FIVE

Storm Drainage for the Plant Site

PROPER DRAINAGE is of utmost importance to any industrial plant. Drainage failure due to poor flood-control planning can inundate building floors, work areas, and roads, thus interrupting plant operation. Flooding can also undermine critical foundations, break up pavements, and weaken floor slabs. Rapidly moving storm water can scour and erode gullies through plant property and generally wreak havoc on the plant site. To prevent this expensive and disruptive damage, the plant engineer must plan for proper drainage.

Preparation of an effective drainage plan begins with the study of a topographic map of the plant site and, if possible, of the adjacent areas. This map may have contour lines, which are lines joining all points of equal elevation or only indications of spot elevations. In that case the plant engineer can develop his own contour lines by interpolation between the known elevation points.

Topographic maps showing both contour lines and spot elevations appear in Figs. 5-1 and 5-2. A steep gradient causes the contour lines to group closer together, while a flattening makes them spread. Shading often indicates a sudden embankment, and hachure marks mean a depression. The slope or grade is determined by the vertical distance divided by the horizontal distance stated as a ratio or a percentage.

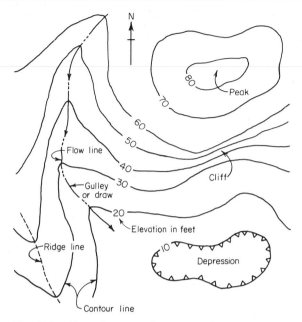

Fig. 5-1. Typical topographic map, showing contour lines, flow lines, ridges, peaks, and depressions.

The "ridge" or "crest line" divides two drainage areas. The region from which the rainfall will drain to a particular channel or area is referred to as the watershed of that area. The natural water course can be a gully, valley, or a ditch.

By studying the topographic map, the plant engineer can determine the location of all natural watercourses. He can also locate the source of runoff from the land upstream of his plant as well as the drainage courses downstream from his property. It is generally accepted that the historic location of drainage courses cannot be changed without the prior approval of the owners of the lands involved. Because of this, a knowledge of the historic drainage courses becomes important to the plant engineer. A recommended source of this type of information is the U.S. Geodetic Survey. Quadrangle maps prepared by the federal government are another source. Yet another source is the local road department or storm-drain department, which can provide the plant engineer with valuable data.

A basic understanding of hydrology and hydraulics will better prepare the plant engineer for the phenomenon of rainfall. Hydrology is the study of precipitation and the runoff caused by the precipitation. Hydraulics is the science dealing with the flow of water. Rainfall is measured in either total depth in inches for a given storm or season or at a rate of inches per hour during a specific storm. Frequency and the amount of rainfall vary widely from month to month, year to year, and even within a given area for a single storm. A plant engineer will find it useful to refer to isohyetal maps, which show relative amounts of rainfall much as contour lines show relative elevations on a topographic map.

In designing culverts or storm sewers within his plant site, the civil engineer is interested in three aspects of a storm: from the weather bureau records he must determine (1) the maximum rate of rainfall per hour of a maximum storm, (2) the duration in hours of the maximum storm, and (3) the frequency of the maximum storm. The frequency of a storm of a certain intensity is the probability that such a storm will occur within a certain number of years. As an example, a 5-year storm means one which will occur once every 5 years. The plant engineer can expect a severe storm of a given magnitude to occur once in 5, 10, 25, or 50 years. Obviously, for economic reasons the plant engineer may not be justified in constructing drainage devices for an intensity of rainfall that may occur only once in the life of the plant.

For the design of a drainage system, which may include a channel, ditch, or pipe, the amount of expected flow must first be determined.

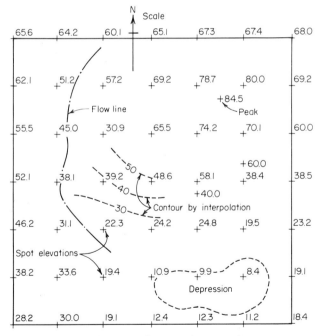

Fig. 5-2. Typical topographic map by spot elevations.

Among the many formulas found in reference books, the "rational method" is probably the simplest and the most commonly used:

$$Q = CIA$$

where Q = runoff of water, cu ft/sec
C = coefficient of runoff
I = intensity of rainfall in inches per hour based on time required for rain falling at most remote point to reach discharge point
A = drainage area, acres

Values of C, which represents the ratio of runoff to rainfall, can vary depending on such surface characteristics as vegetation, condition of soil, and steepness of slopes. Approximate values of C are given in Table 5-1.

Changes in land use during the lifetime of the drainage system should also be considered. The plant engineer who wishes a more detailed derivation and explanation of the rational method should refer to King's *Hydraulics* or Seelye's *Civil Engineer's Handbook*.

Having calculated the quantity of runoff, the design engineer can then select the drainage device. Generally, he has three methods from which to choose: sheet drainage, an open channel, or a closed conduit.

Sheet drainage is simply a properly graded surface. It is best paved to prevent erosion. As a rule, the slope should be made steep enough to avoid ponding and flat enough to prevent erosion. The criteria for grading of sheet drainage are shown in Fig. 5-3a.

Where conditions allow, open channels are most economical. They can be circular, rectangular, or triangular. Some of the typical open-channel drainage devices are street gutters, diversion ditches, and ditches surfaced and unsurfaced (Figs. 5-3, 5-4, and 5-5).

Closed conduits are used when underground devices are required. The common types are circular pipes, pipe arches, arches, and box drains. Examples of closed conduits as well as open channels are shown

TABLE 5-1

	Approximate C values
Watertight roof surfaces	0.75–0.95
Asphalt pavements	0.80–0.95
Concrete pavements	0.70–0.90
Gravel pavements	0.35–0.70
Impervious heavy soils, 1 to 2 percent slope	0.40–0.65
Moderately pervious soils, 1 to 2 percent slope	0.05–0.40

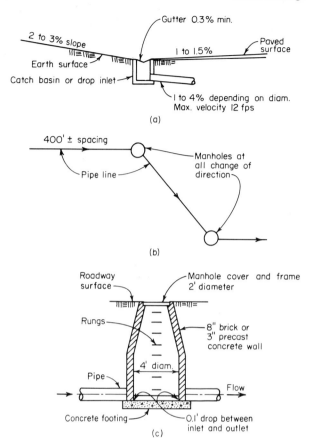

Fig. 5-3. Typical drainage devices. (*a*) Surface-drainage criteria for slopes; (*b*) manhole locations; (*c*) typical manhole.

in Fig. 5-5. Some are manufactured from galvanized steel, concrete, or clay and are named as follows:

1. Corrugated metal pipe (CMP)
2. Reinforced concrete pipe (RCP)
3. Vitrified clay pipe (VCP)

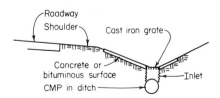

Fig. 5-4. Typical side-ditch drainage.

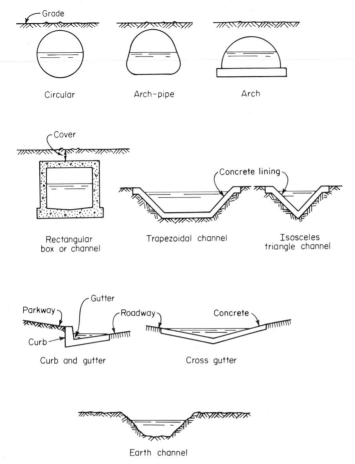

Fig. 5-5.   Typical open-channel drainage.

Valuable data for sizing and installation of these pipes can be obtained from handbooks published by Armco Co., American Pipe and Construction Co., and the Clay Pipe Institute.

The quantity of water that can be carried by any specific drainage device is a function of the various properties of the device—the size, shape, slope, condition of surface, and depth of water at inlet and outlet. Drainage conduits are usually part of a gravity system, and so hydraulic pressure head normally is not involved except at pump-lift stations, where the water must be lifted to a higher elevation.

The plant engineer who has the time and inclination to size an open channel or pipe should refer to hydraulics textbooks.   The relationship of flow to other properties is shown in Fig. 5-6.   Most design is based

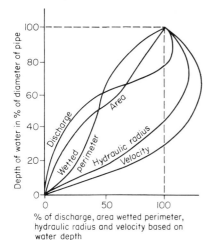

Fig. 5-6. Relationship in drainage pipe between discharge, wetted perimeter, area, hydraulic radius, and velocity.

upon the Manning formula (Fig. 5-7), which is

$$Q = a \times \frac{1.486}{n} \times R^{2/3} \times S^{1/2}$$

where Q = discharge or flow, cu ft/sec
a = cross-sectional area of flow, sq ft
n = coefficient of roughness or surface coefficient
R = hydraulic radius
S = slope

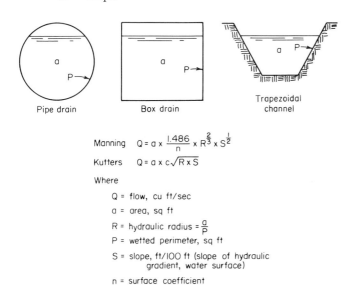

Manning $Q = a \times \dfrac{1.486}{n} \times R^{\frac{2}{3}} \times S^{\frac{1}{2}}$

Kutters $Q = a \times c\sqrt{R \times S}$

Where

Q = flow, cu ft/sec
a = area, sq ft
R = hydraulic radius = $\dfrac{a}{P}$
P = wetted perimeter, sq ft
S = slope, ft/100 ft (slope of hydraulic gradient, water surface)
n = surface coefficient

Fig. 5-7. Determining capacity of open channels.

TABLE 5-2

Surface	n
Cast-iron and wrought-iron pipe...	0.012
Vitrified-clay pipe................	0.013
Concrete pipe....................	0.013
Corrugated-metal pipe............	0.020
Earth canal.....................	0.017–0.0225

Values of n (coefficient of roughness) are given in Table 5-2.

The plant engineer has available well-tested standards for design of plant-drainage devices. These are the same standards used by the local city and county engineering departments dealing with storm drains and road design.

The following suggestions supplement the checklist to be followed in preparation of a plant-drainage design.

1. A topographic plan of the plant site should be made with contour lines at 5-ft intervals except on high banks shown. This map should show both existing and new conditions.
2. The scale of the topographic map should not be smaller than 1 in. to 20 ft; ⅛ in. to 12 in. would be better if the plant is not too large.
3. Finished elevations for hard surfaces should be to the nearest 0.01 ft; they should include floor elevations and the tops of man-holes, curbs, concrete gutters, and all tank foundations.
4. Finished elevations for earth surfaces should be to the nearest 0.1 ft. These elevations should be in grid form, and all sudden changes of grade, ridge lines, flow lines, top and bottom of banks, and spot elevations at change of direction of these items should be shown.
5. All walks and paved areas must be pitched away from all buildings and equipment foundations.
6. Minimum slope for all paved surfaces should be no less than 1 percent grade.
7. All flow lines below a rate of 0.50 percent should be constructed in concrete gutters.
8. Minimum slope for flow lines should be at 0.75 percent minimum grade.
9. All building roof drains should be directed to storm drains if they are available.
10. Storm drainpipes with less than 1-ft cover should be encased in concrete or be constructed of cast-iron pipe, except in the ve-

hicular traffic areas where all pipes with less than 1-ft cover should be encased in concrete.

11. All drainpipes should have cleanouts or Y's every 150 ft and at each change of direction of line to facilitate maintenance.

12. Manholes should be spaced at least 400 ft apart on long straight lines.

13. The crown of all roads should be sloped from the centerline 1.0 to 1.5 percent to allow drainage off the roadway (Figs. 5-3 and 5-8).

14. Gutters adjacent to roadways which collect drainage from the roadway should have a minimum slope of 0.3 percent.

15. Parkways draining to gutter should have a slope of 2.0 to 3.0 percent.

16. When designing drain pipes, the maximum velocity of flow in pipelines should be 12 ft/sec.

17. The maximum slope for paved or planted banks is normally 2 ft horizontal to 1 ft vertical.

18. Planting areas should not drain across traffic areas. Drainage should be diverted along edge of paving or pickup in drainage system.

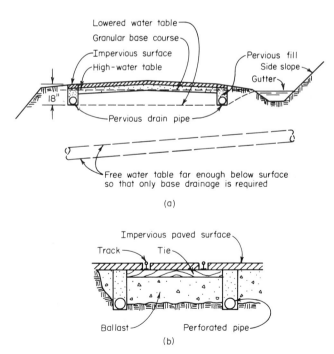

Fig. 5-8. Typical subterranean drainage methods.

19. Graded planes on the plant site should join public sidewalks where possible.
20. Planes should not intersect to concentrate drainage across public or plant sidewalks.
21. Where concentration is unavoidable, it should be diverted into a sidewalk culvert and spilled directly into the street gutter.
22. Roof downspouts spilling into unpaved areas must have splash blocks to minimize erosion.
23. On drainage plans, all storm-drain systems should indicate the following information:
    a. Size and type of drainpipe.
    b. Rate of slope, invert elevation at each change in rate of slope and/or direction, elevation and depth of catch basins (Fig. 5-9), manholes, and junction chambers, and size of culverts.
    c. Profile of major storm-drain lines.

The selection of every new plant site should be made with a thorough examination of the potential hazards from storms. In the study of the new site, the plant engineer should investigate the location and nature of all the local and natural drainage courses affecting the property. A natural drainage course is a wash, swale, ditch, or gully that is well defined and in an unimproved or partially improved condition. When a natural drainage course has been found, there should be no doubt where the water runs or what the extent of the watershed is. In the design of the new facilities, a natural drainage course can be realigned, but great care should be taken to ensure that the storm waters that are released downstream are at their natural outlet and at their natural velocities. If this is not done, the property downstream will be damaged by the relocation of the natural drainage courses.

The plant engineer should also look for existing sumps within the

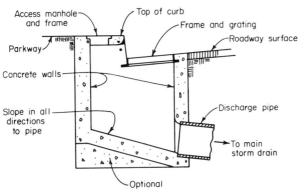

Fig. 5-9. Typical curb-type catch basin.

plant site. A sump is a low-lying area that has no outlet or only an inadequate one. If a sump is of a limited area and the depth of water ponded is less than 6 in., provision should be made for draining the sump within 4 hr after the storm. All foundations within a sump area should be extended at least 12 in. above the grade. Where the sump covers an extensive area, the land can be reclaimed in one of four ways: (1) a drainage system may be daylighted through an acceptable outlet; (2) the water may be pumped to an acceptable outlet; (3) the land may be filled; or (4) a retention basin may be provided. If the water is to be pumped, the pump should be sized to handle at least a 25-year storm. The discharged water must be conveyed to an improved outlet capable of receiving the additional water from the sump. If the site is improved by filling, the grading operation should be undertaken with great care so that diversion of the water does not cause detriment to the adjacent properties. Retention basins are normally used for large sites, and they should be large enough to accommodate the quantity of flow that will accumulate as a result of a major storm. Combinations of pumping and retention facilities can also be utilized.

Another condition demanding careful preparation is a plant site located on a flood plain, that is, a relatively flat area or lowland adjoining the channel of a river, stream, watercourse, ocean, lake, or other body of standing water which has been or may be covered by floodwater. In general, the existing watercourse is not large enough to confine the tributary storm flows. In many cases, there is no channel at all except a low flow ditch or shallow, poorly defined swale. When tributary storm waters will cause a depth in excess of 6 in. anywhere on the site, the property is generally considered subject to a flood hazard due to overflow. If it is determined that the tributary storm waters will flow at depths of less than 6 in. across a plant site, the property is considered to be subject only to sheet overflow. Therefore, grading, street drainage, or construction of drainage facilities can reduce the depth of overflow to 6 in. or less, and the entire site can then be considered to be exposed only to sheet overflow.

Another problem that can cause trouble to a plant site is high groundwater. In areas where available historic data indicate that the groundwater may rise to within 10 ft of the ground surface, serious problems may arise, especially if sewage is to be disposed of by using septic tanks or other percolation methods. Also, difficulties may arise during the construction or maintenance of subsurface structures, such as basement pits and underground tanks. This condition can be relieved by the construction of a subsurface drainage system of adequate capacity to keep the groundwater down to a required level or by selection of improvements which will not be harmed by such a condition.

In summary the plant engineer must understand the history and the future drainage characteristics of his plant site, which he can learn through studying topographic maps of his own site and of the adjacent areas. He can also study the storm-drain devices designed and installed by the local government engineering departments for their storm-drain designs. In this way he can tie his plant design in with that of the adjacent culverts, gutters, catch basins, and storm drains.

EXAMPLE

Over the past 5 years, a large soap company was frequently flooded during major rainstorms. Although some effort was made in pumping and grading, it appeared that the intensity of the flood got progressively worse.

The foundry downstream from the soap company had filled their land, but when they were threatened by a lawsuit, the management defended its actions. The entire flooding problem was turned over to the plant engineer. The results from his investigation ultimately led to a solution.

1. The first step was to obtain and study the original topographic maps of the area. This was easy since the U.S. Geodetic Service quadrangle maps were available from the local federal office.
2. From these maps it appeared that the soap company's property was situated in a natural watercourse to the riverbed adjacent to the property.
3. The riverbed had been improved by the flood control district about 10 years earlier. This improvement consisted of a 20-ft-high levee or dike at each side of the river to increase its capacity and to protect adjacent land from overflowing of the river. Unfortunately no provision was made to drain the soap company's property, which was now dammed by the dike.
4. The plant engineer looked into other local improvements in the area. A major improvement was a state highway which was widened and ramped up to a bridge crossing the river. The highway was at the upstream side of the property. Review of the plans showed that the highway embankment collected runoff and concentrated the flow through a culvert directly on the street in front of the soap company's property.
5. Since local flooding is the responsibility of the city, the local city engineer's office was visited. It was learned that the city was aware of the flooding caused by the highway culvert and river embankment. When asked for his recommendation, the city engineer said a large underground storm drain starting from the culvert and discharging into the river would solve the problem but the cost was too high for the city to handle.
6. The plant engineer reported to management that the flooding was

due in part to the county flood control district, the state highway department, and the inaction of the city. The plant engineer then suggested a meeting of all parties with the idea of constructing the necessary storm drain with its cost to be shared by all.

7. The meeting was held. Each party accepted part of the blame and agreed to share in the cost. The flooding problem was solved.

Example:
Design of drainage for diked tank farm

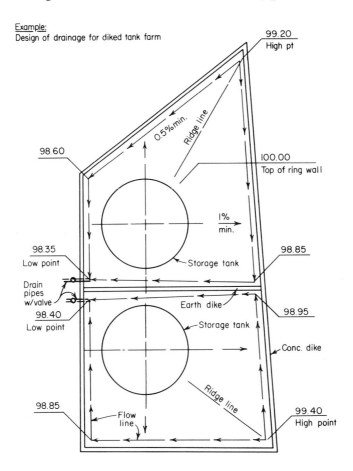

SUMMARY

Funding for protection against storm drainage is too often made after a destructive storm. It is difficult to plan a drainage system around an existing operating plant. For this reason such plans should be made during the initial design of the facilities.

In order to take an active part in storm design the plant engineer must understand topographic maps, plans, and profiles of pipelines and channels.   He must also know the local statistics of rainfall and properties of flow in various types of channels.

Other important aspects of drainage control are the proper design of roads, paved areas, and roofs.   All rain falling upon or flowing toward plant property must be adequately controlled and safely directed off the site.

CHECKLIST FOR PLANT DRAINAGE

1. Plant topographic map
2. Tributary watershed draining onto plant property
3. Expected maximum rainfall intensity
4. Type of surface
5. Types of drainage devices
   a. Gutters
   b. Channels and ditches
   c. Pipelines
6. Roof drainage
7. Public storm-drain systems
8. Industrial-waste contamination of storm water
9. Quantity of runoff
10. Velocity of runoff
11. Protection of underground structures
12. Roadway drainage
13. Catch basins
14. Manholes

BIBLIOGRAPHY

American Institute of Architects and Charles George Ramsey, and Harold Reeve Sleeper: *Architectural Graphic Standards,* 6th ed., John Wiley & Sons, Inc., New York, 1970.

Armco Drainage & Metal Products, Inc.: *Handbook of Drainage and Construction Products,* R. R. Donnelley & Sons Company, Chicago, 1955.

———: *Handbook of Water Control,* Lederer, Street and Zeus Co., Inc., Berkeley, Calif.. 1949.

Blendermann, Louis: *Design of Plumbing and Drainage Systems,* The Industrial Press, New York, 1959.

Davis, Calvin Victor, and Kenneth E. Sorensen: *Handbook of Applied Hydraulics,* 3d ed., McGraw-Hill Book Company, New York, 1969.

Fairbanks, Morse & Co.: *Hydraulic Handbook,* Kansas City, Kans., 1959.

Hydrology Committee: *Hydrology Handbook,* The American Society of Civil Engineers, New York, 1949.

King, Horace Williams, and Ernest F. Brater: *Handbook of Hydraulics,* 5th ed., McGraw-Hill Book Company, New York, 1963.

Los Angeles City School Districts: *School Planning Manual,* Los Angeles, 1963.

Los Angeles Department of County Engineer: *Sanitary Sewer and Industrial Waste Ordinance,* Los Angeles, 1966.

Merriman, Thaddeus, and T. H. Wiggin: *American Civil Engineers' Handbook,* John Wiley & Sons, Inc., New York, 1947.

Merritt, Frederick S.: *Standard Handbook for Civil Engineers,* McGraw-Hill Book Company, New York, 1968.

New York State Department of Health: *State Building Construction Code Applicable to Plumbing,* Albany, N.Y., 1964.

Peckworth, Howard F.: *Concrete Pipe Handbook,* American Concrete Pipe Association, Arlington, Va., 1966.

Steel, Ernest W.: *Water Supply and Sewerage,* 4th ed., McGraw-Hill Book Company, New York, 1960.

Urquhart, Leonard Church: *Civil Engineering Handbook,* 4th ed., McGraw-Hill Book Company, New York, 1959.

Vennard, John K.: *Elementary Fluid Mechanics,* John Wiley & Sons, Inc., New York, 1947.

CHAPTER SIX

Plant Transportation:
Roads and Railroads

PLANT TRANSPORTATION SYSTEMS include roadways, railroads, truck-loading areas, and parking facilities. Roadways can range from an inexpensive but temporary hardened dirt driveway to a reinforced-concrete pavement, which is both costly and permanent. The type of industrial road selected should depend upon such factors as traffic density, the weight of the vehicles, and the condition of the subsoil.

Occasionally, the plant engineer must lay out a new roadway through the plant, and it is useful to understand the basics of road design.

The centerline of a roadway and the parallel edges of the pavement are laid out in a series of straight lines connected by simple curves. These curves are made with a large enough radius for easy turning but not so large that they occupy too much land. The customary width of each traffic lane is 12 ft, and the total number of lanes required determines the overall width of the roadway. When composed of dirt, the curbs and shoulders should be lightly oiled for stability; or they should be paved with asphalt. The shoulders are made to drain away from the roadway to parallel drainage ditches or toward the roadway to paved gutters.

Concrete curbs and gutters are constructed to collect the surface water from both the roadway pavement and parkway. A parkway, which is the strip of land between the curb and the property line, is public property. Many large plants with a great deal of foot traffic require the construction of a concrete sidewalk adjacent to the curb. Sidewalks are usually 3 to 4 ft wide and 3 in. thick. The vertical distance between the center of the roadway and the flow line of the gutter is called the "crown" of the road. Its purpose is to drain the roadway toward the gutter. In some single-lane roads, and in most alleys, the center of the roadway is lower than the edges. In this condition, called an "inverted crown," the water runs down the center of the road.

For good design of plant roadways, consideration should be taken of the following points:

1. The cut and fill should be balanced to avoid or at least minimize the need to import or export earth.
2. The existing drainage system of the plant site should be retained as much as possible. Do not fight the natural flow of water. Use sump pumps as a last resort.
3. Gutters should be designed to collect, transfer, and discharge rainwater fast enough to carry suspended matter without causing excessive erosion.
4. The gutter should be placed at an elevation that will allow the collection of drainage from areas adjacent to roadway.
5. A 25-ft-wide roadway will handle most types of two-way plant traffic.
6. Roads should be wide enough to provide a minimum 2-ft clearance between passing trucks with an additional 1-ft clearance at the side of each truck. This means that a 20-ft-wide roadway is the minimum requirement for an 8-ft-wide vehicle, although some states recommend a maximum width of 8 ft 6 in. for a truck.
7. A 4-ft-wide pedestrian walk should be provided where pedestrians also use the roadway.
8. Gates for one-way traffic should be 20 ft wide, and for two-way traffic 30 ft wide.
9. Recommended curbs and gutters consist of a 2-ft-wide gutter with a curb that is 6 in. thick and 6 or 8 in. high. The height of the curb is governed by the amount of drainage anticipated.
10. The parkway should slope to the top of the gutter with a slope of $\frac{1}{4}$ in. to 12 in. so that water does not stand on the parkway. The top of the curb is usually at the same level as the crown of the street.
11. Shoulders should be provided for roadways having no curbs or gutters.
12. Inverted-crown roadways should have concrete gutters at the center of the road to prevent erosion.

13. Catch basins, drop inlets, guardrails, fire hydrants, signs, culverts, and fencing should be provided where required.

When discussing or reviewing plans for plant roads with civil engineers, the plant engineer should know all the basic terms used. Most roadway-design terminology takes the centerline of the roadway as its frame of reference. A straight run of the centerline between curves is called the "tangent," since it is tangent to the curve. The point where the tangent line meets the curve is called the "beginning of curve" (BC). The point where the curve meets the tangent again is called the "end of curve" (EC). Both points are also known as the "point of curve" and "point of tangent" (PC and PT). The point at which the projection of two intersecting tangents meet is called "point of inter-section" (PI). The angular difference between two tangent lines is called the "deflection angle" of the curve or "delta." Delta is also equal to the angle at the "radius point" encompassing the curve. The distance between the PI and the arc of a curve is called the "external" (E), and the distance between the arc of a curve and its chord is called the "median" (M).

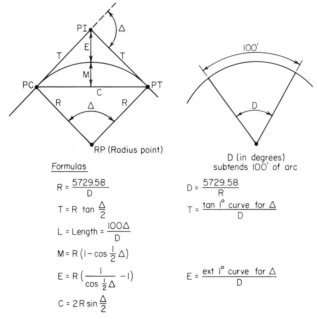

Formulas

$$R = \frac{5729.58}{D}$$

$$T = R \tan \frac{\Delta}{2}$$

$$L = \text{Length} = \frac{100\Delta}{D}$$

$$M = R \left(1 - \cos \frac{1}{2}\Delta\right)$$

$$E = R \left(\frac{1}{\cos \frac{1}{2}\Delta} - 1\right)$$

$$C = 2R \sin \frac{\Delta}{2}$$

D (in degrees) subtends 100' of arc

$$D = \frac{5729.58}{R}$$

$$T = \frac{\tan 1° \text{ curve for } \Delta}{D}$$

$$E = \frac{\text{ext } 1° \text{ curve for } \Delta}{D}$$

Fig. 6-1. Horizontal-curve data used in design of roadways. Tangent offsets: the approximate offset from the tangent to the curve at any distance from the PC = distance²/2R.

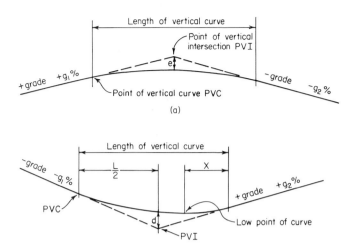

Fig. 6-2. Vertical curves used in the design of roadways: (*a*) convex and (*b*) concave curve. Formulas used for determining curves:

$$A = \text{algebraic difference of grades } +g - (-g)$$

$$e = \frac{AL}{8}$$

$$d = \frac{l^2 A}{2L}$$

The "degree of curvature" (D) is defined as the interior angle subtended by a 100-ft arc (Fig. 6-1). It is significant that this definition differs from the railroad-design definition, where the degree of curvature is the interior angle subtended by a 100-ft chord and not the arc.

The "gradient" *g* of a roadway is defined as a change in the elevation in feet per 100 ft of horizontal distance (Fig. 6-2). An uphill gradient is known as a positive grade (+g) while a downhill gradient is a negative grade (−g). The primary grade is called g_1, and a secondary grade is g_2. The point of vertical intersection (PVI) refers to the point where the projections of two grades meet. The curve joining the two grades is called the "vertical curve." The vertical distance between the PVI and the curve is *e* on a convex curve and *D* on a concave curve. The horizontal length of the vertical curve is *L*, and *A* is the algebraic difference between the two grades. The relationship between these properties is

$$A = +g_1 - g_2$$

and

$$e = \frac{AL}{8}$$

MATERIALS AND CONSTRUCTION OF ROADWAYS

There are two major subdivisions of road surfacing, the rigid type and the flexible, or bituminous type (Fig. 6-3). Rigid roadways are made of concrete and reinforcing bars or welded wire mesh. The reinforcement is usually placed 2 in. from the top surface of the pavement. The thickness of the concrete and the amount of reinforcement vary with the traffic load, the type of base used, and the nature of the subsoil under the base. The base is the layer of granular material under the pavement. The weaker the base or soil, the stronger and more rigid the pavement must be.

The H values given for road classification are based on the maximum wheel loading of the vehicles. The theory behind the rigid pavement is that the wheel load will deflect the slab and cause a depression or dimple in the subsoil. Therefore, the concrete slab should be capable of distributing the wheel load to the soil. Because of this, the softer

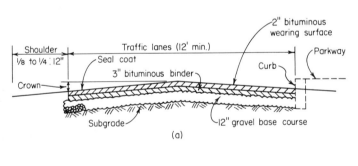

(a)

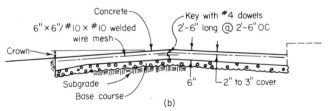

(b)

Fig. 6-3. Typical flexible and rigid roadways. (These are sample designs for reference only.) (*a*) High-type bituminous and (*b*) high-type rigid. Portland cement concrete, plain or reinforced (for mixed traffic under 300 vehicles per day).

the subgrade, the bigger the dimple and the greater the flexural stress in the concrete.

JOINTS IN CONCRETE SLABS

Because of the nature of concrete, large slabs almost always develop cracks caused by contraction, settlement, and thermal expansion.   Contraction joints are used to control the inevitable cracking due to the curing shrinkage of the concrete.   They are usually sawcuts, ⅛ in. wide and ½ in. deep, into the surface of the cured concrete slab.   These joints are usually spaced 10 to 20 ft apart.

To control the problem of cracking caused by settlement, it is advisable to provide a keyway from one slab pour to another at all construction joints.   Reinforcing bars should also be introduced to tie adjacent slabs together.   With properly constructed joints, the slabs will tend to settle together as a unit.

Expansion joints are recommended for large concrete slabs (Fig. 6-4). Expansion joints usually consist of a resilient type of filler material, such as neoprene or asphalt-saturated felt, which is placed in the joint and which can contract as the concrete expands.   To further prevent vertical movement, steel dowels are extended from one slab and allowed to slide into the other.   Proper design and construction of all joints will result in a rigid, continuous concrete roadway with a minimum of unwanted cracks and settlement.

FLEXIBLE ROADWAY SURFACING

Flexible road surfaces may be divided into three types, low, intermediate, and high.   The low type is merely a surface treatment of one or two

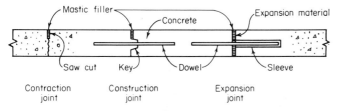

Fig. 6-4.   Typical joints in rigid-type pavement.

coats of asphalt over existing native soil.   The intermediate type, also called "road mix," is a 2- to 3-in. layer of asphalt mixed with selected sandy soil over a 6-in. base course of crushed rock, decomposed granite, or similar granular material.   The high type is approximately 3 in. of asphaltic concrete placed over 6 to 9 in. of a properly selected base course.

Automobile and truck parking areas are normally surfaced with 3 to 6 in. of asphaltic concrete over a 3- to 6-in. base course. Here again, the thickness of the base and surfaces is governed by the conditions.

A properly constructed flexible pavement consists of the surface seal coat, a binder course below the seal coat, a base course, and a prepared subgrade. The seal coat, as its name implies, makes the surfacing impervious to water. The binder course gives the surfacing enough strength to distribute the load from the wheels. The base course supports the binder course and distributes the wheel load to a greater area of the subgrade. Since the base course consists of rock and gravel, it also prevents water from rising to the surface by capillary action. The subgrade is normally graded away from the crown to permit subgrade drainage away from the roadway.

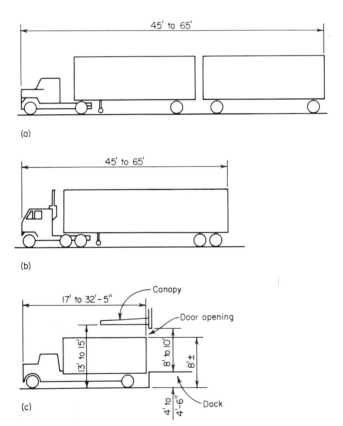

Fig. 6-5. Three types of trucks: (*a*) truck tractor, semitrailer, and full trailer; (*b*) truck tractor and semitrailer; (*c*) van.

PLANT TRUCKS

Planning economical and efficient shipping and receiving areas is a plant engineer's responsibility. He must first know the types and dimensions of trucks (Fig. 6-5).

There are two major classifications of trucks, the two-axle truck and the multiaxle tractor-truck with a semitrailer. The absolute maximum vehicle width allowed without special permit is 8 ft. Vertical clearance must be 14 ft above roadway, and the horizontal minimum clearance is usually 10 ft. Curb-to-curb clearance for a two-lane road is at least 6 ft wider than the roadway but not less than 26 ft.

The maximum allowable length of a truck may vary from state to state, but the average length of a semi-tractor-trailer runs from 45 to 64 ft. State size and weight limits for tractors and trailers are shown in Fig. 6-6.

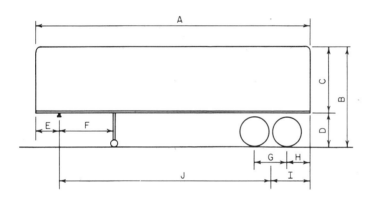

CONVENTIONAL DIMENSIONS

A	Overall length	22' - 40'
B	Overall height	12'-6" - 14'
C	Body height	7' - 10' (more for drop frame)
D	Floor height	4' - 4'-6"
E	Front to C/L kingpin	2' - 3'-6"
F	C/L kingpin to landing gear	82" (SAE)*
G	Tandem axle spacing c to c	4' - 4'-4"
H	C/L rear axle to rear end	2' - 7'
I	C/L tandem assembly to rear end	4' - 10'
J	C/L kingpin to C/L of tandem assembly	14' - 34'

*Minimum dimension with three axle tractors

Fig. 6-6. Trailer lengths: conventional dimensions of a truck-trailer. (*Truck-Trailer Manufacturers' Association, Inc.*)

TRUCK LOADING

Weights of trucks are determined by the H-loading classification, which is given in tons per vehicle. Therefore an H20 is a 20-ton vehicle, H15 is a 15-ton vehicle, and H10 is a 10-ton vehicle. The total weight is distributed with 20 percent of the total load on the front axle and 80 percent of the total load on the rear axle. With single wheels at each axle, these axle loads are equally divided between the two wheels. An H20 truck has 8,000 lb on the front axle and 32,000 lb on the rear axle, while an H15 vehicle has 6,000 lb on the front axle and 24,000 lb on the rear axle. To determine contact loads, the loading under the tire is usually considered to be 1 in. per ton width of total truck weight.

Trucks and trailers are classified as H20/S16, which means that the rear axle carrying the trailer has a 16-ton load on it. The weight carried by each axle load of an H20/S16 truck-trailer is 8,000 lb at the front axle, 32,000 lb on the middle axle, and 32,000 lb on the rear axle.

Since this chapter cannot cover all the many aspects of proper dock design, the following list gives suggestions for good design where conditions permit (Fig. 6-7).

1. Angle docks if you have a space problem.
2. Consider dock levelers, dockboards, and dock plates.
3. Provide for conveyors and portable ramps if needed.
4. Set columns on 25-ft centers, thus providing room for two 12-ft-wide dock stalls.
5. Install vertical sliding doors and keep them high enough to clear forklifts.
6. Keep dock height 50 to 52 in. without dock levelers.
7. Keep dock height 48 in. with dock levelers.
8. Provide ramps or elevators for forklifts.
9. Keep stalls 10 to 14 ft wide.
10. Build recess dock 10 ft longer than the legal limit of truck-trailer.
11. Install bumper guards out of shock-absorbent material and not of wood.
12. Install canopy 14 ft wide cantilevered over trailer.
13. Do not permit water to spill on the ground in the loading dock area where freezing occurs since ice will cause a loss of traction and a great loss of efficiency.

PARKING FACILITIES FOR TRUCKS

When planning docking facilities, roadways, and apron space for truck maneuvering, it is good practice to secure and keep the following information at hand:

1. Length of truck and trailer unit allowed
2. Width of truck and trailer unit allowed
3. Turning radii required for the units involved
4. Height of trailer
5. Drainage requirements
6. Composition of roadway including soil conditions

The apron space is the area required to maneuver a tractor-trailer into or out of a docking stall. The size of the space depends on such things as the number of other trucks and the width of the berth itself. Over the past 20 years this length of apron space has been increased in half the states. If your state is considering an increase in length,

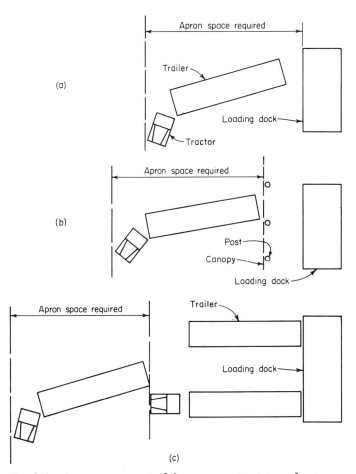

Fig. 6-7. Apron space required for maneuvering into and out of position: (*a*) unobstructed dock, (*b*) post-supported canopy, (*c*) alongside other vehicles.

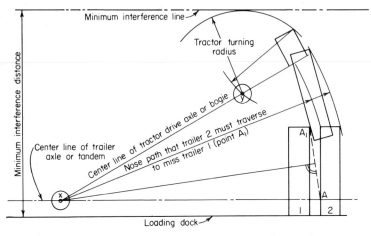

Fig. 6-8. Recommended method for determining radius and clearance for a large truck.

1. Draw to scale trailers up against the loading dock at the expected minimum spacings. (Use measurements of the longest and widest trailer expected at the dock with rearmost axle or tandem position.)

2. Extend trailer 2 or tandem centerline in direction of turn.

3. Draw chord AA_1 from that point on the side of the trailer 2 where the axle or tandem centerline intersects the side of the body to the nose corner of the adjacent trailer (1). This is a chord of the curve through which point trailer 2 must traverse to miss trailer 1.

4. Bisect chord AA_1 and extend a perpendicular line until it intersects the extension of trailer 2 axle or tandem centerline at point X. This is the point about which all points on trailer 2 must rotate to miss striking trailer 1.

5. With the compass point on point X, swing trailer 2 nose around until point A reaches A_1. Sketch trailer 2 in its position as shown.

6. Through the location of the kingpin, extend a line back through point X. This line then represents the centerline of the tractor drive axle or bogie. From this drive-axle centerline, draw the tractor with the greatest turning radius in its proper position with respect to trailer 2 in its second position.

7. With the compass point on the tractor front bumper (opposite side from the direction of the turn) scribe an arc equal to the turning radius of the tractor so that it intersects the centerline of the tractor drive axle at point Y.

8. With the compass set at the turning radius of the tractor, place the point at Y and scribe an arc that represents the curve through which the bumper will travel.

For the result, measure the distance from the dock to that point on the curve just drawn which represents the greatest distance from the dock. *Based on a single continuous forward movement. This represents the absolute minimum distance away from the dock needed for maneuvering area.*

Minimum interference distances can be decreased by increas-

it would be wise to assume that the increase will become effective and provide for it in your design.

Since the legal width of trailers is 8 ft, the width of a dock berth should be no less than 10 ft. Some stalls are as much as 14 ft wide, which may be required in rare cases. In most designs the suggested minimum width for the berth is 12 ft. A rule of thumb for estimating the necessary apron space, assuming a 12-ft-wide stall, relies on the length of the truck-trailer itself. From the loading dock to the nearest obstacle that must be cleared the "minimum interference distance" should be twice the maximum allowable length of the tractor-trailer. This method is not exact, however. See Fig. 6-8 for a precise method of determining maneuvering clearance.

Before making a final decision on the apron space and the minimum interference distance, the state trucking association or the Truck-Trailer Manufacturers' Association should be consulted, particularly if the situation is at all unusual. It is also advisable to ask the local traffic department for suggestions.

An additional item for consideration is the grade immediately adjacent to the dock. If the merchandise is liquid, it is good practice to slope the grade toward the dock so that in the event of breakage or spillage, the trailer can be emptied easily.

In docking areas asphalt paving is not always practical since it will not withstand the harsh treatment that accompanies docking procedures when trailers are spotted for loading. It is therefore essential that a 6-in. minimum thickness concrete slab be installed. The slab should run the full length of the dock area. The slab should be at least as wide as the wheelbase of the trailer plus the distance between the wheels and the dock. Normally, the width of slab is about 40 ft, which assures that the landing gear will rest on concrete rather than asphalt. It is recommended that the plant engineer consult with the trucking firm involved for a careful discussion of the problems of grade, traction,

---

ing the minimum spacing between trailers; using trailers with the axle or tandem advanced as far forward as possible; using tractors with smaller turning radii, and using a saw-toothed loading platform design. Power steering can be of some help in a practical operation since for a given turning radius the less effort required to turn a tractor, the shorter the distance required to maneuver the vehicle.

As a matter of practical consideration, an additional allowance over and above the dimension shown in the graphical computation should be provided to allow a safety margin.

It should be noted that the illustrated design and explanation can be used to solve other problems of combination vehicle maneuvering and offtracking, such as determining width of an entrance gate, space required for saw-toothed dock designs, etc.

and protection against snow and ice conditions. Under bad weather conditions some fully loaded rigs cannot be hauled out of loading pits.

Restrictions in trailer height also vary considerably. To be safe, a minimum overhead clearance of 15 ft should be specified for all pipe bridges over docks, yards, and driveways where normal truck traffic will occur. In addition, special provisions should be made to provide a route in and out of the plant for unusually large machinery and tanks that exceed the normal 15-ft clearance when placed on a low trailer.

Every plant site comes complete with its own special problems. No one plan will suit all conditions. Though it is almost a cliché to emphasize the importance of planning for future needs, one cannot state too often that the effort is absolutely necessary and will never be regretted. Planning for the future almost invariably improves the efficiency of the layout under consideration. All states have restrictions on length, width, and height of tractor-trailer combinations. The information given, while recent, should be checked periodically with the state highway department or state trucking association to ensure that it is up to date.

PARKING FACILITIES FOR AUTOMOBILES

Automobile parking requirements for industrial facilities are usually governed by code and vary with the community involved; the following general comments are representative (Fig. 6-9).

1. There should be a surface parking area within 400 ft of the plant property that provides adequate space for all vehicles directly involved with plant operations.
2. In addition, one parking space should be provided for every two employees on the shift having the largest number of employees, or one space should be provided for every 500 sq ft of total plant building, whichever is greater. An area should also be designated for visitors' parking.
3. Each parking space should be a minimum of 8 ft wide by 18 ft long except at the dead end of an aisle, where the last parking space should be 11½ ft wide to facilitate turning.
4. Parking spaces may be perpendicular, or 90°, to the aisle, diagonal, or 30 to 60° to the aisle, or parallel. For parking layout, Fig. 6-9 shows recommended widths and lengths for double-row stalls at various angles.
5. As shown on the parking layout, the minimum required backup space behind each parking stall regardless of orientation is 25 ft.
6. For parallel parking, aisles should maintain a minimum width of 10 ft.

7. Traffic flow should be marked with painted arrows and designated as one-way or two-way traffic.
8. One-way aisles should be at least 12 ft wide and two-way aisles at least 20 ft wide.
9. The parking area should be paved with at least 3 in. of asphaltic concrete graded properly for surface drainage.
10. The recommended minimum slope is 1 percent, and the maximum slope is 5 percent.   A slope of 2 percent is considered best.

Zoning codes of many urban communities require that at least 2 percent of the total area devoted to parking having 20 or more parking spaces should be landscaped and continuously maintained.   These codes also require that the selection of planting, which includes shrubs, bushes, or trees, be approved by the planning commission.

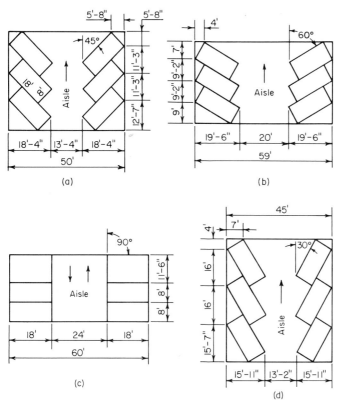

Fig. 6-9. Typical parking-lot layouts. (All dimensions are net. Allowance must be made for required fences, walls, or obstructions.) (a) 45°, (b) 60°, (c) 90°, and (d) 30° parking.

Also required are sprinklers or irrigation systems to these areas and select topsoil to be placed in the planting areas.

The edge of a paving should be trimmed with a 2 by 6 in. rough redwood header, set 2 in. above the top of the paving. The headers are held in place with 2 by 4 in. stakes set 4 ft on center (Fig. 6-10).

An alternative to the redwood header would be a 6-in.-wide concrete curb set 4 to 8 in. above the surface of the paving and 2 in. above the adjacent top of the topsoil in the planter.

Industrial parking areas, when adjacent to residential areas, should be screened off by a 6-ft-high wall.

Lighting for parking areas should be so oriented that it will not annoy adjacent landowners.

For proper parking-area layouts, many city codes prohibit maneuvers on public sidewalks for access to parking spaces, as well as tandem parking. Also prohibited is backing into public streets when leaving a parking lot. Therefore the parking area should be designed so that exit from the parking lot always entails forward motion.

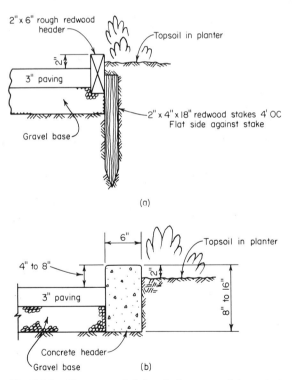

Fig. 6-10. Recommended details for automobile parking area: (a) redwood header for edge of asphalt pavement and (b) concrete header for edge of asphalt pavement.

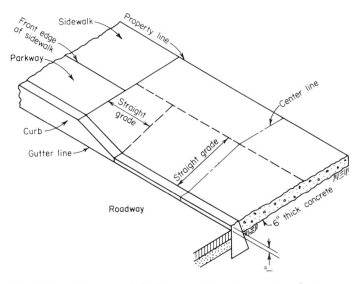

Fig. 6-11. Recommended driveway through street curb to industrial property.

When designing a parking area, it should be remembered that all dimensions given are net and additional allowance must be made for required fences, walls, and obstructions.

For parking areas requiring ramps, special care should be made in the design of ramps to prevent the rear ends of cars from scraping the roadway. The maximum recommended ramp slope is about 12 percent, and each end of the ramp should be curved for easy transition to the level planes. Driveways should be similar to that shown in Fig. 6-11.

In summary, the best guidance the plant engineer can have for the layout of his parking area is conformance to the codes of the planning department of his local government. These codes are based on the combined efforts of traffic engineers, architects, civil engineers, landscape architects, and the automobile industry.

PLANT RAILROAD FACILITIES

The layout of railroad facilities within the plant site requires a fundamental understanding of railroad engineering. The principles used in cross-country lines and railroad yards also apply in a smaller degree to the industrial plant's spur tracks, switching, clearances, and hardware.

The most important component of railroad is the rail, which is described by the weight of the rail per yard of length, for example, "a 120-lb rail." The depth, width, and configuration of each rail is based on its weight. The heavier and faster the train, the heavier the rail used. Rails, which are usually 39 ft long, are bolted together although some railroad tracks use welded rail.

Recent automatic-welding techniques permit economic welding over long runs, but they are not for plant-site installations and are used mainly for high-speed transcontinental tracks.

Standard rails are set with a distance of 4 ft 8½ in. between the inside surface of the rails. This distance, called the "gage," is common for all railroads in the United States. There are nonstandard gages for tracks carrying mine cars or other special cars. For railroad work in foreign countries, the plant engineer should check the local railroad company standards.

Rails are supported by crossties that are normally made of wood and measure about 8 by 9 in. and 8 ft 6 in. in length. Spacing of ties is approximately 21 in. on center. The rails are fastened to the ties with two spikes per tie. On curves, a tie plate is added under the rail to resist centrifugal forces of the railroad car.

Ties are laid on a bed of compacted crushed rock called "ballast." The depth of the ballast is between 20 and 24 in., 8 to 12 in. of which is below the bottom of the tie. The top of the ties is about 2 in. above the top of the ballast. The purpose of the ballast is to absorb and distribute the weight of the railroad cars. The soil below the ballast, called the "roadbed," should be compacted and graded to provide a firm drained surface, as the track could settle if the roadbed became soft. Proper drainage away from the track and roadbed must always be provided.

State public utility commissions (see Fig. 6-12) require that minimum clearances be maintained adjacent to and above all tracks. On a straight track a minimum clearance distance of 8 ft 6 in. is required, while on a curve, the clearance should be 1 ft greater. The minimum overhead clearance above the rail should be 22 ft 6 in. Many telephone and power companies would like to maintain as much as 26 to 27 ft clearance. It is a wise practice for the plant engineer to check the required overhead clearances with the serving railroad and utility companies when planning the construction of any overhead structures, such as a pipe or conveyor bridge spanning a railroad track.

The railroad clearances required for tracks within a plant building can be an exception. The overhead clearance above a rail located inside a building may be reduced to 18 ft provided that the track terminates within the building and that all railroad cars are brought to a stop before entering the building.

For parallel tracks, the minimum distance between centerlines of adjacent tracks should be 14 ft. Side clearance of railroad tracks should be as follows. A side clearance to a pole is 8 ft 3 in.; for switchboxes, switch-operating mechanisms, and accessories necessary for the control and operation of the signals projecting 4 in. or less above the top of the rail it is 3 ft; for signals and switches projecting more than 4 in. and less than 3 ft above the top of the rail it should be 6 ft. For other detailed regulations refer to the public utility commission orders.

Although the design of a railroad-switch curve is the responsibility of the railroad engineer, the plant engineer is frequently involved during the planning stage and should be familiar with some of the important railroad engineering terms. A brief description of some of these terms follows.

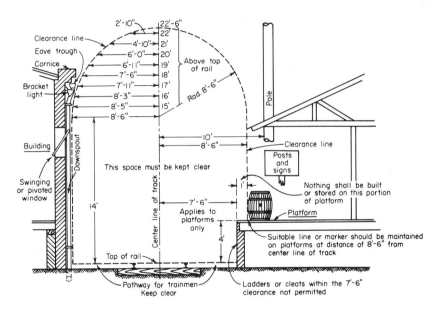

Notes

Overhead wire clearances shall conform to commission's general order No. 95 or amendments thereof

Posts, poles, signs, and similar facilities may have minimum clearance of 8'-6", but clearance of 10' is recommended where practicable

All side clearance dimensions are for tangent track. In general, side clearance for curve track to be 1' greater than that for tangent track

When track is used principally for loading or unloading refrigerator cars, platform with height of 4'-6" above top of rail may be maintained, provided that minimum side clearance to center line of track shall be 8'

Platforms 4' or less in height with minimum clearance of 7'-3" may be extended at existing clearances if such extension is not in connection with reconstruction of original platform

Icing platforms and supports shall have minimum clearance of 7'-8"

Fig. 6-12. Typical clearance of structures from standard-gage railroad tracks. (*Public Utilities Commission, State of California.*)

A "frog" is a section of rail which is used at the intersection of two rails to support the wheels and provide passageway for their flanges, thereby allowing the wheels on either rail to cross the other. Each frog is known by its number, which determines the angle between tracks. The procedure for track layout is to select a particular frog from the table which conforms to the required angle between tracks. A radius of curve is then selected that will suit the site conditions. Once the radius is known, the degree of curve can be determined. The degree of curve for a railroad is defined as

$$D = \frac{100\Delta}{L}$$

where Δ is the interior angle and L is the length of chord. As an example if Δ equals 75° and L equals 300 ft, then $D = 100 \times 75/300$ or 25°. See Fig. 6-13 for railroad curves and nomenclature.

The length and width of most common railroad cars are shown in Fig. 6-14. Weights are given in Table 6-1. Occasionally, the plant engineer must determine the data of an existing railroad curve. Figure

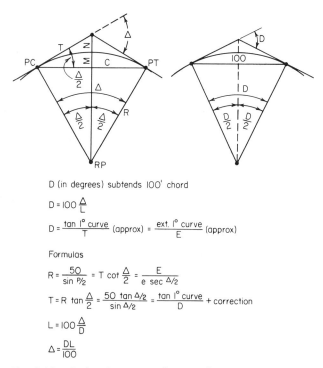

D (in degrees) subtends 100' chord

$$D = 100 \frac{\Delta}{L}$$

$$D = \frac{\tan 1° \text{ curve}}{T} \text{ (approx)} = \frac{\text{ext. } 1° \text{ curve}}{E} \text{ (approx)}$$

Formulas

$$R = \frac{50}{\sin P/2} = T \cot \frac{\Delta}{2} = \frac{E}{e \sec \Delta/2}$$

$$T = R \tan \frac{\Delta}{2} = \frac{50 \tan \Delta/2}{\sin \Delta/2} = \frac{\tan 1° \text{ curve}}{D} + \text{correction}$$

$$L = 100 \frac{\Delta}{D}$$

$$\Delta = \frac{DL}{100}$$

Fig. 6-13. Railroad curves and nomenclature.

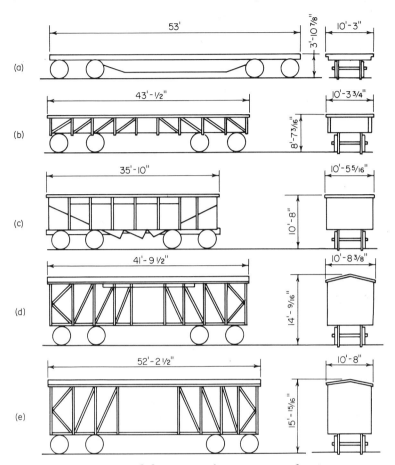

Fig. 6-14. Diagrams and dimensions of average sizes of various types of freight cars. Not to be used for close clearances since many roads operate cars both larger and smaller.

TABLE 6-1 Weights of Railroad Cars

Type of car	Tare weight of car, lb
Flatcar	48,700
Gondola	42,800
Hopper car	30,000
Boxcar	48,200
Automobile car	53,300

6-15 shows the streamlined method that may be used to find the curve of a section of track where original railroad drawings are not available.

Parts of a typical railroad switch are shown in Fig. 6-16. The distance from the point of the frog to the point of the switch is called the "lead." The distance from the point of switch to the pivot point of the switch rail is called the "length of the switch rail." The angle of the frog is called the "frog angle." The length of frog is divided into two distances called the "toe" and the "heel." Other parts of the switch curve are as follows: point of intersection (PI), point of curve (PC), point of tangent (PT), the radius point (RP), the radius (R). The length of switch rail, frog, curve-closure rail, and lead are all properties of the frog number and can be found in frog tables.

SUMMARY

The fundamentals for good plant-transportation design are maximum durability and minimum maintenance. Proper subsoil preparation and adequate drainage are the most important factors for roads, loading docks,

TRACK INFORMATION

$1°$ curve $1"$ for $5,730'$ radius $1" = 100'$ (standard R. R. dwg.)

Permissible $33° \sim 174'$ ($\mathcal{C}$ track)

To find curve of track:

1. Layout $62'$ chord distances on track
2. Tie knot at halfway point in string $62'$ long;
   stretch string between two points
3. Measure height (h) at knot
4. Solve $\dfrac{5,730}{h}$ for radius

Proof:

Assume you measure $h = 2'-6" = 30"$

$5,730$ ft/$30" = 191'$ radius

$c^2 = a^2 + b^2$

$b^2 = 191^2 - 31^2 = 36,481 - 961$

$b = \sqrt{35,520} = 188'-6"$

$191' - (188'-6") = 2'-6"$ OK

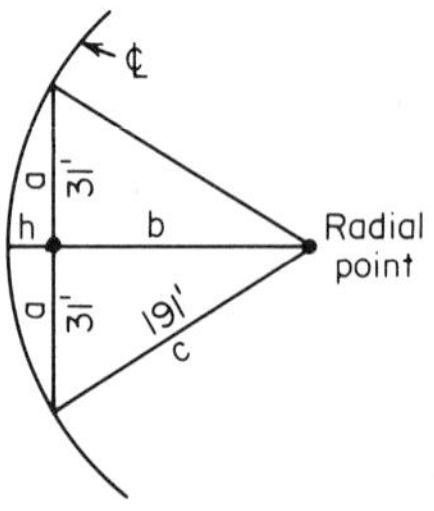

Fig. 6-15. Streamlined method of finding curve of section of track.

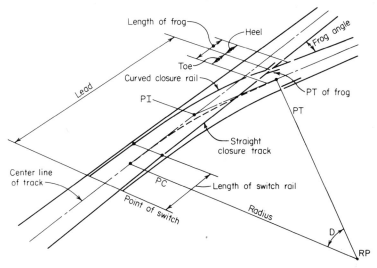

Fig. 6-16. Main components of a typical railroad switch.

parking areas, and plant railroads. With poor drainage, the plant engineer will be burdened with costly and continuous repairs.

Plant-transportation facilities deal mainly with methods of handling trucks, automobiles, and railroad cars within the plant site. Each has its own specific requirements for roadways, curves, clearances, and gradients.

The design of plant roads follows the same rules of design as public roads, which vary from the most inexpensive to the most durable and costly. Road surfaces are either flexible or rigid type.

Planning for trucking on plant property requires a knowledge of the types of trucks and trailers to be used for receiving and for shipping. This includes their weights, turning radius, and dimensions.

Although plant railroads are usually designed by railroad engineers, the plant engineer must make the preliminary layouts, as required by his plant's operation. It is therefore important that he have a knowledge of the fundamentals of railroad design. He should also be aware of the safety requirements of the public utility commission.

CHECKLIST FOR TRANSPORTATION

1. Truck and trailer sizes, width, length, and height
2. H loading
3. Number of truck-docking spaces required
4. Truck parking apron
5. Truck maneuver area, turning radius
6. Truck roadway width for one-way and two-way traffic

7. Roadway paving, concrete, asphaltic concrete, or other
8. Road curves
9. Guardrail
10. Signs
11. Number of passenger cars
12. Parking stall sizes
13. Number of parking stalls
14. Drainage of parking area
15. Striping
16. Parking bumpers
17. Fencing
18. Lighting
19. Landscaping
20. Ramps

BIBLIOGRAPHY

The Asphalt Institute: *Asphalt in Pavement Maintenance,* College Park, Md., 1967.
————: *Asphalts, Paving and Liquid,* Berkeley, Calif., 1970.
————: *Asphalt Paving Manual,* College Park, Md., 1965.
————: *Asphalt Surface Treatments and Asphalt Penetration Macadam,* College Park, Md., 1964; rev. ed., 1969.
————: *Construction Specifications for Asphalt Concrete and Other Plant-mix Types,* College Park, Md., 1969.
————: *Drainage of Asphalt Pavement Structures,* College Park, Md., 1966.
————: *Thickness Design Full-depth Asphalt Pavement Structures for Highways and Streets,* College Park, Md., 1969.
Bateman, John H.: *Introduction to Highway Engineering,* John Wiley & Sons, Inc., New York, 1942.
State of California Public Utilities Commission: *General Orders,* California Office of State Printing, San Francisco, 1967.

CHAPTER SEVEN

Construction Codes

THE FIRST EXPERIENCE a plant engineer has with codes may leave him confused and discouraged. If he is to have a building designed on plant property, he finds that he has to obtain approval from the planning commission, the building and safety department, the fire department, the sanitation district, the storm drain department, and often many other regulatory departments. If he has to add a chemical neutralizing tank next to the building, he may find that he needs additional approval from the industrial waste and the water pollution control department.

The plant engineer can look upon this formidable list of agencies as an endless row of obstacles, or he can consider agencies and their codes and regulations for what they are—a valuable, up-to-date source of safe design guides that are available to him at no cost.

As industry and construction become more complex, codes will undoubtedly continue to be an important consideration in any factory building program. Virtually every community, no matter how small, has codes. To be familiar with these local governing codes becomes one of the prime responsibilities of the plant engineer, and it is to his advantage to keep a copy of the governing codes on his desk for frequent reference and study.

NEED FOR CODES

Building codes and regulations are not meant to harass but to provide minimum standards to safeguard life, limb, and property. Ensuring the protection of the whole community is the prime reason for building regulations.

Considerable thought has been given to the question of the best kind of code to adopt—whether a local, state, federal, or model code. Many cities have developed adequate local codes but at a considerable expense. State codes duplicate much that is in local codes, though their proponents argue that state codes such as California's General Industrial Safety Orders and Electrical Safety Orders provide guidelines for smaller municipalities that cannot underwrite the cost of a local code. To most people in the construction industry the idea of a federal code is anathema.

THE MODEL CODE

Another solution is the model code, of which four are available. Developed by individuals representing organizations with a wealth of experience in regulating building design, these codes are well organized and well written. One of the four will suit the needs of most areas. They all contain sufficient information for the plant engineer who is interested in becoming acquainted with good, sound technical-construction guidelines.

The first model code, the National Building Code, was published by the National Board of Fire Underwriters in 1905. In 1927, the International Conference of Building Officials published the Uniform Building Code. Because of problems peculiar to the South, the Southern Building Code Congress adopted the Southern Standard Building Code in 1945. Finally, in 1950, the Building Officials Conference of America developed and published the Basic Building Code.

The evolution of the Uniform Building Code is a very good example of the care that goes into the publication of a model code.

The main objectives of the Uniform Building Code are to provide regulations for public health, safety, and welfare; to provide safety from fire; to establish uniformity in building department procedures; and to reduce fire-insurance base rates to a minimum.

In 1922 a group of building officials met to discuss the possibility of developing a code to set forth minimum requirements for safe construction. It took 5 years of preparation and compilation before the first edition of the Uniform Building Code was printed. The code was compiled with the aid of many well-known technical and material associations, including:

1. The American Institute of Steel Construction
2. The American Concrete Institute
3. The American Welding Society
4. The American Society of Testing Materials

The recommendations of these various associations were then incorporated into the Uniform Building Code. The code is continually upgraded in order to include new construction materials and practices, to accommodate new process operations, and to meet the new social problems caused by population changes. The Uniform Building Code was first adopted by 37 cities. Now over 300 communities in all parts of the country have adopted this code.

TYPICAL CODE REQUIREMENT

As an example of the contents of a code, the following are excerpts from the California Administrative Code, Title 8, which is typical of local or state building codes. The articles illustrate the thoroughness of building-code provisions. While the scope of the requirements will vary somewhat with the plant site, the code is very specific in order to protect life and limb.

TYPICAL ITEMS REGARDING STAIRWAYS, RAMPS, PLATFORMS, AND HANDRAILS

A standard railing around a platform, which is defined as an elevated working level for people, shall consist of a top rail, midrail, and posts having a vertical height of not less than 42 in. nor more than 45 in.

All standard railings, including connections, shall be designed for a live load of 20 lb per linear foot applied vertically or horizontally at the top rail.

Platform railings shall have a minimum inside diameter of 1 in. The spaces between posts shall not exceed 8 ft.

Toeboards shall be installed where the platform, runway, or ramp is 6 ft or more above places where employees walk.

Platforms, runways, ramps, or other elevated working levels 4 ft or more above the working area shall not be less than 2 ft wide.

Permanent elevated platforms that are frequently used shall be equipped with a permanent stairway or ladder.

Fixed ladders having a slope of more than 60° and serving locations over 30 ft high shall have a cage unless the ladder sections are offset and equipped with rest platforms at intervals of less than 20 ft.

Cages shall extend from the top of the ladder to a point not less than 7 ft above the ground. Cages shall be at least 24 in. wide, and the back of the cage shall not be less than 24 in. nor more than 30 in. from the face of the ladder.

No stairways shall be less than 22 in. wide.

No corridor shall be less than 42 in. wide. (A corridor is defined as a passageway that is at least 7 ft long.)

Stairways shall not have a slope in excess of 50° nor less than 20°. If less than 20°, a ramp shall be used. For any slope exceeding 75°, fixed or portable ladders shall be used.

No ramp shall have a more than 10 percent slope excepting temporary ramps, which may have a 12.5 percent slope.

TYPICAL ITEMS REGARDING AISLES FOR INDUSTRIAL TRUCKS

One-way traffic aisles for industrial trucks shall be at least 2 ft wider than the widest vehicle. Two-way traffic aisles shall be at least 3 ft wider than twice the width of the widest vehicle.

MISCELLANEOUS ITEMS

Surfaces having an external temperature capable of burning animal tissue shall be insulated if within 7 ft measured vertically from the floor or 15 in. measured horizontally from the stairways, ramps, or fixed ladders.

Compressed air in excess of 10 psi shall not be used to blow dirt, chips, or dust from clothing while it is being worn.

TYPICAL ITEMS REGARDING TOILET FACILITIES

Toilet facilities shall be provided for each sex according to the following table:

No. of people	Facilities	No. of people	Facilities
1–15	1	46–60	4
15–30	2	61–80	5
31–45	3	81–100	6

Thereafter one toilet is required for every 25 additional employees or fraction thereof. For males, one urinal may be substituted for one toilet facility except that the number of toilet facilities shall not be reduced to less than two-thirds of the number specified above.

ENFORCEMENT OF CODES

Codes have become such an integral part of industry that it is unlawful for any firm to violate any provision or to fail to comply with any of the requirements of the code.   In many communities the law states that those who fail to comply with the code are guilty of a misdemeanor which is punishable by a fine of not more than $500 or imprisonment of not more than 6 months, or both.   In addition, a firm shall be guilty of separate offenses for each and every day the violation is continued. Therefore a plant engineer who knowingly violates the code exposes his company to severe punishment.

CODES RELATING TO PLANT EXPANSION

It is of the utmost importance that the plant engineer be aware of all the codes and regulations affecting the expansion of his plant.   He should be familiar not only with the zoning laws of his plant site but also of the adjacent land.   He must be cognizant of all easements, zoning regulations, public utilities, and building and safety rules affecting the plant buildings and other facilities of his site.   He must know the permissible present use of the buildings and property of his company as well as limitations of their future use.

To plan a legal and safe building, the plant engineer must consider every aspect of its design and the use to which it will be put.   The structure must be resistant to collapse from operating loads, wind, and earthquake.   There must be adequate exits in accordance with the use of the building and the number of occupants.   The more hazardous the use of the building, the more fire-resistant it must be; and the greater the number of occupants in the building, the more severe the fire-resistance requirements.   Other factors, such as proximity to residential properties or other types of dwellings, also affect the type of construction and occupancy of the industrial building.

The plant engineer should have in his reference library copies of all the codes pertinent to his plant, including local city or county building and safety codes, state industrial safety codes, fire department codes, planning commission or zoning ordinances.   He should also have for reference the recommendations of the various technical and material manufacturing associates, such as the *Handbook of the American Institute of Steel Construction* and the reference books of the American Concrete Institute.

The plant engineer must deal not only with the published building and safety codes but also with all unpublished rulings of governmental agencies under whose jurisdiction his plant falls.   Many government agencies have no formally printed codes. Their regulations may be controlled through policy bulletins, department memos, notices, or court decisions. These regulations are normally not printed for public distribution but constitute public regulations nevertheless. The plant engineer should confer with these agencies during the planning stage of all projects. It is the responsibility of the conscientious plant engineer to keep in personal contact with these agencies in order to keep up to date with the laws governing his plant.

The following are some of the main governmental agencies that have control of the design and construction of a plant and its facilities.

1. Planning commission, which may include zoning department
2. Department of building and safety, which may include
   a. Grading department
   b. Engineering department
   c. Mechanical department
   d. Plumbing department
   e. Dangerous chemicals department
   f. Inspection department
3. Engineering department, sometimes known as the office of the city engineer or county engineer, which may include
   a. Storm drain division
   b. Street department
   c. Industrial waste division
   d. Sanitary waste division
   e. Air-pollution control board
   f. Water-quality control board
4. State division of industrial safety
5. Public utilities commission, which controls
   a. Railroad design
   b. Plant services such as gas, water, and electricity
6. Fire department

PLANNING COMMISSION

The planning commission has the responsibility of preparing and maintaining a master plan for the physical development of a community, including such elements as industry, civic centers, public works facilities, and general land use.

Another function of the planning commission is to prepare a general zoning plan, which divides the community into various agricultural, residential, commercial, and industrial zones. In addition to zoning, it regulates the yard space required for each development, the maximum height and floor areas of buildings, and the amount of automobile parking space required with various kinds of improvements.

A comprehensive modern zoning ordinance has been the prerequisite for continued growth and development of communities. As industry is a vital and important part of community growth, the plant engineer must be aware of and alert to the requirements of the planning commission as they affect his plant's present and future plans.

ZONING DEPARTMENT

The zoning department, which is often a subdivision of the planning commission, regulates and restricts the location of buildings, their occupancy, and use. The plant engineer should become familiar with these zoning regulations, which govern the type of improvement permitted on the land for which he is responsible.

The four major zone classifications—(1) residential, (2) commercial, (3) agricultural, and (4) industrial—are the most pertinent for a plant engineer.

As an example, the Los Angeles City Zoning Regulations describe the various industrial zones as follows (Fig. 7-1):

1. Commercial manufacturing (CM) includes wholesale business, storage buildings, and limited manufacturing
2. Limited industrial (M1) includes CM uses and limited industrial and manufacturing uses
3. Light industrial (M2) includes M1 uses, additional industrial uses, and storage yards of all kinds
4. Heavy industrial (M3) includes M2 uses, any industrial use, and nuisance type 500 ft from any other zone

The purpose of zoning is apparent: to group plants with similar uses together and to protect residential and commercial areas from offensive noise, smoke, and odors. Zoning regulations also control the yards around buildings, the height of buildings, and the amount of parking facilities rquired. A typical parking requirement is one parking space for each 500 sq ft of floor area in buildings containing 5,000 sq ft or more. Parking is not required for buildings under 5,000 sq ft.

Another section of the zoning laws which may affect plant expansion is the establishment of a "building line," which is the minimum distance from the street at which buildings, structures, and improvements may be built. The building line serves to preserve the commonly accepted characteristic of the district, to protect and maintain the master plan of highways, and to provide sufficient open space for public and private

Summary of zoning regulations
City of Los Angeles

Classification	Zone	Use	Height (Stories)	Height (Feet)	Yards (Front, ft)	Yards (Side, ft)	Yards (Rear, ft)	Area (Per lot)	Area (Per dwelling unit)	Minimum lot width, ft	Parking space
Residential	RE	Residential estate — One-family dwellings, Parks, Playgrounds, Community centers, Truck gardening — Horses	3	45	25	5 or 6 (3 stories)	25 max.	11,000 sq ft	11,000 sq ft	70	One garage per dwelling unit
Residential	RS	Suburban — One-family dwellings, Parks, Playgrounds, Truck gardening — Horses, RS uses	3	45	25	5 or 6 (3 stories)	20	7,500 sq ft	7,500 sq ft	60	One garage per dwelling unit
Residential	R1	One-family dwelling — RS uses	3	45	20	5 or 6 (3 stories)	15	5,000 sq ft / R1-H 15,000 sq ft	5,000 sq ft / R1-H 15,000 sq ft	50	One garage per dwelling unit
Residential	R2	Two-family dwelling — R1 uses, Two-family dwellings	3	45	20	5 or 6 (3 stories)	15	5,000 sq ft	2,500 sq ft	50	One garage per dwelling unit
Residential	R3	Multiple dwelling — R2 uses — Apartment houses, Multiple dwellings	3	45	15	5 or 6 (3 stories)	15	5,000 sq ft	800 to 1,200 sq ft	50	Varies from one for one to 1¼ for one
Residential	R4	Multiple dwelling — R3 uses — Churches, Schools — Hotels	Unlimited *	Unlimited *	15	5 plus 1 for each story above 2nd 16 max.	15 plus 1 for each story above 3rd 20 max.	5,000 sq ft	400 to 800 sq ft	50	Varies from one for one to 1¼ for one
Residential	R5	Multiple dwelling — R4 uses — Clubs — Lodges, Hospitals — Sanitariums	Unlimited *	Unlimited *	15	5 plus 1 for each story above 2nd 16 max.	15 plus 1 for each story above 3rd 20 max.	5,000 sq ft	200 to 400 sq ft	50	Varies from one for one to 1¼ for one
Agricultural	RA	Suburban — RE uses — Limited agricultural uses — Golf courses	3	45	25	5 or 6 (3 stories)	25	20,000 sq ft	20,000 sq ft	70	One garage per dwelling unit
Agricultural	A2	Agricultural — RA uses — Extensive agricultural uses	3	45	25	25 max.	25	2 acres	1 acre	150 minimum average lot width	One space per dwelling unit
Agricultural	A1	Agricultural — A2 uses	3	45	25	25 max.	25	5 acres	2½ acres	300 minimum average lot width	One space per dwelling unit
Parking	P	Automobile parking – Surface & underground — Property in a P zone may also be in an A or R zone. Parking permitted in lieu of residential or agricultural uses.	*	—	0.5 or 10 depending on zoning in block	5 to 16 if abutting A or R zone	5 to 16 if abutting A or R zone	None	Area per lot and unit	None unless also in an A or R zone	—
Parking	PB	Parking building — Automobile parking within or without a building	*	—					Loading space	None	—

108

Fig. 7-1. Typical zoning regulations table (City of Los Angeles).

	Zone	Uses			✱	10 interior lot except on major highway	5 to 10 corner lot only	15 plus 1 for each story above 3rd	Same as R5 for dwellings Otherwise none	Loading — Where lot abuts alley	50 for residence use	One space for each 500 sq ft of floor area
Commercial	CR	Limited commercia[l] — Most R5 uses — Office buildings, Banks, Business schools, No merchandise display or sale	6	75	✱				Same as R5 for dwellings Otherwise none	Where lot abuts alley →	50 for residence use	One space for each 500 sq ft of floor area
	C1	Limited commercial — R3 uses — Local retail stores, offices or businesses	Unlimited		✱	Only if part of block in dwelling zone	None unless lot adjoins dwelling zone	None unless abutting A or R zone or in residential use	Same as R3 for dwellings Otherwise none	Minimum loading space 400 sq ft	50 for residence use	One space for each 500 sq ft of floor area in buildings containing 5,000 or more sq ft — Must be located within 750 ft of building
	C2	Commercial — C1 and R5 uses — Retail business with limited manufacturing	Unlimited		✱	None	None for comm'l. bldgs. Residential uses — Same as in R4 zone	None for comm'l. bldgs. Residential uses — Same as in R4 zone	Same as R4 for dwellings Otherwise none	Minimum loading space 400 sq ft	50 for residence use	One space for each 500 sq ft of floor area in buildings containing 5,000 or more sq ft
	C4	Commercial — C2 uses (with exceptions)	Unlimited		✱	None	None for comm'l. bldgs. Residential uses — Same as in R4 zone	None for comm'l. bldgs. Residential uses — Same as in R4 zone	Same as R5 for dwellings Otherwise none	Additional space required for buildings containing 50,000 sq ft of floor area	50 for residence use	Must be located within 750 ft of building
	C5	Commercial — C2 uses — Limited floor area for light manufacturing	Unlimited		✱	None	None for comm'l. bldgs. Residential uses — Same as in R4 zone	None for comm'l. bldgs. Residential uses — Same as in R4 zone	Same as R5 for dwellings Otherwise none	Where lot abuts alley →	50 for residence use	One space for each 500 sq ft of floor area
Industrial	CM	Commercial manufacturing — C2 uses — Wholesale business, Storage buildings, Limited manufacturing	Unlimited		✱	None	None for industrial or comm'l. bldgs. Residential uses — Same as in R4 zone	None for industrial or comm'l. bldgs. Residential uses — Same as in R4 zone	— Note — R zone uses prohibited	Minimum loading space 400 sq ft	None	One space for each 500 sq ft of floor area in buildings containing 5,000 or more sq ft
	M1	Limited industrial — CM uses — Limited industrial and manufacturing uses, No R zone uses	Unlimited		✱	None	None	None	— Note — R zone uses prohibited	None	None	Must be located within 750 ft of building
	M2	Light industrial — M1 uses — Additional industrial uses, Storage yards of oil kinds, No R zone uses	Unlimited		✱	None	None	None	— Note — R zone uses prohibited	Additional space required for buildings containing 50,000 sq ft of floor area	None	None
	M3	Heavy industrial — M2 uses — Any industrial use, Nuisance type 500 feet from any other zone — No R zone uses	Unlimited		✱	None	None	None	— Note — R zone uses prohibited	None	None	None

Supplemental use districts: (Established in conjunction with zones)

G Rock and gravel   O Oil drilling   •   S Animal slaughtering

No. 1	Floor area of main buildings may not exceed three times the buildable area of the lot.
No. 2	Floor area of main buildings may not exceed six times the buildable area of the lot.
No. 3	Floor area of main buildings may not exceed ten times the buildable area of the lot.
No. 4	Floor area of main buildings may not exceed thirteen times the buildable area of the lot.

✱ Height district   ✱ PB zone height

No. 1	2 stories and roof
No. 2	6 stories
No. 3	10 stories
No. 4	13 stories

Note: All information general   For specific details check with Department of Building and Safety

Fig. 7-1. Typical zoning regulations. (*City of Los Angeles.*)

transportation.   For fire prevention, the enforcement of a building line is to prevent the spread of fire and to facilitate the fire fighting.

THE DEPARTMENT OF BUILDING AND SAFETY

The department of building and safety controls the occupancy of the building as related to its size and type of construction.   Inversely, it also controls the building construction as related to its occupancy and size (Tables 7-1 and 7-2).   Other regulations of the department of building and safety govern exits and stairs, structural design, plumbing, fire-resistant construction of interior and exterior walls, openings of exterior walls adjacent to property lines, and electrical distribution.   Other divisions of the department make regulations dealing with construction-related earthwork, including fill and excavations.

The regulations of the department of building and safety are based on three main aspects of the building: the occupancy, the type of construction, and the area.   (The term "occupancy" means the use to which the building is put.)   Most building codes have classified the various occupancies as follows: group A, assembly; group B, assembly buildings under 1,000; group C, schools with more than 8 hr/week; group D, hospitals.   Most important for all plant engineers are industrial occupancies, which fall under groups E, F, and G (Table 7-3).   Group E is considered the most hazardous of the occupancies and is in turn subdivided into five categories.   E1 covers the storage and handling of hazardous and highly inflammable or explosive materials other than flammable liquids.   Group E2 covers the storage and handling of class I, II, and III flammable liquids.   Also covered under this division are

TABLE 7-1   Basic Allowable Floor Area for One-story Buildings

	Type of construction								
	I	II	III		IV		V		
Occupancy			1-hr or H.T.*	N	1-hr	N	1-hr	N	
E 1,2	11,250	5,600	4,200	2,800	4,200	2,800	3,300	1,900	
3–5	Unlimited	11,300	8,400	5,600	8,400	5,600	6,600	3,800	
F 1–3	Unlimited	18,000	13,500	9,000	13,500	9,000	10,500	6,000	
G	Unlimited	27,000	20,300	13,500	20,300	13,500	15,800	9,000	

*H.T.—Heavy Timber.

TABLE 7-2   Maximum Height of Building

Occupancy	Type of construction							
	I	II	III		IV		V	
			1-hr or H.T.*	N	1-hr	N	1-hr	N
	Maximum height, ft							
	Unlimited	95	65	55	65	55	50	40
	Maximum height, stories							
E 1	Unlimited	2	1	1	1	1	1	1
2–5	Unlimited	2	2	1	2	1	2	1
F 1–3	Unlimited	6	4	2	4	2	3	2
G	Unlimited	6	4	2	4	2	3	2

SOURCE: City of Los Angeles.
* H.T.—Heavy Timber.

paint stores with bulk handling, paint shops, and spray-painting rooms and shops.   Group E3 covers woodworking establishments; planning mills and box factories; shops where loose, combustible fibers or dust are manufactured, processed, or generated; and warehouses where highly combustible material is stored.   Repair garages are covered under subdivision E4, and aircraft repair hangars under E5.

Occupancies of less hazard than group E are in group F and include buildings where combustible material is stored, manufactured, or sold. F1 covers gasoline and service stations, and storage garages where no repair work is done except exchange of parts and maintenance that requires no flame, welding, or use of highly flammable liquids.   F2 concerns wholesale and retail stores; office buildings; drinking and dining establishments with an occupant load of fewer than 100 persons; printing plants, factories, and workshops using material not highly flammable or combustible; storage and sales rooms for combustible goods; and paint stores without bulk handling.   Open parking garages and aircraft hangars where no repair work is done except exchange of parts and maintenance which requires no open flame, welding, or use of highly flammable liquids also fall under the F3 division.

Group G occupancy comprises buildings in which no combustible material is manufactured or stored.   A typical example is a steel-fabricating shop.

TABLE 7-3   Industrial Occupancy Groups and Requirements for Exterior Walls

Group	Description of occupancy	Fire zone	Fire resistance of exterior walls	Openings in exterior walls
E	1. Storage and handling of hazardous and highly inflammable or explosive materials other than flammable liquids	* 3	4 hr less than 5 ft 2 hr less than 10 ft 1 hr less than 20 ft	Not permitted less than 5 ft; protected less than 20 ft
	2. Storage and handling of class I, II, and III flammable liquids, as specified in code; dry-cleaning plants using flammable liquids; paint stores with bulk handling; paint shops and spray-painting rooms and shops	1	4 hr less than 20 ft 1 hr elsewhere	
	3. Woodworking establishments, planing mills, and box factories; shops, factories where loose, combustible fibers or dust are manufactured, processed, or generated; warehouses where highly combustible material is stored	2	4 hr less than 5 ft 2 hr less than 10 ft 1 hr elsewhere	
	4. Repair garages	3	4 hr less than 5 ft 2 hr less than 10 ft 1 hr less than 20 ft	
	5. Aircraft repair hangars	* 3	1 hr less than 60 ft	Protected less than 60 ft
F	1. Gasoline and service stations, storage garages where no repair work is done except exchange of parts and maintenance requiring no open flame, welding, or the use of highly flammable liquids	1	2 hr less than 20 ft 1 hr elsewhere	Not permitted less than 5 ft; protected less than 20 ft
	2. Wholesale and retail stores, office buildings, drinking and dining establishments having an occupant load of less than 100, printing plants, municipal police and fire stations, factories and workshops using material not highly flammable or combustible, storage and sales rooms for combustible goods, paint stores without bulk handling	2	1 hr	Not permitted less than 5 ft; protected less than 10 ft
		3	1 hr less than 10 ft	
	3. Aircraft hangars where no repair work is done except exchange of parts and maintenance requiring no open flame, welding, or the use of highly flammable liquids	1	2 hr less than 20 ft 1 hr elsewhere	Not permitted less than 5 feet; protected less than 20 feet
		2	1 hr	
		3	1 hr less than 20 ft	
G	Ice plants, power plants, pumping plants, cold storage, and creameries, factories and workshops using incombustible and nonexplosive materials; storage and sales rooms of incombustible and nonexplosive materials	1	2 hr less than 20 ft 1 hr elsewhere	Not permitted less than 3 feet; protected less than 20 ft
		2	1 hr	Not permitted less than 3 ft; protected less than 10 ft
		3	1 hr less than 3 ft	Not permitted less than 3 ft

Types IV and V construction: Type V construction is not permitted within fire zone 1.   Exceptions to limitation for Type IV and Type V construction, as provided in Code.

Types I, II, and III construction: Exterior walls and protection of openings shall be as specified in Code.

   * Not permitted in fire zones 1 and 2.

SOURCE: Uniform Building Code; International Conference of Building Officials.

TYPES OF CONSTRUCTION

The building code classifies types of construction according to their fire-resistance properties.   The five main classifications are designated as types I, II, III, IV, and V (Figs. 7-2 and 7-3).   Type I is the most fireproof, while type V is the least fireproof.   A type I building is one in which all structural members are not only of incombustible material

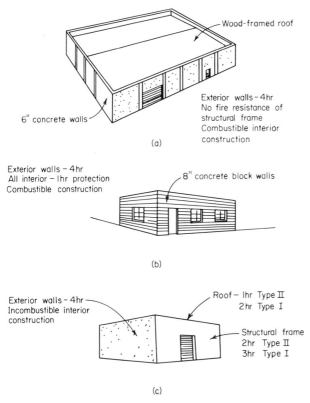

Fig. 7-2. Construction of types I, II, and III. (*a*) Type III-N. Example: a tilt-up warehouse with wood roof construction. Exterior concrete walls are 4-hr fire-resistive construction. Interior framing includes glue/laminated girders, wood purlins, rafters, and roof sheathing. (*b*) Type III–1 hr. Example: concrete-block office building with exterior walls. 8-in. concrete block (4-hr) and all interior combustible framing protected with 1-hr fire-resistive plaster. (*c*) Types I and II. Example: an all-concrete chemical-storage building with exterior walls of 6-in. concrete (4-hr), interior all-incombustible construction. All framing protected by 2- or 3-hr fire-protective plaster (type II or I, respectively).

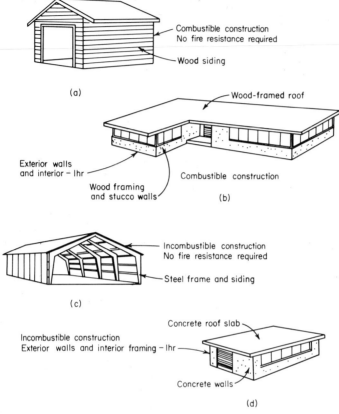

Combustible construction
No fire resistance required

Wood siding

(a)

Wood-framed roof

Exterior walls
and interior – 1hr

Combustible construction

Wood framing
and stucco walls

(b)

Incombustible construction
No fire resistance required

Steel frame and siding

(c)

Concrete roof slab

Incombustible construction
Exterior walls and interior framing – 1hr

Concrete walls

(d)

Fig. 7-3. Typical types of construction. (*a*) Type V-N. Example: a wooden toolshed with exterior walls and framing of combustible material. No fire-resistive construction. (*b*) Type IV-N. Example: a wood frame and stucco laboratory building protected by 1-hr fire-resistive plaster. (*c*) Type IV-N. Example: an all-metal shop building without fire-resistive protection. (*d*) Type IV–1 hr. Example: a steel frame and stucco reagent-storage building. Exterior walls and framing protected with 1-hr fire-resistive plaster.

but are protected by a 3-hr fireproofing. Type II is similar to type I except 2-hr fireproofing is required instead of 3-hr. Type III structures are combustible framed buildings in which all exterior walls are 4-hr fire-resistant. Type III is further subdivided into III-N or III–1 hr. Type III-N requires no fire-resistive construction other than the exterior walls while type III–1 hr must have all its structural frame protected with 1-hr fire-resistant material. A building entirely constructed of incombustible material is a type IV building. A steel-framed building, being totally incombustible, can be classified as type IV. A type IV–1 hr is a totally incombustible building with all its structural parts protected by 1-hr fire resistance while a type IV-N has no fire resistance. Combustible buildings whose frame is protected by 1-hr fire-resistance covering are classified as type V–1 hr, and those without protection are type V-N.

Division Wall

A building or installation that includes two different types of occupancies adjacent to each other can be separated by a properly rated division wall without imposing the more stringent requirements of the hazardous area on the less hazardous part. This wall completely separates the

TABLE 7-4 Required Separations by Division Walls in Buildings of Mixed Occupancies (in Hours)

Group	A	B	C	D	E1	E2	E3	E4,5	F1	F2	F3	G	H	I	J
A	N	N	N	3	4	4	4	4	4	3	3	3	1	1	1
B		N	N	3	4	4	4	4	3	1	1	1	1	1	1
C			N	1	4	4	4	4	4	1	1	1	1	1	1
D				N	4	4	4	4	4	4	4	4	1	1	3
E1					N	1	1	1	2	2	2	2	4	4	1
2						N	1	1	1	1	1	1	3	3	1
3							N	1	1	1	1	1	3	3	1
4,5								N	1	1	1	1	3	3	1
F1									N	1	1	1	3	1	1
2										N	1	1	1	N	1
3											N	1	1	N	1
G												N	1	N	N
H													N	N	1
I														N	1
J															N

SOURCE: Uniform Building Code.

building (Table 7-4).   Any openings in this wall must be automatically closed in time of fire.

BUILDING AREAS

It is obvious that the allowable area of a building increases with the higher type of construction and less hazardous occupancy.   The basic allowable floor area for one-story buildings having E, F, or G occupancy is shown in Table 7-1.   A building having the maximum area for the maximum danger would be the most fireproof building.   Figure 7-4 illustrates the relationship between types of construction, occupancies, and allowable areas.

Often area requirements have been already established by the time the project gets to the plant engineer.   Sales figures dictate warehousing

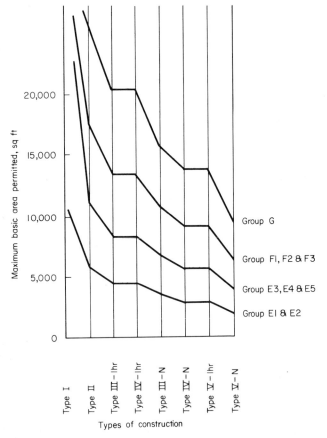

Fig. 7-4.   Relative basic building areas versus types of construction for group G, F, and E occupancies.

needs, or a process installation demands a certain minimum amount of space. Whatever the requirements, the plant engineer usually has to decide how to get the maximum area and whether the more expensive type of construction is justifiable.

An increase in the permitted areas may be accomplished in several ways besides using more fire-resistive methods of construction. One of these techniques is to build more than one story. The total permissible area for a multistory building may be 200 percent of the tabulated basic area, but this 200 percent increase represents the maximum regardless of the number of stories, and no single floor can have more than the basic area listed for one-story buildings.

A permissible increase in the basic area can also be achieved by providing a clear yard on two or more sides of the building. When there are two yard areas, each over 20 ft, an increase in basic area is permitted at the rate of $1\frac{1}{4}$ percent for each foot over 20 ft of yard space. A maximum 50 percent increase is allowed.

A rate of $2\frac{1}{2}$ percent is permitted with three yards, but the maximum is 100 percent. With four yards, the maximum increase is 200 percent. Under certain conditions a building surrounded on all four sides with yards 60 ft or more in width has unlimited area.

Another common method of increasing the allowable area of a new building is to install an automatic sprinkler system. If the sprinkler system is not required for other reasons, such as occupancy, the basic area can be tripled.

When the property is located in a relatively light-density area, or fire zone 3, the code permits an automatic increase of $33\frac{1}{3}$ percent in the basic area.

In summary, the conditions for area allowance are:

1. Type of construction
2. Group occupancy
3. Yards
4. Sprinklers
5. Fire zone
6. Number of stories

It is worth noting that each area increase is cumulative; thus the plant engineer has several possible methods of increase to investigate and evaluate. His final choice will depend upon economics, design considerations, or actual physical requirements.

EARTHWORK AND GRADING REQUIREMENTS

While modern earth-moving machines make it possible to level a hill or fill a canyon for a new plant site, the machines and their drivers are not always as careful when replacing the fill they removed as mother nature was when she put it there in the first place. Therefore, to avoid cave-ins, inadequate drainage, uncontrolled "land butchering," and the danger of future construction being done on poorly stabilized fill, permits are required for excavations and fill and backfill operations.

Earthwork which does not require a permit includes fills under 3 ft in depth, excavations to less than 5 ft, work where the quantity of earthwork is under 20 cu yd on one lot, and work done in remote areas.

When permits are required for earthwork, the following is a suggested checklist for the plant engineer to follow:

1. Prepared plans giving the description of the property and the earthwork involved.
2. Retain a supervising civil or soils engineer to assure expert supervision.
3. Provide a statement of the volume of material being moved.
4. Prepare topographic plans showing existing and new contour lines.
5. Draw grading plans showing elevations, locations, and extent of slope.
6. Prepare structural details of all drainage devices to prevent flooding and erosion damage.
7. Complete an application for a grading permit and pay the fee to cover inspection service.
8. Provide a completion bond to the grading department to guarantee proper and complete work of all earthwork shown on plans as required by code.

Proper design and construction of earthwork are as important as for plant buildings and structures, since the stability of all structures depends on the subsoil.

VARIANCE APPEALS

Because it is understood that industry is continually changing, our laws governing construction do not always apply. Therefore the plant engineer should be aware of the right of variance appeals, for he may have to resort to them. If the existing ordinances are not truly applicable to a company's problems, the governing agencies may permit variances if they are not detrimental to the public welfare or injurious to property or to property values. But granting variances is up to the discretion of the agency and subject to pressure from the neighborhood citizenry. The plant engineer must maintain cordial relations with his neighbors if he wishes to run his plant with the least amount of conflict. Every code includes the procedure for petitioning for a variance or exception.

INDUSTRIAL WASTE

As the effects of certain types of industrial wastes upon sewers and sewage-treatment processes can be highly destructive, plant wastes must be controlled. Authorization must be given by governing agencies before industrial waste can be discharged into trunk sewers, and if subsequent inspection shows continued noncompliance with regulations, permission can be revoked by the governmental agency.

To facilitate inspection and control of industrial wastes, the industry must separate industrial waste from sanitary wastes (rest rooms, showers, drinking fountains, etc.) until such industrial wastes have passed through a stabilizing tank and sampling manhole. The latter may serve as a junction manhole with the sanitary sewer. The manhole should be located off the premises.

Some of the materials specifically required to be removed from industrial waste are as follows:

1. Sand, metal filings, and similar material which will settle out in sewers
2. Excessive grease and oil (floatable or dispersed)
3. Wastes which cause excessive putrefaction or sulfide formation
4. Compounds which give off toxic or flammable gases in amounts considered dangerous
5. Blowdown or bleed from cooling towers or other evaporative coolers equal to not more than half of the evaporation loss
6. Chemical solutions containing nitric acids or salts in excessive amounts
7. Storm waters from yard or roof runoff (they must go to suitable storm-water channels)

A sanitation district is an agency of the county government which operates the system of trunk sewers serving homes, commercial establishments, and industry. The district builds and operates only trunk sewers and sewage-disposal systems. Local sewage-collecting systems or lateral sewers are built and operated by the various cities under their engineering department's control. All liquid wastes originating from the district's boundaries are removed by the district's sewerage systems provided that the wastes do not (1) damage structures, (2) create nuisances such as odors, (3) menace public health, (4) interfere with sewage-treatment processes, or (5) impose abnormal costs on the district for their collection and disposal.

Storm waters or uncontaminated waters of any origin are not permitted to discharge into trunk sewers.

CONNECTIONS TO PUBLIC MAINS

An industry seeking to connect directly to a district trunk sewer must prepare plans, specifications, and descriptions of the proposed connection to be submitted with the application.   The district engineer will review these plans to see that they conform to regulations and will issue a permit when approved.

THE PUBLIC UTILITIES COMMISSION

Another important agency with whose regulations the plant engineer must comply is the state public utilities commission, which regulates the railroads (whether on public or private land), power lines, gas lines, water supply, and any other public utilities involved with the plant.

Some typical regulations relating to plant railroads are as follows: plant-railroad spur tracks must maintain minimum clearance from buildings, poles, fences, and other obstacles.   These clearances vary with straight or curved tracks.   Headroom clearances over the top of the rail must also be maintained.   Violations of these clearances can prevent the railroad company from using the plant's tracks.

THE FIRE DEPARTMENT

The fire department has control of the type of construction; fire-protection devices (such as hydrants), fire-water supply, and distribution sprinklers; and flammable-tank-storage systems.   They also control the construction of dikes, the location and accessibility of fire-fighting equipment, the type of valves used, and the maximum stored quantities of flammable materials.

The local fire department, whether city or county, often adopts a fire code to protect life, property, and public welfare from the hazards of fire and explosion.   It also controls the handling, use, and storage of dangerous and hazardous materials.   In order to effect this control, the fire department has the power to inspect existing facilities and issue permits for new facilities.   These permits are usually handled through the department of building and safety as an additional check of the plans.

Incorporated into the fire code are certain recognized national standards adopted from the following sources:

1. Association of American Railroads
2. American Petroleum Institute
3. American National Standards Institute

4. American Society of Mechanical Engineers
5. American Society of Testing Materials
6. National Fire Protection Association
7. Underwriters Laboratories, Inc.

The fire code regulates the handling of many types of dangerously flammable products including rebuilt automobile tires, motion-picture films, combustible fibers, compressed gases, explosives, flammable finishes, and all kinds of flammable liquids.

The plant engineer will find that the fire code has specific requirements governing the design of underground storage tanks in relation to depth of cover, venting, and proximity to buildings and property lines. For above-ground tanks, the code covers the capacity of dikes, the spacing between tanks, their location relative to property lines and buildings, and the design of the tanks themselves.

Many fire departments keep on file for emergency a plot plan of each industrial plant. In this way the firemen are aware of the location of pipelines and control valves and the location and nature of fire-fighting equipment at the plant. Therefore, it is definitely to the industry's advantage for the plant engineer to keep the fire department fully up to date on the situation at his plant.

The case of a roofing-material manufacturing company where a serious fire occurred illustrates how important the practice can be. When the firemen turned their water hoses on a group of open-top tanks, they did not know that the contents was liquid asphalt. The displaced burning asphalt flowed over the tops of the tanks. The ensuing flaming flood spread the fire throughout the plant. This was a tragic example of the firemen not being aware of the nature of the tank and its contents until it was too late. These facilities had been built without the knowledge or approval of the governing agencies.

EXAMPLE

A large national manufacturing firm purchased the entire West Coast facility of a pressure-vessel fabricator. After taking over the plant, management began plans for expansion and modernization.

The new plant engineer was requested to prepare a report on the status of the buildings with local building and zoning regulations.

He visited the local building department and asked to see the complete file of all permits ever issued on their property. All such records are public property, and the plant engineer was acting within the rights of his management.

The records showed there were 12 permits issued on various buildings and other structures over the past 18 years. These included:

1. A 123,000 sq ft manufacturing building group G type IV
2. A 16,100 sq ft office building group F type IV
3. A relocated 3,200 sq ft executive office building group F type V
4. A stress relief furnace
5. A grit blast building
6. A carpenter and paint shop
7. Two research and development buildings group F type IV
8. Various other rooms, buildings, walls, and electrical and plumbing permits

But the most important documents found in the files were a "yard letter" and a signed commitment by the previous owner relating to future construction of fire walls.

A yard letter is a commitment that acknowledges the approval of a building permit on maintenance of a clear 60-ft yard around all sides of the main building in which no construction will ever be permitted.

In addition, another letter agreed that the owner would construct a 200-ft-long fire wall along the building adjacent to the property line should the adjacent railroad ever be abandoned.

The plant engineer also found that certain buildings were granted permits based on occupancies which were no longer valid.

Using these findings, the plant engineer and management proceeded to replan their expansion program to conform to certain restrictions and to reclassify the use of each building.

This investigation was of utmost importance, as it saved much time and expense in future expansion and remodeling.

SUMMARY

Each governmental agency has a definite role to perform in the industrial community. The rules and regulations set by each department have usually come about as a result of previous tragedy and economic loss suffered by the members of the community due to uncontrolled and faulty construction.

Governing agencies are made up of technical experts whose sole purpose is to aid and protect the total community. They have the depth of specialized experience due to the continuity of their offices and the breadth of knowledge gained by sharing their experience with their national counterparts from all communities. All this knowledge and experience is available to the plant engineer through the codes.

CHECKLIST FOR NEW BUILDING CODES

Check for new building construction codes on:

1. Occupancy of building
2. Type of construction

3. Building floor area
4. Building height
5. Number of occupants
6. Number of required exits
7. Fire-resistance value of exterior walls, roof, and exit corridors
8. Required division walls
9. Distance to property lines
10. Distance between buildings
11. Parking requirements
12. Sprinklers
13. Fire zone

CHECKLIST FOR REGULATORY AGENCIES

1. Planning commission
2. Building and safety department
3. Grading department
4. Sanitation department
5. Public works department
6. Air-pollution control
7. Industrial waste
8. Fire department
9. Storm-drain department
10. Health department
11. Industrial-safety department
12. Gas utility company
13. Electric utility company
14. Water utility company
15. Telephone utility company

CHECKLIST FOR TANK-FARM REQUIREMENTS

1. Classification of liquids stored
2. Quantity of liquid stored
3. Types of tanks to be used
4. Sizes of tanks to be used
5. Volume of liquid contained
6. Height of dike
7. Size of dike
8. Drains
9. Access stairs
10. Distance between tanks
11. Distance between tanks and property lines

BIBLIOGRAPHY

Air Pollution Control District: *Rules and Regulations Los Angeles County*, Los Angeles, 1967.

American Institute of Architects and Charles George Ramsey, and Harold Reeve
    Sleeper: *Architectural Graphic Standards,* 6th ed., John Wiley & Sons, Inc., New
    York, 1970.
Building Codes Bureau: *State Building Construction Code Applicable to One- and
    Two-family Dwellings,* New York, 1964.
City of Los Angeles: *Building Code,* Building News, Inc., Los Angeles, 1970.
————: *Zoning Code,* Building News, Inc., Los Angeles, 1967.
County of Los Angeles: *County of Los Angeles Uniform Building Laws,* Building
    News, Inc., Los Angeles, 1968.
County of Los Angeles Uniform Building Laws: *Building Code, Plumbing Code,
    Mechanical Code, County Electrical Code,* Building News, Inc., Los Angeles,
    1968.
Department of Building and Safety Grading Division: *City of Los Angeles Official
    Grading Regulations,* Building News, Inc., Los Angeles, 1963.
Housing and Building Codes Bureau: *State Building Construction Code Applicable
    to General Building Construction,* New York, 1964.
————: *State Building Construction Code Applicable to Multiple Dwellings,* New
    York, 1964.
Los Angeles County Regional Planning Commission: *Los Angeles County Zoning
    Ordinance,* Los Angeles, 1966.
Los Angeles Department of County Engineer: *Sanitary Sewer and Industrial Waste
    Ordinance,* Los Angeles, 1966.
Merritt, Frederick S.: *Standard Handbook for Civil Engineers,* McGraw-Hill Book
    Company, New York, 1968.
New York State Department of Health: *State Building Construction Code Applicable
    to Plumbing,* New York, 1964.
Southern California Chapters, American Public Work Association, Associated General
    Contractors of America: *Standard Specifications for Public Works Construction,*
    Building News, Inc., Los Angeles, 1967.
State of California Human Relations Agency, Department of Industrial Relations:
    General Industry Safety Orders, Division of Industrial Safety, Sacramento, Calif.,
    1969.
State of California Printing Division: *Laws Relating to Subdivided Lands,* Sacra-
    mento, Calif., 1961.
State of California Public Utilities Commission: *General Orders,* California Office
    of State Printing, San Francisco, 1967.
Uniform Fire Code of the California Fire Chiefs Association: *County of Los Angeles
    Fire Code,* Los Angeles, 1968.
Urquhart, Leonard Church: *Civil Engineering Handbook,* 4th ed., McGraw-Hill
    Book Company, New York, 1959.
U.S. Department of Labor, Bureau of Labor Standards: *Safety Subjects,* Government
    Printing Office, Washington, 1956.

CHAPTER EIGHT

Construction Materials

THE MODERN INDUSTRIAL PLANT is constructed primarily of steel, wood, concrete, and masonry. Each material should be used to its best advantage. Most structural materials need not be the most costly or the highest grade, but they should be of the strength and quality necessary for safe and enduring service. Since there should be an economic balance between service and quality the plant engineer must be aware of the relative costs and the advantages and disadvantages of all the materials being specified in the construction of plant facilities.

STRUCTURAL STEEL

To aid the designer and the plant engineer in the selection of structural steel, the American Society of Testing Materials has published certain specifications covering structural steel. Steel meeting specifications of the ASTM is identified by letter and number. The five common grades of structural steel presently used in construction are ASTM A7 and A36, used for bridges and buildings; A440, a high-strength structural steel; A441, a high-strength low-alloy structural manganese-vanadium steel; and A242, a high-strength low-alloy structural steel.

For ordinary industrial buildings and structure, the A7 and A36 are by far the most popular, of which the A36 is now replacing the older A7 steel. When special conditions of high strength are required, one of the other four types of steel may be specified. Three types of bolts are normally specified. In normal connections of low-carbon A7 and A36 structural steel, A307 bolts are used; the high-strength steel bolts conforming to ASTM A325 and A354 are usually specified when heavy loading conditions are involved. The latest edition of AISC specifications should be referred to for the most recent classification of steel types.

CONCRETE

The type of concrete used in industrial construction is often classified by the ratio of cement and aggregate used in the concrete mixture. It may also be identified by the amount of cement used per cubic yard of concrete in the final mix. As an example, a five-sack mix is five sacks per cubic yard of concrete.

Portland cement is the most important ingredient in concrete; there are five major types: type I portland cement is used for general concrete construction where the special properties of the other types are not required; type II is for general concrete construction when exposed to mild sulfate action and where moderate heat of hydration may be required; type III is for use where high early strength is required when normal curing time cannot be tolerated; type IV is for use when low heat of hydration is required, as in massive concrete pours; type V is for use when high sulfate resistance is required, normally a condition where spillage of acids occurs frequently.

Concrete aggregate is generally divided into two types. "Regular aggregate" is crushed granite rock, while "lightweight aggregate" comes from volcanic material or by expanding, calcining, or sintering porous materials such as blast-furnace slag, diatomite, fly ash, shale, perlite, vermiculite, or slate.

Chemical admixtures must often be added to concrete to improve or change its properties, for example, water-reducing, retarding, and accelerating admixtures and combinations of these admixtures.

REINFORCING STEEL

The reinforcing bars for concrete are available in three types of steel: structural grade, intermediate grade, and hard grade. In time of extreme shortage there is also available rerolled rail steel. Another reinforcing material used in concrete slabs is welded wire fabric made from cold-drawn steel wire. In prestressed-concrete construction a special, extremely high-strength steel wire is used.

MASONRY

In masonry construction many types of shapes and materials are available. The oldest is the building brick, made from clay or shale, classified into grades SW, MW, and NW brick. Grade SW is used for a high degree of resistance to frost action and exposure occurring when the brick is permeated with water. MW brick is intended for use where it will be exposed to temperatures below freezing but permeation with water is unlikely. NW brick is intended for backup or interior masonry; it is also used where no frost action occurs.

There are also concrete building bricks and hollow concrete masonry units, more commonly known as "concrete block." For interior construction work, there are structural-clay non-load-bearing tiles, structural-clay floor tile, gypsum partition tile or block, reinforced gypsum concrete, and precast reinforced gypsum slabs.

WOOD

Over 180 different kinds of commercial wood are grown in the United States, but only a few have properties suitable for construction. Wood is often classified as hardwood or softwood. Softwood comes from trees with needlelike leaves (usually cone-bearing), while hardwood comes from trees with broad leaves. This classification can be misleading because some hardwood is softer in the mechanical sense than the softwoods and vice versa.

In timber construction, only a few species of wood are commonly used. These include douglas fir, pine, and redwood. The wood is classified by most building codes as utility grade, standard grade, construction grade, dense construction grade, and select structural grade, the highest quality being dense select structural grade and the lowest utility grade.

Another method of grading wood is by allowable stress. Stress-grade lumber is classified by its use and known as "beams and stringers," "joists and planks," and "posts and timbers." To each grade is assigned proper allowable stresses. Plywood is also divided into grade designations according to its use, exposure to moisture, and the number of knots and defects in the outer layers.

MISCELLANEOUS MATERIALS

Other construction materials are fiber glass, plate glass, various types of plastic, aluminum, and copper.

STRESS-STRAIN DIAGRAMS AND
THEIR IMPLICATION

The most important properties of all construction materials can be plotted on a stress-strain diagram (Fig. 8-1), which indicates by a series of points the unit strain or deformation per inch of length versus the unit stress the material is subjected to. Unit stress, which is expressed in pounds per square inch, increases from zero at the bottom of the chart. The unit strain increases from left to right. When a curve is drawn through the points plotted on this diagram for either tensile or compressive stresses, the following facts become obvious.

The slope of the straight portion of the curve is an indication of the modulus of elasticity of the material, which can also be defined as the ratio of the unit strain to unit stress. Another term for the modulus of elasticity is "Young's modulus." If the line is straight, it can be said that deformation is proportional to stress. The point of the curve where there is a sudden change of direction is the elastic limit, and the unit stress at that point is called the "yield strength" of the

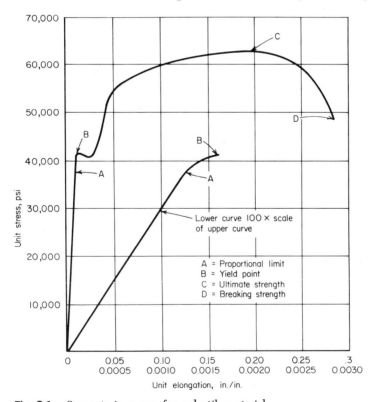

Fig. 8-1. Stress-strain curves for a ductile material.

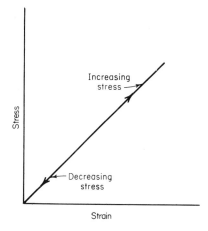

Fig. 8-2. Stress-strain curve showing elastic action.

material. Beyond the yield point, the curve follows a more or less erratic course and may eventually even drop down before complete failure of the material.

Another definition for the elastic limit is the maximum unit stress to which a body can be subjected without permanent deformation. Within the straight portion or the elastic curve, the strain will reduce to zero when the stress is relieved to zero (Fig. 8-2). If the stress is relieved after the yield point has been reached, there will be a permanent deformation, or set, in the material (Fig. 8-3). Consequently, the yield strength is the key point on which allowable stresses are based.

Relatively rigid and brittle material will have a very steep line while elastic and ductile material will have a rather flat curve (Fig. 8-4).

The plant engineer must also be familiar with other important properties and characteristics of structural materials in addition to their

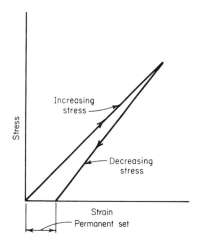

Fig. 8-3. Stress-strain curve showing inelastic action.

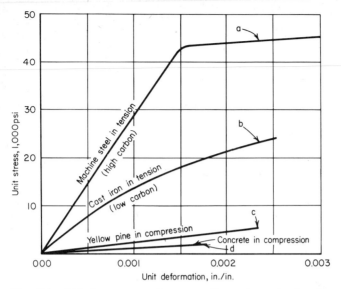

Fig. 8-4. Relative stress-strain curves for various structural materials: (*a*) machine steel, (*b*) cast iron, (*c*) yellow pine, and (*d*) concrete.

strength, namely their chemical, electrical, thermal, and acoustical properties. The electrical characteristics are the conductivity and resistivity of the material, where conductivity denotes the capacity for transmitting electric current and resistance, the opposite of conductivity, denotes the capacity to impede the passage of current.

Thermal conductivity of material is defined as the time rate of transfer of heat by conduction. Another important thermal characteristic of construction material is the change of dimension due to temperature variation. In the chemical characteristics of material, corrosion resistance may be one of the most important properties a plant engineer can be concerned with.

Each of the structural steels must have a minimum ultimate and yield strength to meet the ASTM Specification for A7, A36, A440, and A441 steel.

The ASTM Designation A7 steel, which includes carbon steel plates, shapes, and bars of structural quality, must have a minimum tensile strength of 60,000 to 70,000 psi, a minimum yield point of 33,000 psi, and a 21 to 24 percent elongation at the elastic limit.

The A36 steel, which also includes carbon-steel shapes, plates, and bars of structural quality, must have a minimum ultimate tensile stress of 58,000 to 60,000 psi and a minimum yield point of 36,000 psi.

The A440 steel, which is also a high-strength steel, has an atmospheric corrosion resistance approximately twice that of structural carbon steel. The minimum tensile strength is between 63,000 and 70,000 psi, and the minimum yield point is 42,000 to 50,000 psi.

The ASTM A242 is a high-strength low-alloy steel primarily for use as structural members where savings in weight or added durability are important. This steel also has great atmospheric corrosion resistance. The minimum ultimate tensile strength is from 68,000 to 70,000 psi, and the minimum yield point is from 42,000 to 50,000 psi.

EFFECT OF HIGH TEMPERATURE ON STEEL

The average coefficient of expansion for structural steel between ambient temperature and 200°F is 0.0000065 per degree Fahrenheit. For temperatures between 200 and 1100°F, the coefficient of expansion is given by the formula

$$e = 0.0000061 + 0.0000000022t$$

where e is the coefficient of expansion for each degree Fahrenheit and t is the temperature in degrees Fahrenheit. The modulus of elasticity for structural steel is close to 30,000 psi at room temperature but decreases linearly to about 25,000 psi at 900°F and then begins to drop at an increasing rate at higher temperatures.

It is interesting to note that the ultimate strength of structural carbon steel at about 550°F is approximately 25 percent greater than the strength at normal room temperature and at 800°F its strength is approximately the same at normal temperatures. Therefore in this temperature range, steel becomes stronger! At a temperature of 1000°F the yield-point strength of structural steel (depending on the shape of the member) may be lowered almost to the basic allowable working stress, which is 60 percent of the yield strength.

The coefficients of thermal expansion for other metallic materials are as follows: for aluminum 0.00128 for every 100°F of temperature change and for stainless steel 0.00099.

STRUCTURAL WELDING

The properties of electrodes for submerged arc welding are as follows: the tensile strength for grade SAW1 is from 62,000 to 80,000 psi, and the minimum yield strength is 45,000 psi. Grade SAW2 electrode has a minimum tensile strength of 70,000 to 90,000 psi and a minimum yield strength of 50,000 psi. The latest specifications for welding have revised classifications to AWS A5.17, A5.18, and A5.20.

It should be apparent to the plant engineer that there is a wide range of tensile and yield strengths of the various ferrous metals used in construction. But in general, the most commonly specified steel is the ASTM A36 steel, used in industrial building, structures, tanks, and bins.

ALLOWABLE WORKING STRESSES FOR CONSTRUCTION MATERIALS

The allowable working stress is the maximum computed unit stress which is permitted in a construction material. This value may be set by the local building and safety department or by material associations such as the American Institute of Steel Construction or the American Cement Institute, or it can be determined by the engineer responsible for the design.

The allowable working stress for a given member and its material will depend upon the characteristics of the material and the amount and kind of damage that might result from failure. The higher-risk structure will require a greater safety factor. Since the actual material used in construction is rarely tested for a particular situation, the approximate value of the desired properties must be obtained by correlating similar material from tests.

Another factor to consider is that no engineering material is perfectly uniform. There are nonuniformities in all structural materials. The properties in the material can be changed during the life of its service. Deterioration of metal occurs by corrosion, and wood is weakened by rotting.

The actual live loads on a structure also represent an assumption based upon the experience of the governing agency or the designer. This can vary greatly according to the use of the building. There can also be impact loads, which are not normally considered the design. The structure is often called upon to carry larger loads than anticipated during the construction period, for example, the storage of rolls of roofing paper or other construction material on the roof or the floor of a building. Because of all these unknown factors, a margin of safety is recommended.

The factor of safety is defined as the ratio of the strength of the material to the maximum calculated stress which will exist in that member. A term synonymous with the factor of safety is "factor of ignorance." Allowable working stresses can be obtained by dividing the ultimate strength of material by a given factor of safety. The factor of safety can vary from material to material and from use to use. With this consideration the various agencies have recommended maximum values at which materials can be stressed using these approximate factors of safety:

Material	Factor of safety
Brick and stone.......	15
Timber..............	8–10
Cast iron............	6
Wrought iron.........	4
Structural steel........	4

For structural steel the AISC has defined allowable values for steels of specific yield points. For A7 structural steel, which has a 33,000-psi yield strength, the allowable unit tensile stress is 20,000 psi, except that the allowable unit tensile stress at pinholes is limited to 15,000 psi. The allowable shearing stress is 13,000 psi, and the allowable compressive stress is a function of the length and radius of gyration of the member considered. The allowable flexural tension and compression stress is either 22,000 or 20,000 psi, depending on the type of shape, where the "compact" shape has the greater value.

For A36 steel, which has a 36,000-psi yield strength, the allowable working tensile stresses are 22,000 and 16,000 psi at pinholes, and the allowable shear stress is 14,500 psi. For flexural tension and compression stresses, the allowable stresses are 24,000 and 22,000 psi.

A compilation of allowable stresses recommended by the American Institute of Steel Construction is given in the AISC *Handbook*.

All the allowable stress values listed above are further limited by the configuration of the structure itself. The ratio of unsupported length to least radius of gyration (l/r) of columns or other compression members has a bearing on the allowable compressive stress. For beams, the relationship of unsupported length of the compression flange, depth of beam, width, and thickness of flange can reduce the allowable stress values.

In general, allowable stresses are also given by the following equations:

For tension:
$$F_t = 0.60F_y$$

where F_y is the yield strength and F_t is the allowable tensile stress.

For tension at pinholes: $F_t = 0.45F_y$
For shear: $F_v = 0.45F_y$
For bending: $F_b = 0.66F_y$

but limited to

$$\frac{12,000,000}{ld/A_f}$$

where l = span of compression flange between lateral supports
    d = depth of beam
    A_f = area of compression flange

For welded connections, the allowable stress of fillet, plug, slot, and partial penetration-groove welds is 13,600 psi for the grade SAW2 electrodes on A7 or A373 steels; for the class E70 series electrodes on A36, A242, and A441 steels, the allowable stress for the same types of weld is 15,800 psi.

The allowable tensile stress in A307 bolts when used in A7 and A373 steel is 14,000 psi. The allowable unit shearing stress for A325 high-strength bolts is 15,000 psi and for the A354 high-strength bolts is 20,000 psi.

For momentary loads of stress, such as wind or earthquake, all the above-listed allowable unit stresses can be increased by one-third.

In the case of stress-grade lumber the basic allowable stresses are for the extreme fiber stress in bending f_b, tension stress parallel to grain f_t, maximum horizontal shear H, compression perpendicular to grain q, and compression stress parallel to the grain of the wood c.

For coast-type douglas fir, the maximum allowable stress in extreme fiber in bending and tension parallel to the grain varies according to the grade of lumber from 1,200 to 2,050 psi. The maximum horizontal shear varies from 95 to 120 psi. The maximum allowable compression stress perpendicular to the grain varies from 390 to 455 psi, and for compression parallel to grain, it is between 1,000 and 1,650 psi (Table 8-1). The modulus of elasticity E for douglas fir in bending is between 1,000,000 and 1,760,000 psi. Because wood has a significant difference of strength as a function of the direction of its grain, care must be taken in considering grain orientation for any connection of wooden members. See Table 8-1 for determining allowable unit stress on an inclined surface of timber.

Lumber is cut at the sawmills into standard sizes; depending on how the lumber was cut from the log, there will be resulting effects on warping due to the direction of grain throughout the piece of lumber, as shown in Fig. 12-1.

Lumber associations and building codes control the allowable strength of wood based upon the species of wood and the defects found in the sawn lumber. Some of these defects are knots, cross grain, shakes, checks, rot or decay, pitch pockets, wane, and warping. The number and size of these defects determine the grading of the timber.

Another important condition affecting the property of timber is the percentage of moisture found in the wood (Fig. 8-5). As can be seen in a stress-strain curve for douglas fir, a sample of saturated timber can have a maximum compressive stress of 4,000 psi while an air-dried

TABLE 8-1 Allowable Unit Stresses for Stress-grade Lumber

Species and commercial grade	Abbre-viation*	Allowable unit stresses, psi					
		Extreme fiber in bending (and tension parallel to grain) f (or t)	Maximum horizontal shear H	Compression perpendicular to grain q	Compression parallel to grain c	Modulus of elasticity E	Rules under which graded
Douglas fir, coast region:							
Dense select structural..	LF	2,050	120	455	1,500		
Select structural.......	LF	1,900	120	415	1,400		
1,750f-industrial	LF	1,750	120	455	1,400		
1,500f-industrial.......	LF	1,500	120	390	1,200		
1,200f-industrial	LF	1,200	95	390	1,000		
Dense select structural..	J & P	2,050	120	455	1,650		
Select structural.......	J & P	1,900	120	415	1,500		
Dense construction.....	J & P	1,750	120	455	1,400		
Construction..........	J & P	1,500	120	390	1,200	(All)	U, B, C.
Standard..............	J & P	1,200	95	390	1,000	1,600,000	Standard
Dense select structural..	B & S	2,050	120	455	1,500		25-3-64
Select structural.......	B & S	1,900	120	415	1,400		
Dense construction.....	B & S	1,750	120	455	1,200		
Construction..........	B & S	1,500	120	390	1,000		
Dense select structural..	P & T	1,900	120	455	1,650		
Select structural.......	P & T	1,750	120	415	1,500		
Dense construction.....	P & T	1,500	120	455	1,400		
Construction..........	P & T	1,200	120	390	1,200		

* LF = light framing
J & P = joists and planks
B & S = beams and stringers
P & T = posts and timbers
KD = kiln dried
SOURCE: Uniform Building Code.

NOTE: 1,750f represents 1,750 stress lumber.

sample with only 15 percent moisture can have an 11,000-psi maximum compressive stress. There is almost a 300 percent difference in strength.

One of the disadvantages in the use of timber is its vulnerability to fire and to deterioration. Two main causes of deterioration are termites and dry rot. Fortunately these can be prevented, as there are many types of timber preservatives which are resistant to termite attack. As a rule, however, the best protection is to keep the wood separated from soil and moisture and by keeping it dry and with adequate ventilation. This precaution would also prevent deterioration by dry rot.

MASONRY

The allowable working stresses for building brick are based on three grades of clay brick, the SW, MW, and NW grades. The minimum compressive strength for an average of five tests for the SW grade is 3,000 psi; for the MW grade it is 2,500 psi; and for the NW it is 1,500 psi.

For gypsum concrete as used for precast roof slabs, there are two classifications, A and B. The minimum compressive strength for class A gypsum is 500 psi, and for class B gypsum it is 1,000 psi.

CONCRETE

The Uniform Building Code and the American Cement Institute have listed the recommended minimum allowable stress for portland cement concrete. These stresses are based upon the ultimate compressive stress for each particular grade of concrete. The ultimate compressive stress is defined as the crushing strength of a sample concrete cylinder that has been cured for 28 days and has undergone a standard compressive test. The maximum strength of concrete is greatly affected by the moisture content of the concrete during curing, as seen in Figs. 8-6 and 8-7. According to the results of the compressive test, the concrete is then graded as a function of its ultimate compressive strength. Common grades are classified as 1,500-, 2,000-, 2,500- and up to 5,000-psi concrete. The allowable working stresses in flexural compression and tension in shear, bond, and bearing are all functions of the maximum

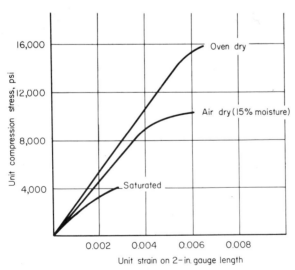

Fig. 8-5. Stress-strain curves showing the effect of moisture upon douglas fir lumber.

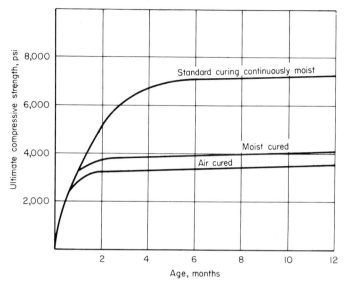

Fig. 8-6. The effect of curing upon compressive strength of concrete.

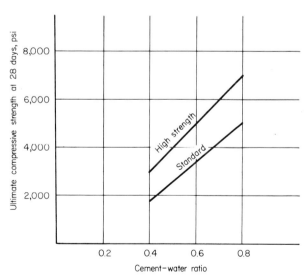

Fig. 8-7. Relationship of concrete strength and cement/water ratio for high-strength and standard concrete.

TABLE 8-2

Flexure, extreme fiber stress in compression	$0.45f'_c$
Shear, beams with no reinforcement	$0.02f'_c$
Shear, beams with properly designed web reinforcement	$0.06f'_c$
Bond for plain bars	$0.04f'_c$
Bond for deformed bars	$0.05f'_c$
Bearing	$0.25f'_c$

compressive stress of the concrete. Table 8-2 shows the allowable unit stresses for concrete in accordance to its ultimate compressive stress noted as f'_c.

The modulus of elasticity of concrete E_c is an indication of its stiffness and is approximately 2,000,000 psi for concrete within the 1,500- to 2,200-psi range. For stronger concrete the value of E_c is higher. For allowable unit stress in various strengths of concrete see Table 8-3.

REINFORCING STEEL

Reinforcing bars, which are made from intermediate-grade deformed steel, have an allowable tensile stress of approximately 18,000 psi based on an ultimate tensile strength of 70,000 to 90,000 psi and a minimum yield point at 40,000 psi. The modulus of elasticity E_s of these bars is about 30,000,000 psi. The ratio of E_s to E_c is known as the n value of reinforced concrete and is the relationship of deformation of the two materials. For properties of types of reinforcing bars see Table 10-2.

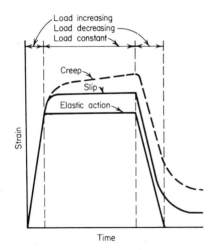

Fig. 8-8. Strain-time diagrams indicating elastic and inelastic behavior.

TABLE 8-3 Allowable Unit Stresses in Concrete

		Allowable unit stresses				
	For any strength of concrete in accordance with code $n = \dfrac{30,000}{f'_c}$		For strength of concrete shown below			
Description		Maximum value, psi	$f'_c = 2,000$ psi $n = 15$	$f'_c = 2,500$ psi $n = 12$	$f'_c = 3,000$ psi $n = 10$	$f'_c = 3,750$ psi $n = 8$
Flexure f_c:						
Extreme fiber stress in compression.......	$0.45f'_c$		900	1,125	1,350	1,688
Extreme fiber stress in tension in plain concrete footings......................	$0.03f'_c$		60	75	90	113
Shear (as a measure of diagonal tension):						
Beams with no web reinforcement v_c......	$0.03f'_c$	90	60	75	90	90
Beams with longitudinal bars and with either stirrups or properly located truss bars, but not both v..................	$0.08f'_c$	240	160	200	240	240
Beams with longitudinal bars and a combination of stirrups and truss bars (the latter bent up suitably to carry at least $0.04f'_c$) v...........................	$0.12f'_c$	360	240	300	360	360
Flat slabs at distance d from edge of column, capital, or drop panel v_c........	$0.03f'_c$		60	75	90	100
Footings v_c.........................	$0.03f'_c$	75	60	75	75	75
Reinforced concrete shear walls............	$0.05f'_c$		100	125	150	187
Bond u						
Deformed bars:						
Top bars*.........................	$0.07f'_c$	245	140	175	210	245
In two-way footings (except top bars)...	$0.08f'_c$	280	160	200	240	280
All others.........................	$0.10f'_c$	350	200	250	300	350
Plain bars (must be hooked):						
Top bars.........................	$0.03f'_c$	105	60	75	90	105
In two-way footings (except top bars)...	$0.036f'_c$	126	72	90	108	126
All others.........................	$0.045f'_c$	158	90	113	135	158
Bearing f_c:						
On full area.........................	$0.25f'_c$		500	625	750	938
On one-third area or less†...............	$0.375f'_c$		750	938	1,125	1,405

* Top bars are horizontal bars so placed that more than 12 in. of concrete are cast in the member below the bar.

† This increase is permitted only when the least distance between the edges of the loaded and unloaded areas is a minimum of one-fourth of the parallel side dimension of the loaded area. The allowable bearing stress on a reasonably concentric area greater than one-third, but less than the full area, should be interpolated between the values given.

SOURCE: Uniform Building Code.

HOISTING ROPES

The most common types of ropes used are the manila hemp (abaca, which comes from a banana tree), sisal fiber, cotton, and steel-wire rope. The maximum tensile load which a manila rope will support is expressed by the formula $T = 7,000 \times D^2 + 600$, where D is the diameter in inches. Sisal rope, which is made from an agave (century plant) grown in Mexico, is about two-thirds as strong as manila. Hemp rope is somewhat stronger than manila but is suitable only for small ropes. For heavy industrial use, the steel-wire rope is by far the most popular. Wire rope usually develops about 90 percent of the ultimate strength of the individual strands making up the rope.

ALUMINUM

Another popular construction material is aluminum because of its light weight and comparatively high strength. Aluminum comes in many alloys, each with its own physical and mechanical properties. The yield strength of the alloys varies from 16,000 psi to as high as 58,000 psi. An ultimate strength as high as 73,000 psi is available in certain alloys. Most structural aluminum shapes are made from heat-treated wrought-aluminum alloy 6061T6. The number 6061 identifies the alloy composition; the letter T shows that the metal has been heat-treated, and the final 6 indicates the type of heat treatment. The physical properties for 6061T6 are shown in Table 8-4.

SUMMARY

The plant engineer must decide on the type of material which best suits his structural problem. He must understand the significance of the fundamental properties of the materials and whether they are best adapted for the service required. Not only are the structural strength characteristics important but also the durability, appearance, quality, availability, and all aspects of economy during fabrication, erection, and maintenance.

The factor of safety is decided on by experienced testing and a good appraisal of the service to which the structure will be exposed. Structural materials can be exposed to stresses of tension, compression,

TABLE 8-4

	psi
Ultimate tensile strength	38,000
Ultimate shear strength	24,000
Yield strength, in tension	32,000
In compression	32,000
In shear	14,000
Modulus of elasticity, tension, and compression	10,000

bearing, shearing, torsion, and all types of chemical, thermal, and electric exposure. Repetition and reversal of stresses in loading can have a serious effect upon the strength of the material. The duration of loading also is an important consideration, that is, whether it is a temporary load or one sustained over long periods of time.

The plant engineer can also determine from the stress-strain diagram whether the material is brittle or ductile, at what point the yield or proportional limit occurs, the breaking strength, and the ultimate strength of the material. He can also determine the modulus of elasticity and anticipate the deformation or elongation of the material under the anticipated load of the structure. All construction material is flexible, ductile, and compressible under outside forces. To aid the plant engineer in his selection of material, the various manufacturing associations publish manuals with specifications citing the conditions under which their products should be used.

CHECKLIST FOR STRUCTURAL MATERIALS

1. Steel
   a. ASTM A7, A36, A440, A441, A242
   b. Yield point, elastic limit
   c. Modulus of elasticity
   d. Allowable working stresses, compression, tension, shear, and bearing
2. Concrete
   a. Ultimate compressive strength
   b. Aggregate type
   c. Portland cement types I to V
   d. Modulus of elasticity
3. Reinforcing steel
   a. ASTM designation
   b. Structural-grade steel
   c. Intermediate-grade steel
   d. Hard-grade steel
   e. Yield strength
   f. Modulus of elasticity
   g. Allowable working stresses, compression, tension, shear, and bond
4. Brick
   a. Grade SW, MW, NW
   b. Size
   c. Mortar
5. Concrete block
   a. Size
   b. Grade
   c. Compressive strength
   d. Mortar

6. Wood

   a. Species of wood

   b. Grade, utility, standard construction, dense construction, or selec structural

   c. Allowable stresses, compression, tension, shear, and bearing

BIBLIOGRAPHY

ACI Committee 317: *Reinforced Concrete Design Handbook, Working Stress Method,* American Concrete Institute, Detroit, Mich., 1965.

American Concrete Institute: *Building Code Requirements for Reinforced Concrete* (ACI-318-56), Detroit, Mich., 1959.

————: *Manual of Standard Practice for Detailing Reinforced Concrete Structures* (ACI 315-65), Detroit, Mich., 1965.

American Institute of Architects and Charles George Ramsey, and Harold Reeve Sleeper: *Architectural Graphic Standards,* 6th ed., John Wiley & Sons, Inc., New York, 1970.

American Institute of Steel Construction: *Steel Construction,* New York, 1961.

American Institute of Timber Construction: *Timber Construction Standards,* AITC 100-65, Washington, 1965.

Boyd, James E.: *Strength of Materials,* McGraw-Hill Book Company, New York, 1924.

Brick Institute of California: *Handbook on Reinforced Grouted Brick Masonry Construction,* Los Angeles, 1962.

Building Codes Bureau: *State Building Construction Code Applicable to- One- and Two-family Dwellings,* New York, 1964.

Callender, John Hancock: *Time-saver Standards,* 4th ed., McGraw-Hill Book Company, New York, 1966.

City of Los Angeles: *Building Code,* Building News, Inc., Los Angeles, 1970.

Concrete Masonry Association: *Concrete Masonry Design Manual,* Los Angeles, 1960.

Concrete Reinforcing Steel Institute: *CRSI Design Handbook,* Chicago, 1952.

County of Los Angeles: *County of Los Angeles Uniform Building Laws,* Building News, Inc., Los Angeles, 1968.

County of Los Angeles Uniform Building Laws: *Building Code, Plumbing Code, Mechanical Code, County Electrical Code,* Building News, Inc., Los Angeles, 1968.

Fling, Russell S.: *ACI Standard Specifications for Structural Concrete for Buildings* (ACI 301-66°), Portland Cement Association, Chicago, 1966.

Grinter, Linton E.: *Design of Modern Steel Structures,* The Macmillan Company, New York, 1948.

————: *Theory of Modern Steel Structures,* The Macmillan Company, New York, 1947.

Grover, LaMotte: *Manual of Design for Arc Welded Steel Structures,* Air Reduction Sales Co., New York, 1946.

Housing and Building Codes Bureau: *State Building Construction Code Applicable to General Building Construction,* New York, 1964.

————: *State Building Construction Code Applicable to Multiple Dwellings,* New York, 1964.

International Conference of Building Officials: *Uniform Building Code,* Pasadena, Calif., 1967.

————: *Uniform Building Codes,* vol. III, Los Angeles, 1961.

The James F. Lincoln Arc Welding Foundation: Modern Welded Structures, Cleveland, Ohio, vol. 1, 1963; vol. 2, 1965.

Knudsen, Vern O., and Cyril M. Harris: *Acoustical Designing in Architecture,* John Wiley & Sons, Inc., New York, 1965.

Laurson, Philip Gustave, and William Junkin Cox: *Mechanics of Materials,* 3d ed., John Wiley & Sons, Inc., New York, 1954.

The Lincoln Electric Company: *Procedure Handbook of Arc Welding Design and Practice,* Ohio, 1951.

Masonry Research: *Masonry Code and Specification,* Los Angeles, 1963.

Merriman, Thaddeus, and T. H. Wiggin: *American Civil Engineers' Handbook,* John Wiley & Sons, Inc., New York, 1947.

Merritt, Frederick S.: *Standard Handbook for Civil Engineers,* McGraw-Hill Book Company, New York, 1968.

Metal Building Manufacturers Association: *Recommended Design Practices Manual,* Cleveland, Ohio, 1959.

Murphy, Glenn: *Advanced Mechanics of Materials,* McGraw-Hill Book Company, New York, 1946.

————: *Properties of Engineering Materials,* International Textbook Company, Scranton, Pa., 1947.

Parker, Harry: *Simplified Engineering for Architects and Builders,* 4th ed., John Wiley & Sons, Inc., New York, 1967.

Plummer, Harry C., and John A. Blume: *Reinforced Brick, Masonry and Lateral Force Design,* Structural Clay Products Institute, Washington, 1958.

Portland Cement Association: *Simplified Design of Concrete Floor Systems,* Portland Cement Association, Chicago.

Priest, H. Malcolm, and John A. Gilligan: *Design Manual for High-strength Steels,* United States Steel Corporation, Pittsburgh, Pa., 1962.

Reese, R. C.: *CRSI Design Handbook,* Concrete Reinforcing Steel Institute, Chicago, 1952.

Roark, Raymond J.: *Formulas for Stress and Strain,* 4th ed., McGraw-Hill Book Company, New York, 1965.

Rossnagel, W. E.: *Handbook of Rigging,* 3d ed., McGraw-Hill Book Company, New York, 1964.

Ryerson, Joseph T.: *Ryerson Data Book,* Joseph T. Ryerson & Son, Inc., 1970.

————: *Ryerson Stock List,* Joseph T. Ryerson & Son, Inc., California, 1968.

Southern California Chapters, American Public Work Association, Associated General Contractors of America: *Standard Specifications for Public Works Construction,* Building News, Inc., Calif., 1967.

State of California Public Utilities Commission: *General Orders,* California Office of State Printing, San Francisco, 1967.

Sutherland, Hale, and Raymond C. Reese: *Reinforced Concrete Design,* John Wiley & Sons, Inc., New York, 1946.

Urquhart, Leonard Church: *Civil Engineering Handbook,* 4th ed., McGraw-Hill Book Company, New York, 1959.

Wallin, R. E.: *Construction Specifications,* Plant Engineering, Barrington, Ill., 1970.

West Coast Lumbermen's Association: *Douglas Fir Use Book: Structural Data and Design Tables,* Portland, Ore., 1958.

Western Concrete: *Reinforcing Steel Institute Manual of Standard Practice for Reinforced Concrete Construction,* Calif., 1967.

Winter, George: *Development of Cold Formed Light Gage Steel Structures,* American Iron and Steel Institute, Pittsburgh, Pa., 1959.

CHAPTER NINE

Steel Construction

SINCE MOST BUILDINGS AND STRUCTURES in the modern industrial plant are constructed of steel, the plant engineer must have a basic knowledge of this subject. He must become familiar with the various stages of steel construction, which include structural calculations, design drawings, steel nomenclature, symbols, shop drawings, erection plans, types of fasteners, fabrication, and erection of structural steel.

The American Institute of Steel Construction, founded in 1921 as a nonprofit technical organization, furnishes advisory services to designers, fabricators, and contractors. The *Manual of Steel Construction* published by this organization is as indispensable to the plant engineer as it is to the structural engineer. It covers all the most important aspects of steel construction, including dimensions and properties of steel shapes, design of beams, columns, and connections, and recommended specifications and codes.

Steel is formed in rolling mills into standard structural shapes (Fig. 9-1). Each rolled shape is known by an accepted name used in the industry, and the names are listed in the manual. (Recently much of the nomenclature has been changed. The changes will appear in parentheses.) The tables list dimensions and the cross-sectional properties of each member. Steel constitutes the major framing of most build-

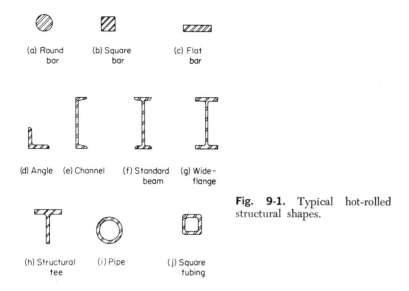

(a) Round bar   (b) Square bar   (c) Flat bar

(d) Angle   (e) Channel   (f) Standard beam   (g) Wide-flange

(h) Structural tee   (i) Pipe   (j) Square tubing

Fig. 9-1. Typical hot-rolled structural shapes.

ings and plant structures including towers, platforms, conveyor bridges, and pipe supports.

For the convenience of the users of steel, the AISC employs a system of designating rolled steel shapes with an economy of symbols. For example, a typical equal-leg angle 6 ft 2 in. long is written as L6 × 6 × ½ × 6′2″. Angles with unequal legs can be written as L6 × 4 × ¼ × 6′2″. An American Standard beam is written as 24I100 (S24 × 100). A light beam is written as 14B26 (W14 × 26). Wide-flange shapes can be written as 24WF76 (W24 × 76), and a miscellaneous shape is 8M17 (M8 × 17).

Designers customarily select the lightest beam of each size since these are the most commonly stocked in warehouses. For instance, of the four 10-in. channels available, the 10⌷15.3 (C10 × 15.3) is the lightest while the heaviest beam is almost twice its weight at 30 lb/ft. Shapes other than the lightest ones may mean a mill order, slower delivery, and additional cost. It is more economical to use the next size member rather than the next weight.

In addition to the many structural shapes rolled by steel mills, known as hot-rolled or mild steel, another very popular shape is the cold-formed structural member (Fig. 9-2), which is the type used by the prefabricated-building manufacturers. Cold-formed shapes are used most economically in construction as secondary members. Instead of standard hot-rolled structural shapes for girts, purlins, angles, and struts, a cold-formed shape made from 12-, 14-, or 16-gage sheet steel is used. These shapes are formed from high-strength steel with yield strengths up to

50,000 psi. This can be compared to the typical rolled shapes, which have a yield strength of only 36,000 psi.

These cold-formed members are formed into Z's, G's, and C's, shapes having bending-resistance properties equivalent to rolled sections weighing over three times more.

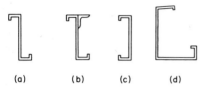

(a)   (b)   (c)   (d)

Fig. 9-2. Typical cold-formed steel shapes made from 12- and 14-gage sheets: (a) Z shape, used for girts and purlins; (b) Z and angle, used as a strut; (c) channel, used for girts, purlins, and light beams; (d) G shape, used as an eave strut.

The main structural frame of prefabricated buildings is usually made of built-up beams of mild steel. For the sake of economy, the rigid frames, columns, and rafters are usually tapered so that the moment of inertia of the section conforms to the bending moment, thus reducing the weight normally required by constant-depth rolled sections.

In addition to the structural framing system which includes columns, beams, purlins, girts, and the metal covering, many accessories make up steel industrial buildings, for example, gutters, downspouts, rake angles, ridge closures, corner trims, closure strips, and flashing.

Most prefabricated-building manufacturers offer a wide assortment of options which include doors, windows, canopies, roof ventilators, wall louvers, insulation, and bridge crane runways.

There are several building profiles available; all are considered to be standard. The roof may have a single or double slope. It may be a low profile, which is a slope of 1 in 12 in., or a standard profile, which is a slope of 4 in 12 in. The width, height, and spacing between columns are usually offered in many choices, so that the plant engineer can simply select the building which most closely fits his needs.

INDUSTRIAL BUILDINGS

In order to communicate with the designers and manufacturers of steel buildings, the plant engineer should know the language of the trade. The various components have their own peculiar names in the steel industry. In a typical industrial mill building, the walls of the building are made of "columns" which support the "roof trusses" or "girders." The interior columns at the end of a building are called "wind columns." They do not carry the weight of the roof but support the siding and resist the horizontal wind forces.

The horizontal framing between columns used to support the siding is called "girts." Girts are usually spaced from 4 to 6 ft apart, depending upon the wind condition and the type of siding used. Vertical rods used to prevent the girts from sagging between columns are called "sag rods." They are suspended from the top horizontal member of the wall, which is known as the "eave strut."

Supported from the roof trusses or girders are horizontal members called "purlins." They are also spaced about 4 to 6 ft apart, depending on the type of roofing used and the live-load condition of the area. The purlins are also stayed transversely by sag rods, which carry a portion of the weight of the roofing to the "ridge strut."

Diagonal bracing in the walls is called "wall bracing" and is made of either rods or angles. Similarly, diagonal bracing in the roof plane is called "roof bracing." These are also of rods or angles. When the roof construction is made of trusses, there is another set of bracing in the horizontal plane of the lower chord of the truss, called "lower-chord bracing." Compression members in any bracing system are called "struts" and may occur in the roof or in the wall plane.

When an industrial building supports a horizontal traveling bridge crane, the member supporting the crane rail is called the "rail girder." The building components listed above can be seen in Fig. 9-3.

Various types of siding and roofing materials are used to enclose the building. The most economical is corrugated, galvanized-steel siding. This has been largely replaced by the prepainted, corrugated or ribbed siding formed from a high-strength sheet steel. Sheets are available in a wide range of colors and profiles. Prepainted sheets are not only attractive but are resistant to most industrial fumes and liquids.

In addition to the steel sheets corrugated asbestos-cement sheets and asphalt-protected metal sheets are available in many colors.

Another economical enclosure material is aluminum siding and roofing, which is available as corrugated or ribbed sheets in various thicknesses and profiles.

When natural lighting is desired, many types of translucent plastic sheets have the same corrugations as the type of roofing and siding used. These translucent sheets can be used interspersed with any of the above corrugated sheets to allow light to enter the building. This method has largely replaced glazed windows.

There are two main methods of attaching the corrugated sheets to the building members. The most popular method is by stainless-steel sheet-metal screws. The older method is by steel straw nails.

For industrial buildings requiring waterproofing or some degree of dust control, all siding joints can be sealed by preformed neoprene closure strips. All junctions should be covered by sheet-metal flashing. This is particularly necessary at eaves, doors, and corners of walls.

A steel building is connected to the foundation through its column baseplates, which are usually ½ to 1 in. thick and large enough to distribute the column load over the concrete as well as to provide holes for anchor-bolt attachment.

Many types of roof trusses are used in industrial buildings. Some of the commonly used trusses are the Fink, Howe, Pratt, and Warren types. Other roof-construction systems are the framed portal, the three-hinged arch, and the two-hinged arch.

The various components of an industrial stairway are the treads, stringers, landing, and handrail, as shown in Fig. 9-4. A typical ladder is shown in Fig. 9-5.

Case History

A large aircraft company planned to install new process equipment for cleaning and spraying aircraft components. This new equipment was to occupy one bay of a building 300 by 1,000 ft in size, the bay being

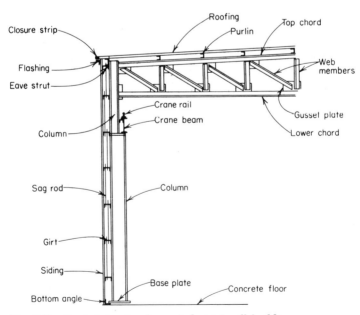

Fig. 9-3.   Typical framing for an industrial mill building.

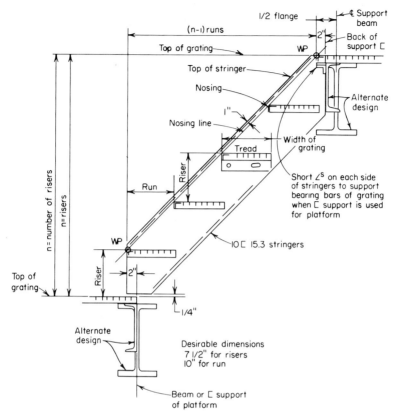

Fig. 9-4. Typical detail of a steel stairway.

60 ft wide and 300 ft long. The process required an extensive overhead conveyor system which traversed the entire bay. The conveyor system carried a maximum load of 2,500 lb spaced 25 ft apart. The aircraft company's plant-engineering department was given the job of supporting this conveyor system from the existing steel roof structures.

From this point the plant engineer followed the following procedure:

1. He acquired a plan of the conveyor system which accurately located the centerline and height of the conveyor, all related drive units, turntables, switches, and drop sections that must be suspended with the overhead conveyor system.
2. After a study of the mechanical plan, he determined the location of all points of support.
3. The plant engineer prepared a plan showing the conveyor as a single line drawing with every point of vertical and horizontal support indicated on this plan.

4. He reviewed the existing roof framing plan of the building to determine the answers to the following questions:
   a. Was there adequate strength in the existing trusses, purlins, and columns to carry the new load of the conveyor system?
   b. What were the critical points of the existing trusses where loads could not be applied?
   c. Were the trusses so highly stressed that no welding or drilling could be accommodated?
   d. Were the columns large enough for the additional load?
   e. Did the existing foundation have adequate bearing value to carry the additional conveyor loading?
   f. Did the new loading of the conveyors add significantly to the lateral or seismic design of this building?
   g. Were any of the existing members of the building to be cut for clearance of the conveyor, and if so, how critical was this cutting?

If the existing plant building calculations were still available, the job of checking the existing structures would be relatively simple. But if

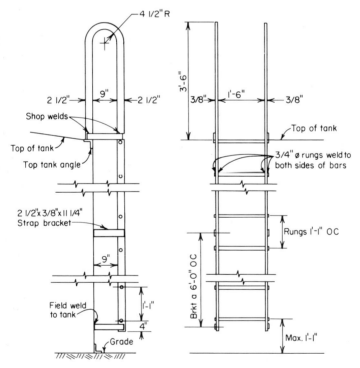

Fig. 9-5. Typical detail of a steel ladder.

the building, as in this case, was built 25 years ago and calculations were not available, a new analysis of the building would have to be made by the plant's civil engineer or an outside consultant.

The result of this analysis showed that the existing trusses were adequate to carry the new conveyor load provided there was no welding to the members or holes drilled into them. The purlins were found to be already loaded to the maximum, and they could not be used for carrying any additional conveyor loads. The foundations were found to be adequate, and the bridge-crane girder was found to be more than adequate since the bridge crane was no longer to be utilized.

The design for the conveyor-supporting structure was a system of beams spanning from truss to truss supported at the panel points wherever possible. When it was found that the new beams had to be supported on the lower chord between panel points, the lower chord had to be reinforced. The conveyor system was to be suspended by a double-angle hanger and diagonal bracing system. Where the suspension system was attached to new steel members, it was field-welded. Where it was attached to existing steel, it was fastened by a method of bolted clamps. The suspension system for the conveyors was designed for an impact factor of 25 percent, a traverse load factor of 20 percent, and a longitudinal load factor of 10 percent. Diagonal bracing hangers and connections were all designed for the various combinations of loading.

It was found that the various members were better cut in the field to assure proper length. All suspension members were light angles no larger than $2\frac{1}{2}$ by $2\frac{1}{2}$ by $\frac{1}{4}$ in. thick, so that they could be easily cut or drilled at the site. In order to estimate the cost of the new supports, the plant engineer found that approximately 30,000 lb of supporting steel and 40,000 lb of suspension steel were necessary to provide adequate structural support for the new conveyor system. By multiplying this weight by a unit cost per pound, it became apparent that the supporting structure was a substantial part of the cost of the project and also a very critical part in terms of safety and operation.

STRUCTURAL STEEL DRAWINGS

During the planning stage of any new steel building, the plant engineer must review the design and shop drawings.

Three general types of drawings are used from the conception to the final erection of a steel building or structure (Fig. 9-6). The conceptual drawing is the design drawing. The fabrication drawing is the shop drawing, and the construction drawing is the erection drawing. As the plant engineer will be involved with all three, he should be familiar with their purpose and use. He must understand the nomenclature, symbols, and all other indications on the various drawings.

The purpose of the design drawing is to furnish basic information to the steel fabricator and the erector. These drawings provide a full description of the project, the names of the customer and the owner, and the name of the organization responsible for the design. The design drawings should also include the grade of steel to be used, the type of paint and steel connections, required inspection in the shop and in the field, the conditions of approval for shop drawings, and the scope of work included and excluded in the contract.

The design drawings should also show the complete structural framing with the size, sections, and relative location of all the steel members. Floor levels and column centers should be dimensioned. The plans should be drawn at a scale large enough to convey the information adequately and should indicate the important details of construction

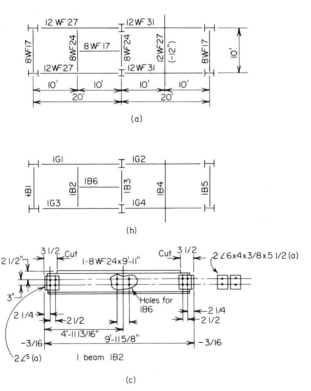

Fig. 9-6. Three types of structural-steel drafting: (a) design drawing, made by design engineer; (b) erection drawing, made by steel fabricator; (c) shop drawing, made by steel fabricator.

to be employed, supplemented by such data concerning the assumed loads, shear, moments, and axial forces to be resisted by all members and their connections.

Design drawings normally include an accepted specification for detailing, fabricating, and erecting the steel. These specifications usually refer to the AISC Code of Standard Practice for steel buildings and bridges. This code should be used as part of the contract documents along with the design drawings.

Good practice in the preparation of structural-steel design drawings requires the inclusion of general notes which provide good control of the construction. It is therefore recommended that a note similar to the following be included in every set of structural-steel drawings.

General Notes

1. The detailing, fabrication, and erection of all structural steel shall conform to the latest AISC Specification Serial Designation A36.
2. The fabricator shall furnish three sets of completed checked shop drawings for approval before fabrication.
3. All field connections are ¾-in. bolts with 1³⁄₁₆-in. holes unless otherwise noted.
4. All steel members shall receive one shop coat of rust-resistant paint except on surfaces to be embedded in concrete, to be welded, or to receive high-strength bolts.
5. Fabricator shall furnish all field bolts.
6. All welding shall conform to the specification of the American Welding Society.
7. All welding shall be done with certified welders and shall have continuous inspection by qualified inspectors.
8. All connections using high-strength bolts are friction-type or bearing-type with regular-head bolts.
9. Material manufacture and installation of high-strength bolts shall conform to the ASTM A325 latest edition.

The notes may vary for each job, but the subjects covered remain the same. The reference to the AISC Specification relieves the designer of the necessity of drafting the many details and connections which are considered standard practice. Most steel fabricators and erectors are well acquainted with the specifications of the AISC and will follow their recommendations for detailing, fabrication, and erection.

It is also good practice for the plant engineer to review the fabricator's shop drawings before fabrication of steel has begun. This is also the last chance to clarify any misunderstanding about the intent of the design drawings and to pick up design and drafting errors in dimensioning and clearances which have escaped checking.

STEEL CONNECTIONS

The bolt usually used in standard steel construction is a ¾-in. machine bolt except when high-strength connections are required.

Since good welding practice is well covered by the Specifications of the American Welding Society, it is preferable to refer to the AWS Specifications to describe methods and materials of welding. Many building and safety departments require continuous inspection of all field structural welding; without inspection only one-half stress is allowed on such welding.

Methods and material for installation of high-strength bolts are covered in ASTM A325 and A490 Specifications.

High-strength bolts are installed by the calibrated-wrench method or by the turn-of-the-bolt method. Holes for this type of connection must be clean and without burrs and the adjacent surfaces must be smooth. Here too, reference to the ASTM Specifications relieves the designer of the burden of detailing the entire procedure of installation for material of high-strength bolts.

PAINTING

All steel should receive at least a shop coat of paint before leaving the fabricator's shop to prevent corrosion if erection is delayed and to serve as a necessary undercoat when the steel is to be painted with a second coat after erection. When only a prime coat is required, the plant engineer may select the type of paint to be specified to match the paint being used in the balance of the plant.

In certain places on structural steel paint is not desired. The unpainted areas are those to be welded, where high-strength connections are to be made, where steel is to be embedded in concrete, or when the steel is to be fireproofed. If this note is not included on the drawings, expensive field costs will result from scraping off the paint.

DESIGN DRAWINGS

The design drawings (Fig. 9-6) are single-line drawings showing the location of each beam, column, or brace and their sizes. Dimensions are given to working lines or working points. A "working line" is either the top of the beam, the center of a column, or the neutral axis of an angle. The "working point" is the intersection of two working lines.

The design drawings are the result of layout and calculation of loads. Although there are single-line drawings, one should always be aware of the depth and width of each member to avoid interferences. Part of the design drawing includes details, usually for unusual connections and complicated construction which cannot be shown on the design drawings and which are not considered standard.

SHOP DRAWINGS

In detailing beams, a system of shipping marks incorporating the sheet number is usually used. One indexing system uses a prefix number to indicate detail-sheet numbers, the letter to distinguish the various types of members, and a suffix number to show that particular member on the sheet. For example, a shipping piece numbered 2B21 which is identified as a beam will be found on shop drawing 2 and is the twenty-first member shown on that sheet. Also, a piece numbered 3G21, which is indicated by its letter to be a girder, will be found on shop drawing 3.

In order to simplify the design of connections some designers add to their plan the reaction load at the end of the beam in kips so that the detailer can select the proper connection from the manual.

Shop drawings include details of each individual piece of steel, whether it is a long column or a small clip angle. The shop detail shows the cutoff length of each member, all cutouts, all holes for bolts, and surfaces to be milled or painted. The shop detailer follows the design drawings but allows for fitup, dimensions, clearances, cutouts, matching holes, and all bevel and diagonal dimensions. Each shop drawing includes a bill of material listing every piece of steel fabricated and shown on that particular drawing.

ERECTION DRAWINGS

The steel fabricating shop and the steel erector utilize two other types of drawings, the shop drawings and the erection drawings. The erection drawings are framing plans and elevations which are similar to the design drawings but also have the shipping number noted beside each member.

DESIGN PRACTICE

The steel designer and fabricator are guided by common industrial practice in the selection of steel members and the standard methods of connections. The method of presenting the intentions of the designer and detailer on the drawings must be in accordance with the accepted procedure outlined in the AISC *Manual*. A misinterpretation of a symbol, notation, or dimension can cause a great deal of difficulty during construction and increase the cost of the job.

The names used for members in steel building are significant only in this industry. Therefore the plant engineer should understand the language when involved in this work. Some of these common terms for components of a building are: trusses, built-up girders, rigid frames, rafters, tapered girders, columns, beams, bents, trestles, knee bracing, ridge struts, eave struts, sag rods, girt lines, purlins, bracing rods, bays, top chord, bottom chord, crane girders, gussets, clip angles, and web members. These components are shown in Fig. 9-7.

In roof construction the main carrying member may be a beam for short spans and a truss for very long spans. As beams carry greater loads and span longer distances, it becomes economical to change from rolled sections to built-up girders and finally to trusses.

For most roofs, a wide-flange or I beam is economical to a 30-ft span. For longer spans up to approximately 100 ft, a built-up girder can be used. For spans over 100 ft, the truss is most economical. For uniform loading it has been found that a tapered girder has the advantage of a varying beam depth which generally follows the bending moment.

Built-up girders are fabricated from plates, angles, or channels in various combinations, as shown in Fig. 9-8.

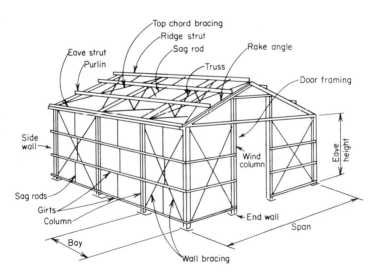

Major components of a steel frame
mill building

Fig. 9-7.   Main components of a steel-framed building.

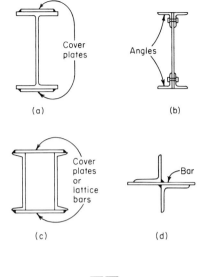

Fig. 9-8. Typical built-up structural sections made from rolled structural shapes: (*a*) wide-flange beam with cover plates, (*b*) girder made from plate and angles, (*c*) girder made from two channels and two plates, (*d*) star strut made from two angles, (*e*) T strut made from two angles.

Lightweight trusses are also common and are known as "open-web steel joists." They have top and bottom flanges of small angles, T's, or formed steel sheet, and the web members are made from bars or angles. They are used for light floor and roof construction. Open-web steel joists are prefabricated and available in many depths and carrying capacities.

DESIGN LOADS

The design of every industrial structure is based on two types of loading, the dead load and the live load. The dead load is assumed to consist of the weight of the steel work and all material permanently attached to the structure. The live load includes all movable loads, such as snow, wind, personnel, equipment, and all temporary loads.

In addition to the consideration of these loads, the designer includes impact loads caused by moving machinery. The impact loads are usually given as a percentage of the live load of that particular machine. The following impact-load factors are recommended by the AISC:

1. Supports of elevators: 100 percent
2. Traveling-crane support girders and their connections: 25 percent
3. Support of reciprocating machines of power-driven units: 50 percent minimum

4. Supports of light shaft or motor-drive machinery: 20 percent minimum
5. Supports for hangers for floors and balconies: 33 percent
6. In addition to the above impact loads, which are vertically directed forces, the designer also must calculate the horizontal forces due to crane movement. The lateral force on a crane runway due to the effect of a moving crane trolley should be no less than 20 percent of the sum of the weight of the lifted load and of the crane trolley acting normal to the rail and 10 percent acting parallel to the rail.

Wind loading is usually governed by local codes. Generally, the code requires about 15 lb/sq ft for the first 30 ft of height, 20 lb/sq ft to 60 ft, and 25 lb/sq ft above that. Localities with high windstorm records have special local requirements.

In areas having an earthquake history, all structures must be designed for lateral forces due to earth movements. These requirements are covered in detail in the local codes.

WELDING

An important part of design drawings is the indication of welding. There is an industry accepted method of drawing welding symbols. Each welding symbol includes the location, size, type, and whether field- or shop-applied.

SHOP PRACTICE

To assist the plant engineer in understanding the function of a steel fabricator, a brief description of the work required for each operation can be helpful. Upon receipt of the design drawings, the following duties are performed by the steel fabricator:

1. Preparation of advance bill for ordering material, especially for long-term delivery items
2. Preparation of erection plans, based on design drawings
3. Preparation of a system of marks, index sheets, and sheet number
4. Preparation of typical details, layouts, and calculation sheets for determining the length of members
5. Preparation and checking of detail drawings
6. Writing shop bill of material
7. Securing approval of drawings from the customer
8. Itemizing field fasteners and weld electrodes

9. Calculating weights of the material
10. Preparing bills for shipping and invoicing of the finished parts

The actual shop practice for the fabrication of steel includes the following operations:

1. Material handling and cutting of steel
2. Template making
3. Layout of steel
4. Punching and drilling
5. Straightening
6. Bending and rolling
7. Fitting and reaming
8. Fastening, including bolting, riveting, and welding
9. Finishing
10. Machine-shop and floor-shop work
11. Inspection
12. Cleaning and painting
13. Shipping to the job site

FIELD PRACTICE

The procedure for erection of structural steel frames is covered by the AISC Code of Standard Practice. Some of the highpoints of this code include the following:

> The frame of the steel structure should be braced so that the structure remains true and plumb at all points; such bracing should be left in place as long as may be required for safety; as the work progresses the structure should be securely bolted or welded to take care of all dead loads, wind and erection stresses; there should be no permanent bolting or welding done until the structure has been properly aligned; all areas to receive field welding should be wire-brush cleaned to remove all shop paint and reduce any paint film to the minimum; there should be cooperation between the steel erector and the owner's inspector, permitting the inspector access to all parts of the work being done.

STANDARD DETAILS AND CONSTRUCTION METHODS

Most of the connections of steel to steel are covered by the *Manual of Steel Construction*. It is unnecessary for the designer to detail these standard connections. Only in the case of bending connections or unusual connections due to the configuration of the members are special

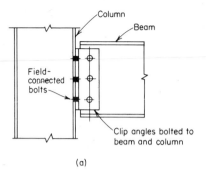

(a)

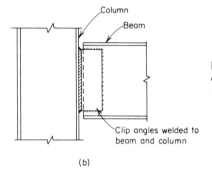

(b)

Fig. 9-9. Two standard beam connections: (*a*) bolted and (*b*) welded connections.

details required. Figures 9-9 and 9-10 show some of the typical standard connections as prepared by shop fabricators.

FAILURE IN CONNECTIONS

The plant engineer should always remember that the most important part of a structural design is the design of its connections. The security and strength of a structure depend mainly on its connections, and great care should be given to the type of design and construction.

The most important part of a structural-steel frame (and yet the most neglected) is the connections. Practically every structural failure that has occurred has been due to inadequate connections rather than undersized beams or columns. When a beam is stressed beyond its designed capability, it will usually deflect, twist, or buckle. These warning signs are noticeable before the beam has reached a point of destruction or collapse. Excessive beam deflection would cause cracking of the plaster or concrete, thus alerting the occupants that the structure has passed its design limit. However, when a connection fails, there is usually very little warning. Stresses in a bolted or welded connection can reach and pass their yield point and give no indication whatsoever to the

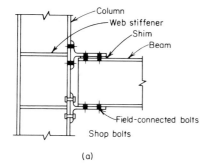

(a)

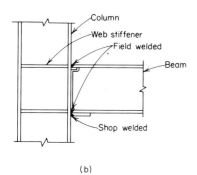

(b)

Fig. 9-10. Two rigid-beam connections: (a) bolted connection with structural T's and (b) welded connection.

eye. Consequently, a failure of a connection may be discovered only after that portion of the structure has collapsed. For this reason the plant engineer as well as the designer must always consider the connection as the most vital part of every framing system.

Figure 9-11 illustrates the sequences of failure of a cantilever beam connection. This entire episode occurred within several seconds after buckling of the column web.

Every connection must resist one or more of the following forces: shear, tension, bearing, compression, flexure, and torque. Connections may be stressed in combinations of two or more stresses.

Connections may fail in many ways (Fig. 9-12). Merely unscrewing a nut from a bolt holding a monorail can cause the monorail, trolley, and load to collapse. By failing in shear a bolt can actually be cut in two by excessive loading. A gusset plate can fail in tension, shear, or in bearing. A column anchor bolt can fail in bond when pulled out of the concrete. Although the bolt could resist the load, the bond between steel to concrete has not been able to sustain the pull of the anchor bolt. A weld can fail by cracking in shear.

The following are suggested checkpoints to prevent potential failure of connections in steel:

1. Loose bolts in friction-type high-strength bolts
2. Oversize holes
3. Unequal stressing of bolts due to poor bolt arrangement
4. Unequal stressing of plate due to poor layout
5. Fatigue of bolt or plate
6. Bolt flexure
7. Tension in bolt
8. Reversal of stresses of connection
9. Secondary stresses due to eccentricity of connection (Figs. 9-13 and 9-14)

The loss of a single bolt in a group can cause a moment or twisting action on those remaining bolts through induced eccentricity in the connection. This eccentricity can create additional secondary loads on the remaining bolts which can cause failure. Therefore, it is not necessarily true that when two bolts out of ten fail, the connection still retains 80 percent of its initial strength. The failure of two bolts can cause

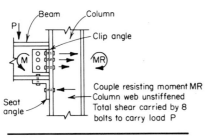

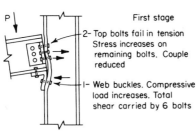

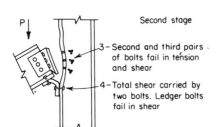

Fig. 9-11. Sequences of failure of a cantilever beam connection.

1. Fabricator neglected stiffener plates in column adjacent to seat angle required to resist compressive forces.

2. Cantilever beam when loaded causes both shear and compressive force on column web.

3. Unstiffened web of column buckles due to high compressive stresses.

4. Because of loss of seat-angle effectiveness, the entire beam moment is taken by bolts in web of beam to flange of column, which causes failure in top bolts due to tension.

5. Top bolts now elongate, causing further increased tension in the second set of bolts until they also fail.

6. Remaining bolts fail in tension and shear.

7. Beam collapses.

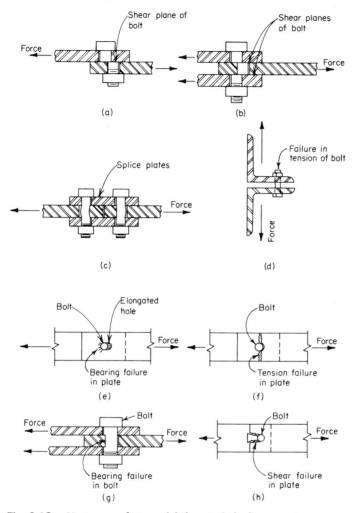

Fig. 9-12. Various conditions of failure in bolted connections: (*a*) bolt in single shear, (*b*) bolt in double shear, (*c*) bolt in bending, (*d*) bolt in tension, (*e*) plate in bearing, (*f*) plate in shear, (*g*) bolt in bearing, and (*h*) plate in shear.

new secondary stresses which may reduce the strength of the connection by as much as 50 percent or more.

BOLTED CONNECTIONS

The most common type of steel-to-steel fastener is the bolt. ASTM A307 bolts include machine, plain, common, rough, and turned bolts. They are used for shop or field connections and are usually not recom-

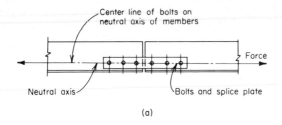

(a)

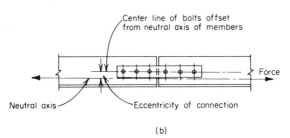

(b)

Fig. 9-13. A concentric and eccentric bolted connection: (*a*) concentric connection: no secondary moment; (*b*) eccentric connection: secondary moment.

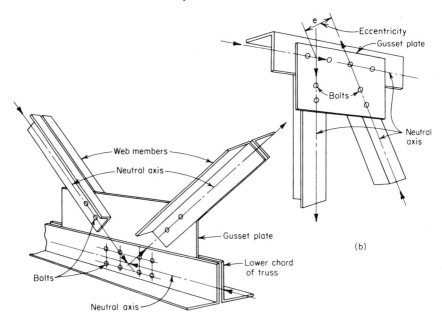

(a)

(b)

Fig. 9-14. Proper and improper design of connections. (*a*) Proper design with neutral axes of all members meeting at one point. No eccentricity or secondary moment created. (*b*) Improperly designed connection with eccentricity between lines of neutral axes causing secondary moment.

164

mended for major, highly stressed connections. The A307 bolt is used for fastening secondary members, such as purlins, girts, stairs, platforms, etc., which are not part of the main structural frame. Nelson studs are also often used (Fig. 9-15).

The high-strength bolts (Fig. 9-16) are known as ASTM Designation A354, A325, and A490. Installation of high-strength bolts is by either the use of a calibrated torque wrench or by the turn-of-the-nut method.

The A325 and A354 high-strength bolts can be either friction type or bearing type (Fig. 9-16). The friction type develops its strength by the frictional forces between the plates caused by the high compression between the head and nut of the bolt. The bearing-type high-strength bolt obtains its strength through bearing contact of the plate to the side of the bolt. For proper installation there should be no paint under the washer with a friction-type high-strength bolt. Bearing-type high-strength bolts should be long enough for the threads to be out of the shear plane.

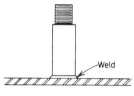

(a) Threaded stud

(b) Shoulder stud

Both the A307 and the high-strength bolts are described by the diameter of their shank in fractions of an inch and by the type of head, which is either square or hexagonal. The length of the bolt is the distance from the inside of the head to the end of the bolt. On high-strength bolts, the washer face is milled on the inside face of the head and the inside face of the nut. The "grip" of the bolt is the distance between the nut and the head which engages the material to be connected, or the distance between washers when two washers are used.

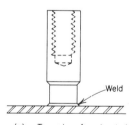

(c) Tapped or female stud

Fig. 9-15. Three common types of Nelson studs.

Beveled washers are required for high-strength bolts when connections are made to the sloping flanges of standard beams or channels. Holes that are drilled or punched in the steel to be connected by all bolts should only be $\frac{1}{16}$ in. larger than the diameter of the bolt shank. In connections for high-strength bolts, all holes must be deburred. On friction-type high-strength bolts, the area around the holes should not be painted to allow proper contact between the bolt head, the washer, and the member.

The minimum distance between centers of bolt holes should not be

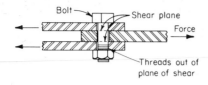

(a)

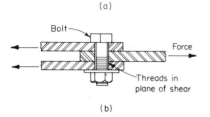

(b)

Fig. 9-16. Installation of two types of high-strength bolts: (*a*) bearing-type high-strength bolt and (*b*) friction-type high-strength bolt.

less than three times the diameter of the bolt, and the distance between the center of any punched bolt hole to any edge should not be less than shown in Table 9-1.

Each steel connection should have a minimum of two bolts, and the center of gravity of the bolt groupings should always coincide with the intersection of the neutral axis of the members being connected. This is to avoid any eccentricity in the connection itself, which would cause secondary stresses.

Another precaution required in the design of bolted connections is the pitch, or distance between bolts in the row. This is important because failure can occur in the material between holes if the spacing is too close, by shear or by tension in the plates being fastened.

Detailing of Connections

On detail drawings of bolted connections, the usual indication for a shop-connected bolt is an open circle. A field-connected bolt is indi-

TABLE 9-1

Bolt diameter, in.	Sheared edge, in.	Rolled edge	
		Plate, in.	Structural shape, in.
$\frac{1}{2}$	1	$\frac{7}{8}$	$\frac{3}{4}$
$\frac{5}{8}$	$1\frac{1}{8}$	1	$\frac{7}{8}$
$\frac{3}{4}$	$1\frac{1}{4}$	$1\frac{1}{8}$	1
$\frac{7}{8}$	$1\frac{1}{2}$	$1\frac{1}{4}$	$1\frac{1}{8}$
1	$1\frac{3}{4}$	$1\frac{1}{2}$	$1\frac{1}{4}$
$1\frac{1}{8}$	2	$1\frac{3}{4}$	$1\frac{1}{2}$
$1\frac{1}{4}$	$2\frac{1}{4}$	2	$1\frac{3}{4}$

cated by a solid black circle. This means the members are to be delivered without a bolt in the hole. All design drawings should clearly indicate size and type of bolts to be used and state that installation should be in accordance with AISC Specifications.

PIN CONNECTIONS

When heavy members are to be connected with free rotational movement, a single large pin is generally used (Fig. 9-17). Structural pins are turned cylinders with treated ends of reduced diameter for nuts. The holes usually drilled for large pins are $\frac{1}{16}$ or $\frac{1}{32}$ in. larger than the diameter of the pin. Pin connections are subjected to many stresses, which include shear, bearing, and bending. The plates attached to the pin are also stressed in bearing, shear, compression, and tension.

WELDED CONNECTIONS

One of the most popular methods of connecting steel to steel is welding (Fig. 9-18). Many building departments require that all structural welding be done by certified welders. In addition, welding done on site must be continuously inspected by deputy inspectors; otherwise, only 50 percent of the allowable unit stresses are permitted. It is best to specify that all welding shall be done in accordance with the specifications of the American Welding Society (AWS). These specifications govern the preparation of the material, the types of welding rods, the method of welding, and inspection methods of the welds.

Steel-to-steel connections are usually made with welding rods and

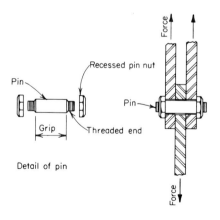

Fig. 9-17. Detail of a pin and a pinned connection.

an application of extreme heat. This fuses the metal of the rod with the steel. The electric-arc method, the most common welding technique, uses an electric generator, cables, and a welding rod which forms one electrode while the base metal forms the other. The heat of the arc fuses the rod and the base metal together.

There are several types of structural welds, including the butt weld, the fillet weld, the plug weld, the stitch weld, the groove weld, and several types of full-penetration welds (Fig. 9-19). The butt weld is used when two plates are joined edge to edge. If the edges of the two plates are square, it is called a "square butt weld." If one of the plates has been beveled, it is called a "single beveled weld." If both plates are beveled, it is called a "double beveled weld." A fillet weld occurs if one plate overlaps the other, and a triangle weld joins the edge of one plate to the side of the other. Small welds that hold component parts together until the final weld is made are called "stitch" or "tack" welds. Welding of holes or slots is called "plug welding." The welding symbols are shown in Fig. 9-20.

Every welded structural connection should have a minimum strength of 10,000 lb. Welds should be designed to avoid eccentricity of connection, which can cause failure. For good welding practice, surfaces to

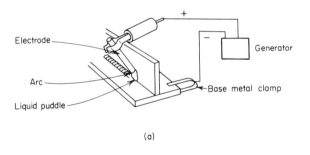

(a)

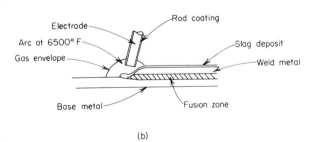

(b)

Fig. 9-18. Structural arc-welding technique: (*a*) electric circuit showing current flow and (*b*) section through weld metal.

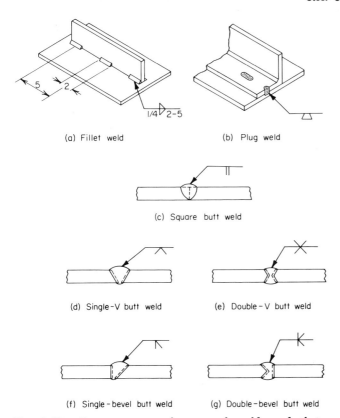

(a) Fillet weld   (b) Plug weld

(c) Square butt weld

(d) Single-V butt weld (e) Double-V butt weld

(f) Single-bevel butt weld (g) Double-bevel butt weld

Fig. 9-19. Common types of structural welds and their symbols.

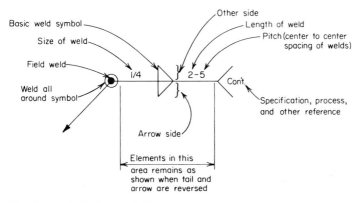

Fig. 9-20. Welding symbols.

TABLE 9-2

Type of stress	psi
Shear on section through throat of butt weld	13,000
Shear on section through throat of fillet weld or on faying surface area or filled plug or slot weld	13,600
Tension, flexural or axial, on section through throat of butt weld	20,000
Compression, crushing on section through throat of butt weld	20,000

be welded should be free from loose scale, slag, rust, grease, paint, or any other foreign material. Joint surfaces should be smooth, uniform, and free from fins or tears. Parts to be joined by fillet welds should not be separated more than $\frac{3}{16}$ in. The maximum fillet weld should be $\frac{1}{16}$ in. less than the thickness of the edge and when used along the toe of an angle or rounded edge of a flange should not exceed $\frac{3}{4}$ in. of the thickness of the angle leg or flange.

The property and strength of a weld are determined by its throat dimension, size, and length. Therefore, a $\frac{1}{4}$-in. fillet weld 4 in. long has an effective weld area of $0.707 \times 0.25 \times 4$, or 0.707 sq in. The permissible stresses in various types of welds are shown in Table 9-2. Therefore, a $\frac{1}{4}$-in. fillet weld 4 in. long is good for $0.707 \times 13,600$, or 9,600 lb.

SUMMARY

Of all construction materials, steel is the most important to the plant engineer. It is the most flexible, easy to change, and the strongest for its volume. He should know the nomenclature for the various shapes in which structural steel is manufactured and the names of each member in a building in accordance with its use.

On most steel-constructed jobs the plant engineer is expected to check and approve the fabricator's shop drawings. In this case, he must be able to read and understand both design and shop drawings.

The design of steel members is set forth in the specifications and *Manual* of the AISC, both of which belong in the plant engineer's office.

As important as selection of the proper member size is the design of the connections. Here, too, the plant engineer should be acquainted with the basic design of bolted and welded connections.

BIBLIOGRAPHY

American Institute of Architects and Charles George Ramsey, and Harold Reeve Sleeper: *Architectural Graphic Standards,* 6th ed., John Wiley & Sons, Inc., New York, 1970.

American Institute of Steel Construction: *Steel Construction,* New York, 1961.
———: *Structural Steel Detailing,* New York, 1966.
———: *Steel Gables and Arches,* New York, 1963.
———: *Structural Shop Drafting,* 2 vols., New York, 1950.
———: *Welded Tapered Girders,* New York, 1956.
American Iron and Steel Institute: *Sectional Properties of Corrugated Steel Sheets,* New York, 1964.
Boyd, James E.: *Strength of Materials,* McGraw-Hill Book Company, New York, 1924.
Building Codes Bureau: *State Building Construction Code Applicable to One- and Two-family Dwellings,* New York, 1964.
Callender, John Hancock: *Time-saver Standards,* 4th ed., McGraw-Hill Book Company, New York, 1966.
City of Los Angeles: *Building Code,* Building News, Inc., Los Angeles, 1970.
Concrete Reinforcing Steel Institute: *CRSI Design Handbook,* Chicago, 1952.
County of Los Angeles: *County of Los Angeles Uniform Building Laws,* Building News, Inc., Los Angeles, 1968.
———: *Building Codes, Plumbing Code, Mechanical Code, County Electrical Code,* Building News, Inc., Los Angeles, 1968.
Editors of Plant Engineering: *Plant Engineering Practice,* F. W. Dodge Corporation, 1958.
Grinter, Linton E.: *Design of Modern Steel Structures,* The Macmillan Company, New York, 1948.
———: *Theory of Modern Steel Structures,* The Macmillan Company, New York, 1947.
Grover, LaMotte: *Manual of Design for Arc Welded Steel Structures,* Air Reduction Sales Co., New York, 1946.
Housing and Building Codes Bureau: *State Building Construction Code Applicable to General Building Construction,* New York, 1964.
———: *State Building Construction Code Applicable to Multiple Dwellings,* New York, 1964.
International Conference of Building Officials: *Uniform Building Code,* Pasadena, Calif., 1967.
———: *Uniform Building Code,* vol. 3, Los Angeles, 1961.
The James F. Lincoln Arc Welding Foundation: *Modern Welded Structures,* Cleveland, Ohio, vol. 1, 1963; vol. 2, 1965.
Kleinlogel, A.: *Rigid Frame Formulas,* Frederick Ungar Publishing Co., New York, 1958.
Laurson, Philip Gustave, and William Junkin Cox: *Mechanics of Materials,* 3d ed., John Wiley & Sons, Inc., New York, 1954.
The Lincoln Electric Company: *Procedure Handbook of Arc Welding Design and Practice,* Ohio, 1951.
Merriman, Thaddeus, and T. H. Wiggin: *American Civil Engineers' Handbook,* John Wiley & Sons, Inc., New York, 1947.
Merritt, Frederick S.: *Standard Handbook for Civil Engineers,* McGraw-Hill Book Company, New York, 1968.
Metal Building Manufacturers Association: *Recommended Design Practices Manual,* Cleveland, Ohio, 1959.
Parker, Harry: *Simplified Engineering for Architects and Builders,* 4th ed., John Wiley & Sons, Inc., New York, 1967.

Priest, H. Malcolm, and John A. Gilligan: *Design Manual for High-strength Steels,* United States Steel Corporation, Pittsburgh, Pa., 1962.

Roark, Raymond J.: *Formulas for Stress and Strain,* 4th ed., McGraw-Hill Book Company, New York, 1965.

Rossnagel, W. E.: *Handbook of Rigging,* 3d ed., McGraw-Hill Book Company, New York, 1964.

Ryerson, Joseph T.: *Ryerson Stock List,* Joseph T. Ryerson & Son, Inc., Calif., 1968.

Smoley, C. K.: *Smoley's New Combined Tables,* C. K. Smoley & Sons, Chautauqua, N.Y., 1951.

Southern California Chapters, American Public Work Association, Associated General Contractors of America: *Standard Specifications for Public Works Construction,* Building News, Inc., Los Angeles, 1967.

State of California Public Utilities Commission: *General Orders,* California Office of State Printing, San Francisco, 1967.

Urquhart, Leonard Church: *Civil Engineering Handbook,* 4th ed., McGraw-Hill Book Company, New York, 1959.

Wallin, R. E.: *Construction Specifications,* Plant Engineering, Barrington, Ill., 1970.

Winter, George: *Development of Cold Formed Light Gage Steel Structures,* American Iron and Steel Institute, Pittsburgh, Pa., 1959.

CHAPTER TEN

Reinforced-concrete Construction

CONCRETE IS USUALLY CONSIDERED the most permanent and stable type of structural material one can use in industrial plants. Wherever long life and strength are required, concrete is specified. It is also valuable for protection against damage from fire, impact, and effects of many corrosive materials.

Relatively inexpensive when used in simple structures, such as foundations, floor slabs, and pavements, concrete can also be used in sophisticated, highly designed structures, such as prestressed, precast bridges, pipe supports, and roof structures. Typical forming techniques are shown in Fig. 10-1.

The plant engineer should be aware of the advantages and the limitations of concrete. He also must be alert to faulty concrete design and improper construction because most errors in concrete work are very difficult to correct.

HISTORY OF CONCRETE

Concrete is the closest thing to nature's own construction material. Concrete construction is an attempt to duplicate nature's ideal mixture of rock, sand, and a cementing agent. A commonly found geological phe-

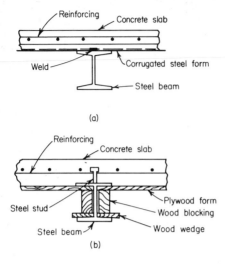

(a)

(b)

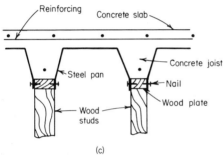

(c)

Fig. 10-1. Typical concrete forming methods: (a) steel-formed slab, (b) wood-formed composite beam, and (c) concrete pan joists.

nomenon known as "conglomerate" is just such a mixture. In nature, the cementing material is usually a lime deposit which has permeated the rock-sand mixture and then solidified the entire mass. The resulting mass has the compressive, bearing, and shearing strength of rock.

Man-made concrete mixtures are an improvement on nature's conglomerate formation and consist of an optimum mixture of sand, gravel, cement paste, and water to form a hard, dense material of any desired shape. Ancient builders built their structures with a mixture of various sized rocks, boulders, sand, and mortar paste of crushed limestone. Structures built in this manner were satisfactory, provided that tensile stresses were avoided by massive construction. Typical of massive construction are the ruins of fortress walls, which are extremely thick at the base. Modern unreinforced concrete is similar to this old structural method.

During the past 60 years, reinforced-concrete design has steadily improved. It now replaces most other structural materials once used in beams, girders, columns, and walls. Modern reinforced concrete is made from portland cement, fine and coarse aggregate, water, and steel reinforcement. The cement binds the aggregate, which is sand, gravel, or crushed rock. The water is needed for a chemical reaction and provides workability; the reinforcement, which can be deformed steel bars, welded wire mesh, or high-strength steel cables, provides the necessary structural strength.

DESCRIPTION OF CONCRETE MATERIALS

The cement paste in concrete is portland cement, which is made by burning crushed limestone and clay, or a similar chalky substance, and then calcining this mixture in kilns at a temperature of 2700°F. The calcined product of the kiln, or "klinker," is then pulverized with gypsum to a powder and becomes portland cement.

In properly mixed concrete, each particle is completely surrounded by the cement paste. Cementing or binding properties of the paste result from the chemical reaction between cement and water. This reaction requires time and favorable conditions of temperature and moisture, being fast at first and then slowing down. Although only a small amount of water is required for chemical reaction, additional water is required to obtain workable mixtures. The plant engineer should be aware that excess water will reduce the strength of cement paste and also cause cavities which make the concrete susceptible to freezing.

Five types of portland cement are available: type I, normal; type II, modified; type III, high strength; type IV, low heat; type V, sulfate resistant. The rates of obtaining full strength in the various types vary considerably. The approximate strength of concretes at certain elapsed times relative to the strength of type I at that time is shown in Table 10-1.

TABLE 10-1 Percent of Type I Strength*

Type of cement	3 days	28 days	3 months
I	100	100	100
II	80	85	100
III	190	130	115
IV	50	65	90
V	65	65	85

* Values based on concrete that is continuously cured moist until tested.

The water/cement ratio is given in gallons of water per sack of cement, where a sack is 1 cu ft in volume and weighs 94 lb. The water/cement ratio is between 4 and 8, the maximum strength being at a ratio of 4:1 and the minimum strength at 8:1.

Water used in concrete mixes should be clean, with few or no impurities. As a simple test, the water should be potable. The concrete mix must not be allowed to dry out too fast or the chemical reaction will stop prematurely. Therefore, concrete should be kept moist during the curing period in order to obtain the maximum compressive strength. If water is added after the chemical reaction has stopped due to premature drying, the reaction will continue and the compressive strength will again increase, but it will not reach the same peak as it would have under continuous moist curing. The longer the dry period, the lower the ultimate strength.

Temperature of curing also has a great bearing on the compressive strength of concrete. The chemical reaction is faster with high temperatures than at lower temperatures, but at temperatures over 100°F, the ultimate compressive strength remains lower than if the concrete had been cured at 70°F. At 40°F concrete is very slow in reaching adequate strength. Therefore, concrete construction in cold weather should be kept artificially warm.

In a properly graded concrete mix, there is an optimum proportion of fine aggregate and coarse aggregate to make as dense a mixture as possible. There is also a proper mixture of cement, so that each particle of the aggregate is completely surrounded by the cement paste. The maximum strength of the concrete is obtained only after the cement has reached its final strength, and then the shearing strength of the concrete is equal to the shearing strength of the rock.

The fine and coarse aggregate, or sand and gravel, should be from hard, clean rock with no attached clay or silt. The surface of each aggregate particle should be angular and sharp rather than round and smooth as found in beach or river sand. Often, the sand used in concrete mixes is the by-product of a rock-plant crushing operation, in which rock is crushed and then screened to required size.

TRANSPORTATION OF CONCRETE

Concrete is most commonly transported by truck-mixer or agitator truck. In some ready-mix operations, the material is dry-batched at the central plant, then mixed en route to the job in truck-mixers. In other cases, the concrete is mixed completely in a stationary mixer, and this mixed concrete is transported to the job in trucks. The trucks are required to continue mixing or agitating the concrete while hauling. In another procedure, known as "shrink mixing," the concrete is mixed in a stationary mixer at the central plant, only sufficiently to intermingle the ingredients, then the mixing is completed en route in mixer trucks.

A truck-mixer consists of a mixing drum, a separate water tank, and a separate measuring device mounted on the truck's chassis. Truck-mixers usually hold from 1 to 8 cu yd. Agitator trucks are similar to truck-mixers, but they do not have the water tanks.

The concrete is mixed in 50 to 100 revolutions of its drum, and any additional mixing is at a slow or just agitating speed. Concrete must be discharged from the mixer within $1\frac{1}{2}$ hr after the introduction of the water. When concrete mixers are used as agitator trucks, they can normally carry about 50 percent more concrete.

PLACEMENT OF CONCRETE

The placement of concrete is very critical. Separation of aggregate must always be prevented. Dumping concrete directly from the mixer into the bucket or hopper tends to throw the heavier and larger rock to one side. The concrete should therefore be unloaded in a concentric method using a vertical chute rather than a sloping chute. In discharging from a buggy into a formed wall, there should always be an effort to avoid ricocheting or bouncing the concrete off one side of the forms. The heavier aggregate will bounce farther than the fine particles, and separation will result.

On large or difficult to reach jobs, concrete can be pumped from one point of a job to another point, but mixer trucks usually dump the concrete into a hopper from which it is pumped through a pipeline to the point of placement. Placement, even on not so difficult jobs, is then a more continuous and efficient operation.

PLACEMENT OF STEEL REINFORCEMENT

The size and placement of steel reinforcement is as important as the concrete itself in a structure (Figs. 10-2 and 10-3). Reinforcing bars are placed in concrete for various important reasons. In large slabs, such as roadways, bars are used to prevent cracking due to thermal expansion and contraction stresses and to distribute wheel loads. As concrete alone is relatively weak in resisting tensile stresses, embedded steel bars are necessary to take up these tensile forces. Therefore, bars are placed in the tension side of concrete members such as at the bottom of simple beams and at the back face of retaining walls. Figure 10-4 shows recommended clearances for concrete reinforcement.

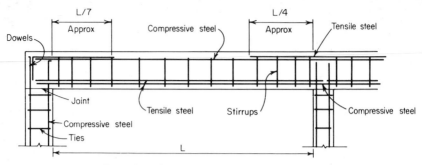

Fig. 10-2. Typical reinforced concrete beam, showing top, bottom column reinforcement, and stirrups.

When bars are parallel to the direction of compressive forces, they carry a portion of the force, thus adding to the load-carrying capacity of the concrete member. A concrete column is a typical example. Reinforcing bars are also used to help concrete resist shearing stresses when used in stirrups in beams and ties in columns.

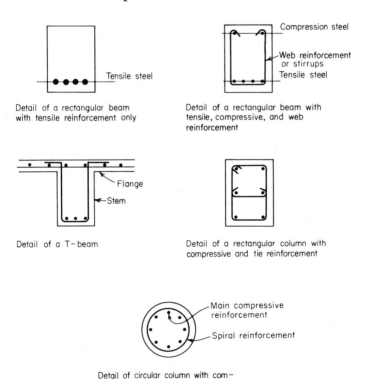

Fig. 10-3. Typical beam and column reinforcement.

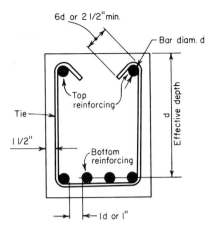

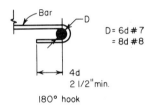

Fig. 10-4. Recommended clearances for concrete reinforcement.

Misplaced bars can cause catastrophic failures in large structures. Therefore, placement of all reinforcing must be done with care in all phases of the concrete construction, design, detailing, fabrication, and installation.

The structural designer determines by calculation the size and placement of all bars and puts this information on the structural drawings. He also designs required connections, as shown in Fig. 10-5. After the bars are fabricated, the reinforcing is placed in the forms according to the plans. An inspection of the forms and reinforcements by the building inspector is usually required before concrete is poured. Once concrete has been poured, there is no way of determining whether the reinforcement has been properly placed. Sometimes the plant engineer may wish to retain the services of a deputy inspector who will provide continuous inspection for all concrete work.

The codes and regulations for the placement of reinforcement in concrete structures are based on years of experience and good practice. Mechanical properties of reinforcement are shown in Table 10-2. Some of these rules recommended to the plant engineer are as follows:

1. At the underside of footings, in walls and where concrete is poured directly against the earth, metal reinforcement should have a minimum covering of 3 in. of concrete.
2. Where the concrete is poured against forms but will be in contact with the earth or water after the forms are removed, a minimum cover of 2 in. should be maintained.
3. In all other cases, except for fire-resistant construction, 1½ in. is the minimum recommended cover.
4. Metal reinforcement in concrete should be supported by chairs, spacers, or hangers or tied to crossing bars in designated positions.
5. The minimum clearance distance between parallel bars, except in columns, should be equal to the normal diameter of the bars.
6. Splices in bars should be 30 bar diameters.

TYPICAL CONCRETE STRUCTURES

Some typical concrete structures are shown in Fig. 10-6. Precast-concrete construction has become a very economical method for plant ware-

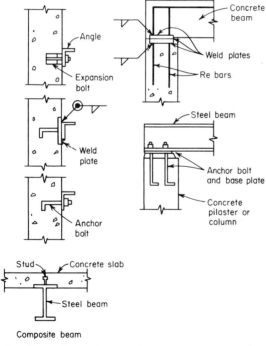

Fig. 10-5. Typical connections in concrete.

TABLE 10-2 Properties of Reinforcing Bars

Type of steel and ASTM Specification No.	Inclusive size numbers	Grade	Tensile strength, psi	Minimum yield,* psi	Minimum elongation in 8 in., %†	Cold bend test‡		
						Size	Angle, deg	d
Billet steel A15	2–11	Structural	55,000–75,000	33,000	1,200,000 / Tensile strength Minimum 16%	Under 6 6–8 9–11	180 180 180	2t 3t 4t
		Intermediate	70,000–90,000	40,000	1,100,000 / Tensile strength Minimum 12%	Under 6 6–8 9–11	90 90 90	3t 4t 5t
		Hard	80,000§	50,000	1,000,000 / Tensile strength	Under 6 6–8 9–11	90 90 90	4t 5t 6t
Billet steel A408	14S, 18S	Structural	55,000–75,000	33,000	13			
		Intermediate	70,000–90,000	40,000	10			
		Hard	80,000§	50,000	7			
Billet steel 60,000 psi	3–11	60,000 psi	90,000§	60,000	1,000,000 / Tensile strength	Under 6 6–8 9–11	90 90 90	4t 5t 6t
Billet steel A432	14S, 18S	60,000 psi	90,000§	60,000	7	14S, 18S		
High-strength, billet steel A431	3–11 14S, 18S	75,000 psi	100,000§	75,000	Varies with bar size, 5–7½%	3–5 6, 7 8, 9 10, 11 14S, 18S	90 90 90 90	4t 5t 6t 8t
Rail steel A16	2–11	Regular	80,000§	50,000	1,000,000 / Tensile strength Minimum 4.5–5%			
Rail steel A61	3–11	60,000 psi	90,000§	60,000	1,000,000 / Tensile strength Minimum 5%			
Axle steel A160	2–11	Structural	55,000–75,000	33,000	1,200,000 / Tensile strength Minimum 16%	Under 6 6 and over	180 180	2t 4t
		Intermediate	70,000–90,000	40,000	1,100,000 / Tensile strength Minimum 12%	Under 6 6 and over	180 90	6t 6t
		Hard	80,000§	50,000	1,000,000 / Tensile strength	Under 6 6–8 9–11	90 90 90	4t 5t 6t
		60,000 psi	90,000§	60,000				

* Yield point or yield strength. See specifications.
† For base sizes of deformed bars. See specifications for adjustment for small and large sizes and for values for plain bars.
‡ d-diameter of pin around which specimen is to be bent, and t-nominal diameter of specimen. Values shown are for deformed bars. See specifications for values for plain bars.
§ Minimum.

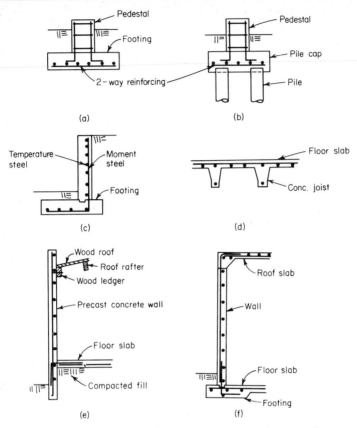

Fig. 10-6. Typical reinforced-concrete structures: (a) spread footing, (b) pile-cap foundation, (c) retaining wall, (d) pan-formed concrete joists, (e) precast tilt-up concrete wall, and (f) cast-in-place concrete wall.

houses and other buildings. The most common forms of this modern method are the tilt-up building, the prestressed- precast-concrete girders for long-span roof beams, precast curtain walls on plant office buildings, and precast-concrete structures for pipe supports. Precast concrete is also used for large storm drains and conveyor tunnels.

The term "tilt-up" does not mean that the precast wall panels are merely tilted up from the floor to the final wall position. Actually, the panels are often lifted by mobile cranes and carried to their proper positions in the building. When possible, similar panels are cast one over the other, forming a stack of precast-concrete panels.

The procedure for precast building construction generally follows these major steps:

1. The floor slab is poured, and all joints are made smooth with mortar. This forms the casting platform.
2. Wood forms are placed on the casting platforms.
3. The forms and casting platforms are sprayed with an antibond agent.
4. Reinforcing bars and necessary inserts are placed in their proper position.
5. The concrete is poured.
6. The concrete curing agent is sprayed over the freshly poured slab.
7. After concrete has cured in the panels, they are raised by a mobile crane.
8. The concrete panels are erected to their final upright position and temporarily braced to the floor slab.
9. Concrete panels are joined together by either cast-in-place concrete pilasters or by field welding to precast-concrete pilasters or steel columns.

The precast-concrete technique is used universally for construction of columns, beams, decking, girders, and curtain walls. The advantage of this type of construction is the speed of erection, a smoother finish on concrete surfaces, and a better control of the placement of the concrete and reinforcing. Caution must be maintained to provide a good casting platform free from indentations or projection, a proper design for lifting hardware and related reinforcing, clear access for mobile cranes, and careful planning for each step of casting and erection.

CONCRETE FLOOR SLABS

The floor of an industrial installation can range from a simple unreinforced concrete slab to a highly reinforced, waterproof, surface-hardened slab. The type of floor selected depends on use, maintenance, and cost.

The following critical items must be considered before deciding on a floor slab:

1. Type of soil under slab
2. Expected concentrated loading on slab
3. Waterproof-membrane requirements
4. Gravel-base requirements
5. Expansion joints
6. Construction joints
7. Control joints or contraction joints
8. Wearing surface
9. Admixtures to concrete

10. Water stops in joints
11. Surface sealants
12. Coloring of finish surface
13. Type of flooring to be installed over slab

A waterproof membrane or moisture barrier is usually installed directly over the subgrade or the gravel base. It is recommended that the membrane be lapped 12 in., with the top lap in the direction of the spread of concrete. The joint should be sealed with pressure-sensitized tape. All pipes and conduits penetrating the membrane should also be sealed. Materials used as a membrane include pure virgin polyethylene, vinyl sheets, rubber, butyl, and neoprene membranes. Thickness varies from 6 to 40 mils.

One of the serious problems confronting all concrete slab work is unwanted cracking. Most cracking is due to the shrinkage of concrete during the curing period. This can be reduced by sealing the freshly poured slab with a coat of curing compound. This sealer acts as a cap to hold moisture in new concrete, thus prolonging the curing by retarding evaporation of water. The sealer also helps to harden, dust-proof, and waterproof the slab.

Abrasion due to steel wheels or heavy moving equipment can cause dusting, which the wearing surface of the concrete slab can be treated to reduce. This is done with a coating of concrete prepared with a variety of admixtures, including sodium silicate, iron powder, emery aggregate, carborundum, aluminum oxide grain, or silicon carbide grain. These ingredients are generally known as "concrete hardeners." Other types of concrete hardeners are made from chemical admixtures such as hydrated lime, ammonium stearate, calcium chloride, and diatomaceous silica. These admixtures also have the advantages of reducing capillarity and shrinkage and increasing watertightness. Water stops, where required, are made from polyvinyl chloride or butyl rubber and are cast into concrete joints. The surface of a concrete slab can be sealed with epoxy polysulfide polyurethane.

Case History: Cracking in Concrete Walls

Soon after the completion of a 12-ft-wide by 120-ft-long concrete tank to be used for an oil/water separator, vertical cracks about 4 ft apart appeared in both walls when the tank was filled with water. Management became concerned and asked the plant engineer to investigate and report the causes and severity of the cracks.

After a visual inspection it was determined that there were several possible causes:

1. Uncompacted soil causing excessive settlement
2. Clayey soil losing strength due to penetration of water
3. Insufficient reinforcement in the wall
4. Incorrect design of walls
5. Weak concrete mix
6. Improper curing of concrete

The plant engineer checked each point in the following manner:

1. He obtained a copy of the soil-compaction report made by a soil engineer, which was found to be adequate.
2. He reviewed the soil-analysis report and determined that the soil was sandy and not affected by moisture.
3. He requested a recheck of the number of bars placed in the wall. Records showed that the bars were according to plans.
4. He requested a recheck on design and plans, which were also found to be correct except that no control joints were called for.
5. He checked the records of the concrete mix delivered to the job. This was found to be better than specified.
6. He checked whether the concrete work was kept continuously moist for 7 days after pouring. Here it was discovered that no effort had been made to wet down the concrete following the pour and that the week following had been unusually hot.

From the above investigation it was determined that the cracking was due to shrinkage of concrete during curing. The number of cracks would have been much less if proper curing procedures had been followed. If control joints had been installed, the cracks would have occurred in the joints and would have been less noticeable. The conclusion was that although the cracks were unsightly, they would not increase but rather decrease in size due to the moisture from the contained water.

STRESSES IN CONCRETE STRUCTURES

To understand the properties of reinforced-concrete structures, the plant engineer should analyze each type of failure. Failure results from exceeding the ultimate strength of a particular stress, whether it is in compression, shear, bond, or bearing. The designer should develop a mental picture of each type of failure and automatically design to prevent its occurrence under expected loads.

An example of failure in compression is a concrete pedestal crushing under a heavily loaded steel column. Figure 10-7a shows a failure in tension of a concrete beam with inadequate reinforcing steel. The bottom of the beam cracks open in failure of tension. Figure 10-7*b* shows a concrete beam failing in a diagonal sheer. These cracks appear diagonally from the point of support sloping in toward the center of the beam. Figure 10-7*c* illustrates a concrete beam failing in vertical shear. The shear is perpendicular to the beam. Figure 10-7*d* shows a concrete cantilever beam failing due to the overstress in bond of the reinforcing bars, which have pulled loose in the concrete.

Since concrete has a very low tensile value compared to its compressive strength, it is customarily assumed that it has no tensile value at all. Therefore, steel bars are used to develop the required tensile strength. Reinforced concrete is concrete with deformed steel bars placed in the areas where tensile stresses occur.

Structural design of concrete beams follows these assumptions: a simple beam supported at its ends will deflect under load. The maximum deflection will occur at mid-span. If a slice of the beam near the midpoint is analyzed, it will be found that the upper portion is in compression while the lower portion stretches or is in tension. This occurs in any rectangular beam whether it is of wood, steel, or plastic.

Figure 10-8 gives the derivation of the formulas for determining the properties of a simple reinforced-concrete beam.

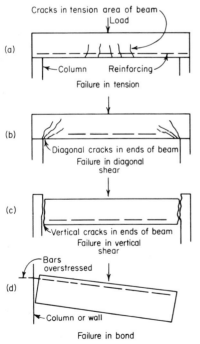

Fig. 10-7. Failures in concrete beams: (*a*) tension, (*b*) diagonal shear, (*c*) vertical shear, and (*d*) bond.

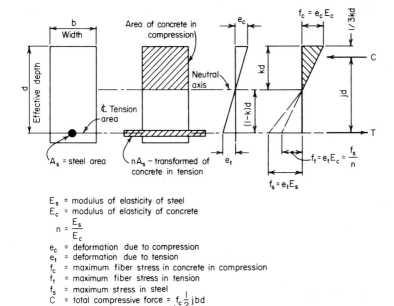

Fig. 10-8. Derivation of flexural formulas for concrete beams.

E_s = modulus of elasticity of steel
E_c = modulus of elasticity of concrete
$n = \dfrac{E_s}{E_c}$
e_c = deformation due to compression
e_t = deformation due to tension
f_c = maximum fiber stress in concrete in compression
f_t = maximum fiber stress in tension
f_s = maximum stress in steel
C = total compressive force = $f_c \dfrac{1}{2} jbd$
T = total tensile force = $f_s A_s$
M = applied moment
M_R = resisting moment = $Tjd = Cjd$
$K = \dfrac{1}{2} f_c \, jk$ or $d = \sqrt{\dfrac{M}{Kb}}$

Certain accepted abbreviations and symbols are used in the design of reinforced concrete, as follows:

A_v = area of web reinforcement, in.^{2}
b = width of a beam, in.
d = effective depth of beam, in.
e = eccentricity, in.
E_c = modulus of elasticity of concrete = $1{,}000 f'_c$, psi
E_s = modulus of elasticity of steel = 30×10^6 psi
f = unit stress, psi
f_c = compressive unit stress in extreme fibers
f'_c = ultimate compressive stress in 28 days, psi
f_s = unit strength in reinforcing bars, psi
f_t = unit tensile strength, psi ·
f_v = unit tensile stress in web reinforcement
I = moment of inertia, in.^{4}
j = ratio of distance between centroid of compression and centroid of tension forces to effective depth by beam
L = span of beam, ft

M = moment, in.-lb
P = concentrated load, lb
n = ratio of E_s/E_c
r = least radius of gyration
Σ_0 = sum of perimeters of bars, in.^{2}
S = spacing of stirrups, in.
t = thickness of slab, in.
u = bond stress per unit of surface area of bar
v = unit shear stress, psi
V = total shear, lb
V' = total shear carried by web reinforcement, lb
C = total compressive force, lb
T = total tensile force, lb
M_R = resisting moment of beam, in.-lb
A_s = area of steel reinforcement, in.^{2}
A_g = gross area of concrete section, in.^{2}

All properties of the concrete mix are based upon its ultimate strength in compression after 28 days in curing, which is also known as the f'_c of concrete. All the allowable stresses for concrete are a function of the f'_c value. For example,

Allowable shear, psi $\qquad\qquad v = 0.03f'_c$

Allowable bond, psi $\qquad\qquad u = 0.07f'_c$

Allowable compression in flexure, psi

$$f_c = 0.45f'_c$$

Allowable tension, psi

$$f_t = 0.03f'_c$$

Allowable bearing, psi

$$f_b = 0.25f'_c$$

The ultimate strength of concrete is affected by the ratio of gallons of water to cubic yard of concrete. According to the Uniform Building Code, a $7\frac{1}{2}$-gal mix is good for 2,000 psi, a $7\frac{1}{4}$-gal mix for 2,500 psi, a $6\frac{1}{2}$-gal mix for 3,000 psi, and a 5-gal mix for 4,000 psi. These values are based on 28 days, but concrete tested at 7 days is approximately 76 percent of its 28-day strength.

In order to design against failures due to various stresses, the designer considers one stress at a time. As an example of compressive stress, let us assume a short column or pedestal with a 200,000-lb load. The allowable stress of the concrete is $f_c = 0.45f'_c$ which equals 1,350 psi. The area of concrete required is $A_g = P/f_c$, which is equal to 200,000/1,350, or 148 sq in. Therefore, a pedestal 12½ by 12 in. would satisfy these requirements.

To determine beam tension, assume a simple concrete beam 12 in. wide by 24 in. deep and spanning 20 ft. A load of 10 kips at center of the span would result in a bending moment $M = PL/4$ or $(10 \times 20)/4$, which equals 50 ft-kips. Although this is not done in practice, let us assume that this is an unreinforced concrete beam. The resulting compressive and tensile stresses from this bending moment is $f = Mc/I$ where M is 50,000 ft-lb or 600,000 in.-lb, c is 12 in., and I is $bd^3/12$ or $12 \times 24^3/12$, which equals 13,824 in.^{4}. Then $f = 600,000 \times 12/13,824$, which equals 520 psi.

Assuming 3,000-psi concrete, f_c is 1,350 psi. Therefore, concrete is adequate in compression but not in tension since f_t is $0.03 \times 3,000 = 90$ psi. Obviously, this concrete is overstressed in tension. Even when concrete appears to be adequate in tension, it is good practice to use reinforcing bars to carry the full tensile loads. The method used to design steel bars in a reinforced beam is different from a homogeneous beam.

The reinforced-concrete beam in bending (Fig. 10-8) shows that C is the total compressive force on the upper area of the beam which is in compression and T is the total tensile force in the steel bars. This is equal to the unit tensile stress times the total area of the reinforcing bars, or $T = f_s A_s$. The location of the neutral axis is not at the center of the beam but depends upon the relative deformation of the concrete and the steel when stressed. An expression for this is n or E_s/E_c.

As C must equal T for equilibrium, the distance between T and C is approximately ⅞ d, or jd, where d is the distance from the top of the beam to the centroid of A_s. The resisting moment in a beam is therefore $M_r = Tjd$ or $f_s A_s jd$. Since this beam is 24 in. deep and there is a 2-in. concrete cover over the steel, assume that $d = 24 - 2$, or 22 in. Therefore, if $M = 600,000$ in.-lb and $f_s = 20,000$ psi, then $A_s = M/f_s jd$, which is $600,000/20,000 \times 0.866 \times 22$, or 1.57 sq in. This beam therefore requires two no. 8 bars, which have a total area of 1.58 sq in.

Another example of design of a reinforced-concrete beam is shown in Fig. 10-9. This beam spans 20 ft and has a moving load of 16 ips. Step by step procedure for determining beam size and amount of reinforcement is shown.

Let us investigate failure as in bond. Without proper bond between the reinforcing bars and the concrete, the bars cannot develop their full strength. The transfer of the full tensile force is through the bond of concrete to the reinforcing bar. Allowable bond stress is $u = 0.07f'_c$. For 3,000-psi concrete, $u = 0.07 \times 3,000$, which equals 210 psi. The

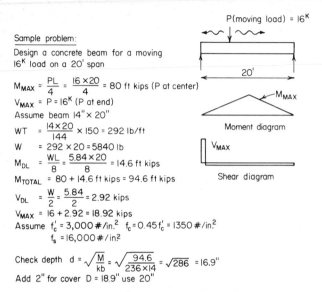

Sample problem:

Design a concrete beam for a moving 16^K load on a 20' span

$M_{MAX} = \dfrac{PL}{4} = \dfrac{16 \times 20}{4} = 80$ ft kips (P at center)

$V_{MAX} = P = 16^K$ (P at end)

Assume beam $14'' \times 20''$

$WT = \dfrac{14 \times 20}{144} \times 150 = 292$ lb/ft

$W = 292 \times 20 = 5840$ lb

$M_{DL} = \dfrac{WL}{8} = \dfrac{5.84 \times 20}{8} = 14.6$ ft kips

$M_{TOTAL} = 80 + 14.6$ ft kips $= 94.6$ ft kips

$V_{DL} = \dfrac{W}{2} = \dfrac{5.84}{2} = 2.92$ kips

$V_{MAX} = 16 + 2.92 = 18.92$ kips

Assume $f_c' = 3,000 \#/in.^2$ $f_c = 0.45 f_c' = 1350 \#/in.^2$

$f_s = 16,000 \#/in.^2$

Check depth $d = \sqrt{\dfrac{M}{kb}} = \sqrt{\dfrac{94.6}{236 \times 14}} = \sqrt{286} = 16.9''$

Add 2" for cover $D = 18.9''$ use 20"

Fig. 10-9. Design of a concrete beam for a moving 16,000-lb load on a 20-ft span.

surface area for 1-in. length of the reinforcing bars is called Σ_0, so to develop the full strength of the bar, $u \times \Sigma_0 \times L = f_s \times A_s$ or $L = f_s \times A_s / u \times \Sigma_0$, where L is the length of the bar in inches.

Good practice requires between $20d$ and $30d$ for acceptable bar anchorage. Therefore, if the tensile bars are to be lapped or spliced at the midpoint of a beam, a lap of 20 to 30 bar diameters is required to transfer tensile forces. For f_c' of 3,000 psi or more, lap 20 diameters and for under 3,000 psi, lap 27 diameters. The ends of a bar can be anchored by a standard hook or a complete semicircular turn, a 90° bend, or any mechanical device capable of developing the strength of the bar in lieu of the hook.

The following are important excerpts from the ACI Building Code:

> In slabs, beams, and girders, splices of reinforcement at points of maximum stress should be avoided wherever possible. Splices where used should be welded, lapped or otherwise fully developed, but, in any case, shall transfer the entire stress from bar to bar without exceeding the allowable bond and shear stresses. The minimum overlap for a lap splice shall be 24 bar diameters, but not less than 12 inches for bars.

Simple direct shear occurs when there is not sufficient cross-sectional area of concrete to resist the force applied perpendicular to this plane. Assume a force of 40 kips on a 10-in.-thick 30-in.-long wall. The total cross-sectional area is $A_g = 10 \times 30$, or 300 sq in. The unit shear on this wall is P/A_g or $40{,}000/300 = 133$ psi. Since the allowable shear stress is $v = 0.03f'_c$ or 90 psi, the wall is inadequate in shear.

Diagonal shear is a function of the total shear at the support of the beam. Assuming a 12 by 24 in. beam, 20-ft span, and a midspan load of 10 kips, the maximum shear is 5 kips. The diagonal shear stress is $v = V/jdb$, where jdb is the area of the beam in compression, as the concrete below the neutral axis is assumed cracked to allow the reinforcing bars to carry their tensile load. Therefore, $v = 5{,}000/0.866 \times 22 \times 12$, equal to 21.8 psi. Failure in the diagonal will occur near the support and is due to a failure in bond of the reinforcing bars, which should prevent cracking. Therefore, the bond should also be checked at the point of maximum shear, or $u = V/\Sigma_0jd$. If $V = 5{,}000$ lb and $\Sigma_0 = 6.3$ sq in. for two no. 8 bars, then $u = 5{,}000/6.3 \times 0.866 \times 22 = 42$ psi.

To determine the resisting moment of a rectangular concrete beam, the following properties should be understood. The resisting moment M_r is equal to Tjd, and to Cjd. The neutral axis of a beam is found by locating the center of gravity of the concrete area in compression and the steel area converted into equivalent concrete area.

For approximation, $j = \frac{7}{8}$ and $k = \frac{3}{8}$. Therefore, the resisting

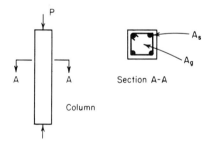

Basic formulas for design of reinforced concrete columns based on both the area of concrete and reinforcing steel

P = total load on an ordinary short column

A = total effective area of concrete

A_s = total area of steel

p_g = ratio $\dfrac{A_s}{A}$ p_g = 0.01 to 0.04

f'_s = minimum yield point of steel

f_c = unit compressive stress in concrete

A_g = total gross area of concrete

$\qquad$ (1) $P = Af_c\left[1 + (n-1)P_g\right]$ transformed area

$\qquad$ (2) $P = A(.225\,f'_c + f_s P_g)$ spiral columns

$\qquad$ (3) $P = .8A_g(.225f'_c + f_s P_g)$ tied column

Formula 1 converts steel into equivalent area of concrete by the factor $(n-1)$

Fig. 10-10. Derivation of formulas for design of concrete columns.

moment of concrete is equal to $(1/2f_c jk)bd^2$ since $(1/2f_c jk)$ equals K, the resisting moment is also equal to Kbd^2, and $d = \sqrt{M/Kb}$.

Some of the general rules of design are that temperature bars should be not less than $0.0020A_g$ and the maximum spacing of bars should be about 18 in. Horizontal reinforcement in walls should have a minimum area of steel of $0.0025A_g$, and vertical reinforcement should have a minimum area of $0.0015A_g$. The minimum size for wall reinforcement is no. 3 bars at 18 in. on center. Walls over 10 in. deep should have two layers of reinforcement. The derivation of formulas for concrete columns is shown in Fig. 10-10.

GENERAL NOTES

The following notes should appear, when applicable, on concrete construction drawings and can also serve as a checklist for the plant engineer.

1. *Placing.* Particular care shall be exercised to tamp the concrete vigorously and thoroughly to get concrete of a maximum density. A mechanical vibrator shall be used to ensure the desired results.

2. *Curing.* All concrete work and cement finish shall be properly protected and the entire structure sprayed with a wax membrane-type sealer after initial set or finishing.

3. *Reinforcement steel.* Steel reinforcement bars shall be intermediate grade and shall conform to the Standard Specifications for Billet-steel Bars for Concrete Reinforcement ASTM A15. All bars other than ¼ in. diameter shall be deformed bars conforming to ASTM A305. Cement pads or wire chairs shall be used to hold all steel above the form bottom or earth. Wall steel shall be wired together at all points where bars cross and shall be lapped unless otherwise indicated, 25 diameters at splices.

4. Flood slab must not be poured until all rough plumbing, piping, and floor conduits are in place.

5. No concrete shall be placed until the forms and reinforcing steel have been placed, inspected, and approved.

6. All bar bends and hooks shall conform to the American Concrete Institute *Manual of Standard Practice.*

7. All steel that is to be continuous shall have a minimum lap of 25 bar diameters or 18 in., whichever is greater.

8. All concrete shall have an ultimate compressive strength of 2,500 psi in 14 days and 3,000 psi in 28 days; it shall have 4- to 5-in. slump plus 1 in. maximum aggregate size. Admixtures shall be approved by the engineer prior to use.

9. Precast panels shall be adequately braced and supported during erection to assure proper alignment and safety, and such bracing shall be maintained until there are adequate permanent connections.

10. Dry pack shall be one part portland cement, one part nonshrink admixture, and one part sand, mixed dry, add water to moisten to hand consistency.
11. Prior to placing concrete, reinforcing steel and embedded items shall be secured in position.
12. The location of all joints other than shown or specified shall be approved by the engineer before placing.
13. All pipes and conduits passing through concrete beams and walls shall be sleeved with standard steel pipes and shall be placed only in such locations as shown on the drawings or approved by the engineer.
14. All water shall be removed from foundation excavations, and the excavation shall be dry before the concrete is placed.
15. Where noted on plans, prior to placing concrete on hardened concrete, the surface shall be roughened, cleaned of foreign matter and laitance, and thoroughly wetted but not saturated. The clean and wetted surfaces of the hardened concrete, including vertical and inclined surfaces, shall be slushed with a coating of neat cement grout against which the new concrete shall be placed before the grout has attained its set. For walls and columns, the grout may be omitted on the horizontal surface, but a layer of mortar having the composition of the mortar in the concrete shall be placed before concreting is resumed. Provide ¾ in. chamfer on all exposed edges of concrete.
16. Slabs on grade shall be reinforced with 6 by 6 10/10 welded wire mesh conforming to ASTM A185 except as noted.
17. Reinforcing steel, except stirrups and ties, shall have a minimum protective covering of concrete as follows except where otherwise detailed:

Position	Minimum thickness of concrete, in.
Concrete placed directly against soil (including slabs)	3
Concrete placed against forms, but exposed to earth or weather	2
Columns	2
Walls: in contact with ground or weather, all interior surfaces	1

EXAMPLE

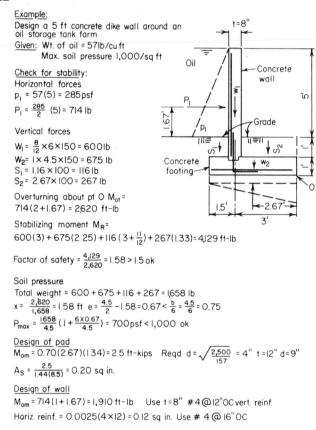

Example:
Design a 5 ft concrete dike wall around an
oil storage tank farm

Given: Wt. of oil = 57 lb/cu ft
        Max. soil pressure 1,000/sq ft

Check for stability:
Horizontal forces
$p_1 = 57(5) = 285$ psf
$P_1 = \frac{285}{2}(5) = 714$ lb

Vertical forces
$W_1 = \frac{8}{12} \times 6 \times 150 = 600$ lb
$W_2 = 1 \times 4.5 \times 150 = 675$ lb
$S_1 = 1.16 \times 100 = 116$ lb
$S_2 = 2.67 \times 100 = 267$ lb

Overturning about pt O $M_{ot} =$
$714(2 + 1.67) = 2{,}620$ ft-lb

Stabilizing moment $M_R =$
$600(3) + 675(2.25) + 116(3 + \frac{11}{12}) + 267(1.33) = 4{,}129$ ft-lb

Factor of safety $= \frac{4{,}129}{2{,}620} = 1.58 > 1.5$ ok

Soil pressure
Total weight $= 600 + 675 + 116 + 267 = 1{,}658$ lb
$x = \frac{2{,}620}{1{,}658} = 1.58$ ft $e = \frac{4.5}{2} - 1.58 = 0.67 < \frac{b}{6} = \frac{4.5}{6} = 0.75$
$P_{max} = \frac{1658}{4.5}(1 + \frac{6 \times 0.67}{4.5}) = 700$ psf $< 1{,}000$ ok

Design of pad
$M_{om} = 0.70(2.67)(1.34) = 2.5$ ft-kips Reqd $d = \sqrt{\frac{2{,}500}{157}} = 4"$ $t = 12"$ $d = 9"$
$A_s = \frac{2.5}{1.44(8.5)} = 0.20$ sq in.

Design of wall
$M_{om} = 714(1 + 1.67) = 1{,}910$ ft-lb   Use $t = 8"$ #4 @ 12" OC vert. reinf.
Horiz. reinf. $= 0.0025(4 \times 12) = 0.12$ sq in. Use # 4 @ 16" OC

SUMMARY

Concrete is one of the most durable of all construction materials. It is resistant to corrosion, fire, and decay. It has high compressive strength but must rely on steel reinforcement for tensile strength. Unfortunately concrete construction is very difficult to change or to add to. For this reason, great care must be given to the dimensional accuracy of concrete structures.

Since concrete is a mixture of sand, rock, water, and cement, it is relatively easy to make a poor mix. Therefore, the plant engineer must insist on a high level of control on the mixing and placement of concrete. This is even more important in the proper placement of steel reinforcement.

Because of its rigidity, concrete is vulnerable to cracks due to contraction, expansion, and differential settlement. Recommended guides for concrete design are available from manuals and specifications published by the Portland Cement Association and the American Concrete Institute.

CHECKLIST FOR CONCRETE CONSTRUCTION

1. Type of concrete specified
2. Type of reinforcements specified (main)
3. Admixtures
4. Forming hardeners
5. Concrete inserts
6. Foundations
7. Columns
8. Pedestals
9. Beams
10. Walls
11. Floor slabs
12. Expansion joints
13. Construction joints
14. Control joints
15. Concrete finishes

BIBLIOGRAPHY

ACI Committe 317: *Reinforced Concrete Design Handbook Working Stress Method,* American Concrete Institute, Detroit, Mich., 1965.

American Concrete Institute: *Building Code Requirements for Reinforced Concrete* (ACI 318-56), Detroit, Mich., 1959.

————: *Manual of Standard Practice for Detailing Reinforced Concrete Structures* (ACI 315-65), Detroit, Mich., 1965.

American Institute of Architects and Charles George Ramsey, and Harold Reeve Sleeper: *Architectural Graphic Standards,* 6th ed., John Wiley & Sons, Inc., New York, 1970.

Building Codes Bureau: *State Building Construction Code Applicable to One- and Two-family Dwellings,* New York, 1964.

Callender, John Hancock: *Time-saver Standards,* 4th ed., McGraw-Hill Book Company, New York, 1966.

City of Los Angeles: *Building Code,* Building News, Inc., Los Angeles, 1970.

Collins, F. Thomas: *Manual of Precast Concrete Construction,* F. Thomas Collins, San Gabriel, Calif., 1955.

Concrete Reinforcing Steel Institute: *CRSI Design Handbook,* Chicago, 1952.

County of Los Angeles: *County of Los Angeles Uniform Building Laws,* Building News, Inc., Los Angeles, 1968.

County of Los Angeles Uniform Building Laws: *Building Code, Plumbing Code, Mechanical Code, County Electrical Code,* Building News, Inc., Los Angeles, 1968.

Editors of Plant Engineering: *Plant Engineering Practice,* F. W. Dodge Corporation, Los Angeles, 1958.

Fling, Russell S.: *ACI Standard Specifications for Structural Concrete for Buildings* (ACI 301-66*), Portland Cement Association, Chicago, 1966.

Housing and Building Codes Bureau: *State Building Construction Code Applicable to General Building Construction,* New York, 1964.

————: *State Building Construction Code Applicable to Multiple Dwellings,* New York, 1964.

International Conference of Building Officials: *Uniform Building Code,* Pasadena, Calif., 1967.

————: *Uniform Building Code,* vol. 3, Los Angeles, 1961.

Laurson, Philip Gustave, and William Junkin Cox: *Mechanics of Materials,* 3d ed., John Wiley & Sons, Inc., New York, 1954.

Merriman, Thaddeus, and T. H. Wiggin: *American Civil Engineers' Handbook,* John Wiley & Sons, Inc., New York, 1947.

Merritt, Frederick S.: *Standard Handbook for Civil Engineers,* McGraw-Hill Book Company, New York, 1968.

Parker, Harry: *Simplified Engineering for Architects and Builders,* 4th ed., John Wiley & Sons, Inc., New York, 1967.

Portland Cement Association: *Simplified Design of Concrete Floor Systems,* Chicago.

Reese, R. C.: *CRSI Design Handbook,* Concrete Reinforcing Steel Institute, Chicago, 1952.

Southern California Chapters, American Public Work Association, Associated General Contractors of America: *Standard Specifications for Public Works Construction,* Building News, Inc., Los Angeles, 1967.

Sutherland, Hale, and Raymond C. Reese: *Reinforced Concrete Design,* John Wiley & Sons, Inc., New York, 1946.

Urquhart, Leonard Church: *Civil Engineering Handbook,* 4th ed., McGraw-Hill Book Company, New York, 1959.

Wallin, R. E.: *Construction Specifications,* Plant Engineering, Barrington, Ill., 1970.

Western Concrete Reinforcing Steel Institute: *Manual of Standard Practice for Reinforced Concrete Construction,* Burlingame, Calif., 1967.

CHAPTER ELEVEN

Masonry Construction

HISTORY OF MASONRY CONSTRUCTION

Next to steel and concrete, masonry is the most common material for industrial plant construction; it was used long before either steel or concrete.

Ancient builders used stone in its natural form or cut into blocks to construct great edifices, but stone was not always available. To provide a building material comparable to stone, the early builders used clay mixed with fiber, formed into blocks, and dried by the sun or in ovens. In many areas of the world it was easier to produce these man-made clay blocks than to cut the stone. Eventually the art of mixing and drying clay developed into the production of brick utilizing high-temperature kilns; there the materials were partially fused and calcined into firm structural units which would not dissolve in the rain.

Masonry construction before the middle of the twentieth century was not reinforced, since it preceded the advent of steel reinforcing bars. To obtain strength, brick walls were constructed in layers and tiers with intermittent interlocking bricks. The names of each type of brick are shown in Fig. 11-1, where a brick running parallel to the length of the wall is called a "stretcher" while one standing vertically is called a "soldier." A brick laid normally to the length of the wall is called

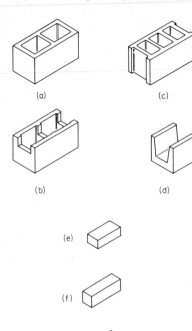

(a)

(c)

(b)

(d)

(e)

(f)

(g)

Fig. 11-1. Typical masonry units: (*a*) 8 by 8 by 16 in. standard concrete hollow block, (*b*) 8 by 8 by 16 in. bond beam block, (*c*) 8 by 8 by 16 in. three-core concrete block, (*d*) 8 by 8 by 8 in. lintel block, (*e*) 3⅞ by 2½ by 8¼ in. common clay brick, (*f*) 3¼ by 3¼ by 10 in. oversize clay brick, and (*g*) 3 by 3⅜ by 11⅜ in. modular clay brick.

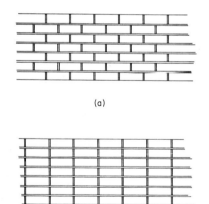

(a)

(b)

Fig. 11-2. Typical wall patterns: (*a*) running bond and (*b*) stacked bond.

a "header." There are two popular patterns of laying the brick. A pattern with alternate vertical joints is called a "running bond." A pattern with all vertical joints lined up directly above one another is called a "stack bond" (Fig. 11-2).

For hundreds of years beautiful buildings were constructed from colorful and permanent bricks. Many, if not most, of the industrial buildings over 50 years old in the United States are constructed of unreinforced brick. Since a plant engineer often finds himself involved with one of these old brick factory buildings, it is important that he be familiar with this original type of construction and aware of its strengths and weaknesses, especially when alterations are to be made.

Little was made of reinforced brick masonry between 1880 and 1906, although there was some experimental investigation of reinforcing techniques. The science of steel-reinforced masonry design and construction was developed only after much of the city of San Francisco had been destroyed by the 1906 earthquake.

As a result of the high cost of structural steel and reinforced-concrete construction, a new effort was made around 1920 to establish allowable working stresses for reinforced masonry. The real effort, however, did not come until after the second major earthquake in California in 1933. Cities that did not feel threatened by earthquakes continued to use unreinforced masonry as their construction standard well into the 1950s.

TYPES OF MASONRY CONSTRUCTION

Masonry is made from a wide range of mineral materials. Some are practically forgotten; others have had a temporary period of popularity until forced out of the market by more competitive products. Among the types of masonry are:

1. Unburned clay, commonly known as "adobe"
2. Stone masonry, made of boulders and large rocks
3. Cavity-wall masonry
4. Hollow-unit masonry, or concrete block
5. Solid masonry
6. Grouted masonry
7. Reinforced grouted masonry
8. Reinforced hollow-unit masonry
9. Structural glass brick
10. Gypsum masonry

Masonry units are made from the following materials:

1. Clay
2. Shale

3. Sand
4. Lime
5. Cement
6. Slag
7. Gypsum
8. Stone
9. Glass
10. Pumice
11. Expanded vermiculite

In areas subject to earthquake, the use of unburned clay units in buildings over one story is not recommended. The unsupported height of walls of unburned clay units should not be more than 10 times the thickness of the walls, and bearing walls should in no case be less than 16 in. thick. It is unlikely that any industrial structure would be made of unburned clay masonry. Precast gypsum units are often used for construction of partitions within buildings and are also used for roof decking. This material is exceptionally good for temperature and sound insulation, but because gypsum is vulnerable to water, care must be taken to protect all units against moisture. Gypsum walls must not be exposed to the elements and therefore should be used only on the interior of a building. Roof decking must be protected against water penetration by a watertight roofing, and condensation should not be allowed to accumulate on the bottom side of the gypsum deck. Gypsum roof decks are 2 to 3 in. thick and are either poured-in-place slabs or precast plank supported by T bars.

Glass masonry is sometimes used as structural self-supporting walls which allow natural light to enter a building. Glass masonry cannot be used for load-bearing walls. Under normal conditions, a glass-block panel for exterior walls should not exceed 144 sq ft in area or 15 ft in either dimension. Every exterior glass-block panel should be provided with ½-in. expansion joints at the sides and the top, which should be entirely free of mortar and filled with a resilient material.

Stone masonry is generally used only for decorative walls and veneers on industrial offices. Walls made of stone masonry should be at least 16 in. thick.

SPECIAL PRECAUTIONS FOR MASONRY CONSTRUCTION

Masonry should never be built on frozen ground and should be protected against freezing for at least 48 hr after being laid. Because of the difference in deflection, wood beams, girders, or columns should never

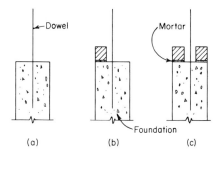

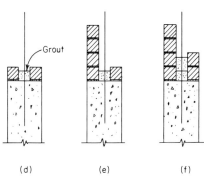

Fig. 11-3. Sequence for erecting a reinforced grouted brick masonry wall: (*a*) dowels extended from concrete foundation wall, (*b*) first brick set on foundation wall, (*c*) second brick set on foundation wall, (*d*) grout placed in space between bricks, (*e*) placement of brick continued on one side, and (*f*) placement of brick on other side and core space grouted in.

be used to support masonry. Only concrete or steel should be used to support any masonry material.

Building codes generally set a limit on the laterally unsupported height of masonry walls. This limit is stated as a function of the thickness of the wall and its height. In bearing walls, the unsupported height of a reinforced grouted masonry wall should be no more than 25 times the thickness of the wall. The wall should not be less than 6 in. thick. The maximum height of nonbearing reinforced masonry walls should be no more than 30 times its thickness for an exterior wall or 48 times its thickness for interior walls. See Fig. 11-3 for the sequence of erecting a grouted brick masonry wall.

DESIGN OF MASONRY WALLS

Because of the critical nature of masonry construction, two sets of allowable stresses are usually given by the building code. The allowable stresses for work without continuous inspection are limited to one-half of the stresses for work with continuous inspection.

The term "continuous inspection" means work overseen by a registered deputy inspector chosen by, and responsible to, the engineer who designed the structure.   When a building has been designed and constructed to utilize the higher stress requiring continuous inspection, the engineer should certify in writing to the building department that this building or portions thereof requiring continuous inspection were constructed in conformity with the approved design of the code.   For non-continuous inspection, or called inspection, a building department inspector will make a periodic inspection at specific stages of construction.

BRICK CONSTRUCTION

Basically, there are two types of brick, building brick and face brick. Building brick is made from clay mined directly from pits and banks and is known as "primary clay."   Building brick comes in various shades of red with smooth and textured faces.   Face brick is made from controlled mixtures of clays or shales containing certain minerals which produce many shades of color when fired in the kiln.

Mortar, which is used to cement the individual bricks together, must be workable, water-retentive, capable of developing a bond, weather-resistant, and subject to minimum volume change.   Mortar is usually composed of one part low-alkali portland cement, $4\frac{1}{2}$ parts mortar sand, and $\frac{1}{2}$ part lime putty or hydrated lime.

Voids between tiers of bricks are filled with grout, which must be sufficiently fluid to flow into the grout spaces (Fig. 11-4).   Grout consists of one part low-alkali portland cement, three parts sand, and sometimes pea gravel.   In exceptionally wide grout space, bricks or pieces of brick may be embedded in the grout, piece by piece, to help fill the gap.

The various joint treatments of brick walls include:

1. Tool joints
2. Rake joints
3. Bevel joints
4. Rubber-ball joints
5. Flush-cut joints
6. Sacked-rubbed joints

The latter two types are not recommended in brick walls.

The formation of (usually white) water-soluble salts which develop from the portland cement in the mortar and the grout within a wall is called "efflorescence."   This is caused when the salts are deposited on the face of the masonry during the drying-out process, the brick masonry acting as a wick.   To avoid efflorescence, a low-alkali portland cement is preferred in both the mortar and grout.   Efflorescence can be cleaned away after the brick is reasonably dry by water under high

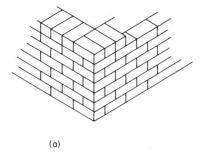

(a)

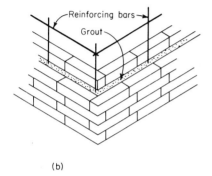

(b)

Reinforcing bars

Grout

Fig. 11-4. Examples of masonry wall construction: (*a*) solid brick masonry and (*b*) reinforced grouted brick masonry.

pressure applied by hose or by a solution of 1 to 20 parts muriatic acid and water, or vinegar and water.

Modern units for brick construction come in several standard sizes: the common brick is $3\frac{7}{8}$ in. wide by $8\frac{1}{4}$ in. long by $2\frac{1}{2}$ in. high. Modular brick is $3\frac{1}{4}$ in. wide by 10 in. long by $3\frac{1}{4}$ in. high (Fig. 11-1). Lately, there has been a movement toward larger unit bricks. One such brick is 3 in. wide by $15\frac{3}{8}$ in. long by $5\frac{3}{8}$ in. high. The design of a wall's length, thickness, and openings is governed by the size of brick used.

The various finishes or textures of the brick include the matte face, rug face, and wire-cut face. The textured surface occurs on two sides and two ends of the brick. The matte-face finish is a surface with very light vertical scratches that present an attractive pattern when left exposed, as well as providing an excellent bonding surface when the brick is grouted or painted. The rug face is a ruffled texture which is produced by making a heavy scratch on the brick surface and rolling the excess material back on the face of the brick. Using this brick in a wall results in an interesting surface of lights and shadows due to the irregular pattern. This ruffled texture exists on one face and one end of the brick. The wire-cut texture, which occurs on two faces of each brick unit, is characterized by the exposure of the aggregate and the slight ruffling of the surface produced as the wire cuts through the ribbon of the extruded clay.

CONCRETE-BLOCK CONSTRUCTION

Just as popular as clay-brick masonry is concrete masonry, which includes concrete block, cinder block, pumice block, and other precast

TABLE 11-1 Maximum Working Stresses for Reinforced Solid- and Hollow-unit Masonry

Type of stress	Solid units				Hollow units* grade A	
	3,000 psi on gross		2,500 psi on gross			
	$f'_m = 1,800$	$f'_m = 900$	$f'_m = 1,500$	$f'_m = 750$	$f'_m = 1,350$	$f'_m = 675$
Special inspection required?	Yes	No	Yes	No	Yes	No
Compression, flexural	600	300	500	250	450	225
Shear:						
No shear reinforcement†	30	15	30	15	30	15
Reinforcement taking entire shear:						
Flexural members. . . .	100	50	100	50	100	50
Shear walls.	60	30	60	30	60	30
Modulus of elasticity‡. . . .	1,800,000	900,000	1,500,000	750,000	1,350,000	675,000
Modulus of rigidity‡.	740,000	360,000	600,000	300,000	540,000	270,000
Bearing on full area§.	450	225	375	187	340	170
Bearing on one-third or less of area§.	540	270	450	225	400	200
Bond, plain bars.	60	30	60	30	60	30
Deformed bars.	140	100	140	100	140	100

  * Stresses are based on net section.
  † Web reinforcement must be provided to carry the entire shear in excess of 20 psi whenever there is required negative reinforcement and for a distance of one-sixteenth the clear span beyond the point of inflection.
  ‡ Where determinations involve rigidity considerations in combination with other materials, or where deflections are involved, the moduli of elasticity and rigidity under columns entitled "yes" for special inspection should be used.
  § This increase is permitted only when the least distance between the edges of the loaded and unloaded areas is a minimum of one-fourth of the parallel side dimension of the loaded area. The allowable bearing stress on a reasonably concentric area greater than one-third but less than the full area should be interpolated between the values given.
  SOURCE: Uniform Building Code.

concrete units. The maximum working stresses are shown in Table 11-1. The most commonly used concrete block is nominally 8 by 8 by 16 in. long. There are also half-blocks 4 by 8 by 16 in. and 8 by 8 by 8 in. units. Blocks are also available in units for 12-, 6-, and 4-in. wide walls. The narrower walls are for fences and special filler walls. The nominal block size of 8 by 8 by 16 in. has net dimensions of 7⅝ by 7⅝ by 15⅝ in. This allows a mortar joint ⅜ in. wide in a completed wall. For layout and modular dimensioning, the block plus the joint dimension is used, and therefore the nominal size is used.

Block units are mass-produced to form walls, bond beams, windowsills, pilasters, and other critical parts of a masonry building (Fig. 11-5). The hollow cells cast into the concrete masonry units provide an air space within the masonry wall, and normally no other insulation is required to insulate the walls for heat or sound. Under extreme temperature conditions the hollow cells can be filled with vermiculite or other insulating material to increase their insulative value.

In addition to the modular flat-surface units, concrete masonry is manufactured with many surface treatments, for example, slump-stone, split-faced block, and veneer block. Cap and solid block units are used for parapets, garden walls, and stepping stones. All units are made in many integral colors. Slump-stone units have rough texture and appear handmade. They are

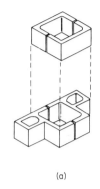

(a)

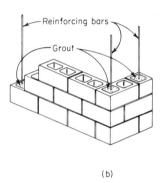

(b)

Fig. 11-5. Typical hollow-concrete masonry construction: (*a*) detail of a pilaster construction and (*b*) detail of a wall-intersection construction.

very effective in certain architectural treatments. Split-faced units are half-height blocks. Veneer blocks are nonstructural and are laid up against a backup wall.

TYPICAL BLOCK-MASONRY CONSTRUCTION

In a typical reinforced-masonry building, the concrete foundations are constructed with reinforcing bars extending vertically at the same spacing as the reinforcing bars in the masonry walls. These vertical bars are called "dowels" and extend above the concrete far enough to provide an adequate bond to the vertical bars placed later in the masonry wall. After the concrete foundations have cured, the placement of blocks proceeds. The blocks are buttered with mortar and set on the top of the concrete wall with dowels projecting through the center of the cell at 16-, 24-, or 32-in. spacing, depending on the design. This procedure continues level upon level until a maximum 8 ft of the height has been reached. At this time wall reinforcement is placed in the same course containing the dowels. Holes are knocked out of the bottom block at the cell containing the reinforcement. When the vertical bars in the walls are properly set, grout is poured or pumped into the cores containing bars until the core is completely full. The holes at the bottom of the cells are for cleaning out the cell and making certain that the grout has reached the bottom. When all cells containing steel bars are filled with grout, reinforced concrete ribs at predetermined intervals have been formed. For lifts of 4 ft or less, knockout holes are not required. Bars are also placed around all corners and openings in addition to the uniform spacing in the walls.

For a well-constructed integrated block wall, each block should be staggered so that there will be no continuous uninterrupted vertical joint extending the full height of the wall. As in brick construction, this pattern is called running-bond pattern. However, for certain architectural reasons a stack-bond pattern may be specified, which then would require each block to be placed directly above the block below. Since this results in a continuous vertical, some type of horizontal reinforcement is required to run between the block to strengthen these vulnerable joints. Horizontal metal ties, wire mesh, or small bars are normally provided at a maximum center spacing of 24 in. to strengthen the wall.

Placement of dowels in the foundation must be carefully measured to be certain that each bar falls in the center of a cell and not in a door opening or the shell of a block. The contractor must be certain to coordinate concrete work and the construction of the block walls.

Using concrete block in building design requires modularly dimensioned doors and windows as well as wall lengths and heights. Usually 4 in. as the smallest unit would be adequate for heights, as blocks are 4, 8, or 12 in. high. Block lengths, which are in 8-in. increments, also govern all horizontal dimensions of a building.

Most door and window manufacturers have standardized certain lines of their products to accommodate concrete-block construction and normally note their details of doors and windows in their term "finish masonry opening dimension" so that their products will conform to the standard masonry wall dimensioning.

Reinforced beams and lintels also can be constructed of special types of concrete block comprising U-shape blocks, bond-beam blocks, and lintel blocks. Masonry beams within a wall are known as "bond beams" and are required to resist horizontal bending moments. Lintel blocks are used to span across window and door openings and resist vertical bending moments.

Foundation walls can be built of concrete block provided that all cells are filled solid with grout and a continuous concrete footing with reinforcement is provided upon which to set the block. Individual piers can also be made from 12 by 12 in. blocks filled with grout.

Thickened portions of a masonry wall designed to carry concentrated vertical loads are called "pilasters." Special blocks are made for 12- and 16-in.-thick pilasters so that the running-bond pattern is continued. All intersections of block walls should be reinforced with a horizontal steel to tie the two walls together.

Another popular use of concrete block is for the construction of retaining walls. Concrete blocks eliminate the forming normally required in concrete construction. It is also easier to construct a concrete-block wall in remote or inaccessible locations when large quantities of concrete are difficult to transport to the work site.

When specifying for concrete masonry construction, many factors must be included (Table 11-2). The masonry units must be grade A units conforming to the ASTM Specification C90. The cement must conform to ASTM C150. The mortar must be freshly prepared and uniformly mixed in a ratio of 1 part cement, $\frac{1}{4}$ part lime putty, and $3\frac{1}{2}$ parts sand and must conform to ASTM Specification C207. The grout should be of a fluid consistency and mixed in a ratio of 1 part cement, 3 parts sand or 1 part cement, 2 parts sand, and 2 parts pea gravel. Reinforcing steel must be deformed bars conforming to ASTM Specifications A15 and A305. The $\frac{1}{4}$-in. ties may be plain bars.

The specifications should also include the scope of work for which the masonry contractors are responsible. Typically, the contractor must furnish all labor and material necessary to complete masonry construction. He must also furnish and place the reinforced steel, inserts, strips, bolts, and anchors. The mason should also cooperate with the plumbing, electrical, carpentry, and all other subcontractors in the layout of his work.

Concrete blocks are manufactured as either "heavyweight" blocks or "lightweight" blocks. Heavyweight blocks are made from conventional sand, gravel, and portland cement, while the lightweight are made from an expanded shale aggregate.

In addition to their structural value, concrete blocks in industrial buildings provide a wide choice of architectural designs for interior and exterior surfaces of walls for office fronts, partitions, and screen walls. Some concrete block is well sculptured with prismatic or curved surface treatment, giving an attractive exposure to the building. Since many modern industrial plants are very conscious of their public image, great use is made of decorative concrete block for screen walls, facades,

TABLE 11-2 Allowable Working Stresses in Unreinforced-unit Masonry

Material	Type S mortar					Type N and N (masonry)		
	Compression*	Shear or tension in flexure†		Tension in flexure‡		Compression*	Shear or tension in flexure†	
Special inspection required?	No	Yes	No	Yes	No	No	Yes	No
Solid brick masonry:								
4,500 plus psi..........	250	20	10	40	20	200	15	7.5
2,500–4,500 psi..........	175	20	10	40	20	140	15	7.5
1,500–2,500 psi..........	125	20	10	40	20	100	15	7.5
Solid concrete unit masonry:								
Grade A...............	175	12	6	24	12	140	14	6
Grade B...............	125	12	6	24	12	100	12	6
Grouted masonry:								
4,500 plus psi...........	350	25	12.5	50	25			
2,500–4,500 psi..........	275	25	12.5	50	25			
1,500–2,500 psi..........	245	25	12.5	50	25			
Hollow-unit masonry.......	85	12§	6§	24§	12§	70	10§	5§
Cavity-wall masonry								
Solid units§:								
Grade A or 2,500 psi plus.	140	12	6	30	15	110	10	5
Grade B or 1,500–2,500 psi	100	12	6	30	15	80	10	5
Hollow units§..............	70	12	6	30	15	50	10	5
Stone masonry:								
Cast stone...............	400	8	4	...	...	320	8	4
Natural stone............	140	8	4	...	...	100	8	4
Gypsum masonry..........	20	...	....	...	...	20		
Unburned clay masonry.....	30	8	4					

* Allowable working stresses in pounds per square inch gross cross-sectional area (except as noted). The allowable working stresses in bearing directly on concentrated loads may be 50 percent greater than these values.

† This value of tension is based on tension across a bed joint, i.e., vertically in the normal masonry work. No tension allowed in stack bond across head joints.

‡ The values shown here are for tension in masonry in the direction of running bond, i.e., horizontally between supports.

§ Net area in contact with mortar or net cross-sectional area.

SOURCE: Uniform Building Code.

and even the construction of the building walls. The range of design of decorative block is almost limitless, as it depends upon the creativity of the designer and the new molds used in the manufacture of the concrete block. The sculptured units also have integral coloring, requiring little or no maintenance.

EXAMPLE

A small chemical company decided to build a garage for its only delivery truck. The building was to be located at the corner of the plant's property. Since no hazardous material was to be stored, the occupancy group classification was determined to be F2, and the type of construction was IIIB.

The building size selected was 26 ft wide by 36 ft long. A door 20 ft wide by 12 ft high was also required. The exterior walls were to be 8-in.-thick concrete block; the roof would be constructed of a

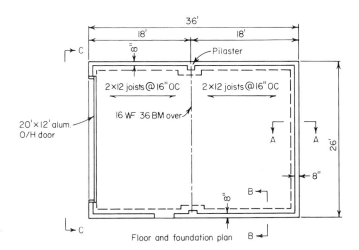

Floor and foundation plan

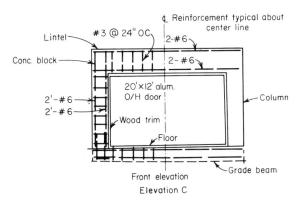

Front elevation

Elevation C

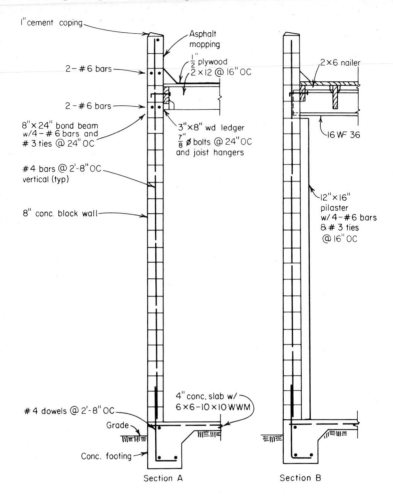

1" cement coping

Asphalt mopping

$\frac{1}{2}$" plywood

2 × 12 @ 16" OC

2 – # 6 bars

2 – # 6 bars

2 × 6 nailer

8" × 24" bond beam w/4 – # 6 bars and # 3 ties @ 24" OC

3" × 8" wd ledger

$\frac{7}{8}$" Ø bolts @ 24" OC and joist hangers

16 WF 36

#4 bars @ 2'-8" OC vertical (typ.)

8" conc. block wall

12" × 16" pilaster w/ 4 – # 6 bars 8 # 3 ties @ 16" OC

4" conc. slab w/ 6 × 6 – 10 × 10 WWM

4 dowels @ 2'-8" OC

Grade

Conc. footing

Section A   Section B

steel beam, wood rafters, and plywood sheathing and was to be strong enough to carry a 50 lb/sq ft uniform load. The floor was to be a 4-in. concrete slab. A 2-ft-high concrete block parapet around the roof was required for fire protection of adjacent property.

These criteria constituted only the shell of the building, as many structural details had to be designed. These main components included the foundation, door lintel, bond beams, pilasters, and roof-support assemblies.

The standard block size selected was 8 by 8 by 16 in., while special blocks were used for pilasters, bond beams, lintels, and the top of the parapet wall.

A lightweight block was selected over the heavyweight block for speed and ease of construction. All building dimensions were made to conform to the block modules. That is, all horizontal dimensions were in 4-in. increments since half blocks were readily available.

Since the actual block dimension is 7⅝ by 15⅝ in., a ⅜-in. mortar joint was selected. In addition, concrete grout was to fill all cells containing reinforcement.

The size and placement of wall reinforcement were based on either a minimum ratio of steel area to wall area or as required by wind, earthquake, or live-load stresses. Reinforcement was then designed for walls, bond beams, pilasters, door lintel, and foundation. The front wall at the door was a rigid frame designed to carry both roof and lateral loads. The side-wall pilasters and the rear wall also carried tributary roof loads.

Special details were drawn for pilasters, foundations, bond beams, lintel, parapet, and ledgers, as well as bar splicing and roof framing.

Much of the design was made directly from tables available in the uniform building code and *Concrete Masonry Design Manual*. The accompanying drawings illustrate the completed structure.

SUMMARY

Masonry is one of the most ancient forms of construction. It is one of the most permanent and resistant to fire, ice, and moisture. There is a broad range of masonry materials available, which are not only structurally strong but also provide attractive architectural treatment.

Because of its weight and low tensile value, masonry walls are susceptible to earthquake forces unless properly reinforced with steel rods. Buildings designed of masonry must dimensionally conform to the module of the masonry unit. This is also true of door and window openings.

The plant engineer should be aware of the local availability of types of masonry before he makes his selection. Long-distance hauling of masonry units is not economical.

CHECKLIST FOR MASONRY CONSTRUCTION

1. Type
   a. Unburned clay
   b. Stone masonry
   c. Hollow-unit masonry or concrete block
   d. Cavity-wall masonry
   e. Solid masonry
   f. Grouted masonry
   g. Reinforced grouted masonry
   h. Reinforced hollow-unit masonry
   i. Structural-glass masonry
   j. Gypsum masonry
2. Type of reinforcement, horizontal and vertical
3. Thickness of walls

4. Treatment of openings
   a. Lintel
   b. Jamb
   c. Sill
   d. Size of openings
5. Mortar joint
   a. Tooled joints
   b. Raked joints
   c. Flush-cut joints
   d. V-groove joints
   e. Rubber-ball joints
   f. Sacked-rubbed joints
6. Grouting
7. Bearing walls
8. Nonbearing walls
9. Pilasters
   a. Size
   b. Reinforcement
10. Columns
    a. Size
    b. Reinforcement
11. Special architectural surface treatment
    a. Slump-stone
    b. Sculptured block
    c. Ribbed block
    d. Split face
12. Joint pattern
    a. Running bond
    b. Stacked bond
13. Bond beams
14. Inspection
    a. Continuous inspection
    b. Called inspection
15. Mortar specifications
16. Grout specifications

BIBLIOGRAPHY

American Institute of Architects and Charles George Ramsey, and Harold Reeve Sleeper: *Architectural Graphic Standards,* 6th ed., John Wiley & Sons, Inc., New York, 1970.

Brick Institute of California: *Handbook on Reinforced Grouted Brick Masonry Construction,* Los Angeles, 1962.

Building Codes Bureau: *State Building Construction Code Applicable to One- and Two-family Dwellings,* New York, 1964.

Callender, John Hancock: *Time-saver Standards,* 4th ed., McGraw-Hill Book Company, New York, 1966.

City of Los Angeles: *Building Code,* Building News, Inc., Los Angeles, 1970.

Concrete Masonry Association: *Concrete Masonry Design Manual,* Los Angeles, 1960.

County of Los Angeles: *County of Los Angeles Uniform Building Laws,* Building News, Inc., Los Angeles, 1968.

County of Los Angeles Uniform Building Laws: *Building Code, Plumbing Code, Mechanical Code, County Electrical Code,* Building News, Inc., Los Angeles, 1968.

Editors of Plant Engineering: *Plant Engineering Practice,* F. W. Dodge Corporation, Los Angeles, 1958.

Housing and Building Codes Bureau: *State Building Construction Code Applicable to General Building Construction,* New York, 1964.

———: *State Building Construction Code Applicable to Multiple Dwellings,* Housing and Building Codes Bureau, New York, 1964.

International Conference of Building Officials: *Uniform Building Code,* Pasadena, Calif., 1967.

———: *Uniform Building Code,* vol. 3, Los Angeles, 1961.

Laurson, Philip Gustave, and William Junkin Cox: *Mechanics of Materials,* 3d ed., John Wiley & Sons, Inc., New York, 1954.

Masonry Research: *Masonry Code and Specification,* Los Angeles, 1963.

Merriman, Thaddeus, and T. H. Wiggin: *American Civil Engineers' Handbook,* John Wiley & Sons, Inc., New York, 1947.

Parker, Harry: *Simplified Engineering for Architects and Builders,* 4th ed., John Wiley & Sons, Inc., New York, 1967.

Plummer, Harry C., and John A. Blume: *Reinforced Brick Masonry and Lateral Force Design,* Structural Clay Products Institute, Washington, 1958.

Southern California Chapters, American Public Work Association, Associated General Contractors of America: *Standard Specifications for Public Works Construction,* Building News, Inc., Los Angeles, 1967.

Urquhart, Leonard Church: *Civil Engineering Handbook,* 4th ed., McGraw-Hill Book Company, New York, 1959.

Wallin, R. E.: *Construction Specifications,* Plant Engineering, Barrington, Ill., 1970.

CHAPTER TWELVE

Wood Construction

OF ALL STRUCTURAL SYSTEMS, the simplest is still timber construction. The earliest industrial plants were framed entirely of heavy wooden timbers. Not only were columns, girders, and trusses made of wood, but tanks, machinery supports, and towers were also constructed of timber. The durability of this method of construction can be attested to by the many structures throughout the country still in operation.

There are two general types of timber construction, heavy-timber construction and light-wood framing construction. Insurance companies and building departments treat each type of construction differently. Although both use wood, their resistance to fire differs considerably. Because of this, insurance rates, allowable areas, and types of occupancy differ in these two types of construction.

Many old mine mill buildings are of heavy-timber construction, as are numerous conveyor and railroad bridges and trestles. The advantages of heavy-timber construction are the structural strength of the timber, its resistance to fire, the ease with which it can be field-fabricated, and its great adaptability in meeting most field conditions. Timber is also very resistant to corrosive liquids and fumes. It can also maintain its strength although continuously wet, as in the case of piling used to support bridges. Although waterfront structures such as piers, wharves, and docks constructed of heavy timber are constantly exposed to moisture, they retain their structural strength for generations.

Heavy timber is also considered more fire-resistant than steel because at approximately 1000°F steel loses its structural strength while a large wood post or beam would merely char. Light members, though, would be completely destroyed.

Another advantage of wood construction is the simplicity of tools. Hand tools including saws, drills, hammers, and wrenches are most often employed. The fasteners for timber are nails, spikes, bolts, split rings, lag bolts, and steel timber connectors.

Light-wood framing construction, most commonly used in residential construction, is also used in industrial facilities for constructing plant offices, change houses, laboratories, gate houses, and small warehouses. This type of construction requires little or no engineering design because most building codes contain tables listing most member sizes and their allowable span. If he is familiar with wood structures, a plant engineer can easily prepare plans of a small building by merely following the building code.

One disadvantage of wood construction is its relative flexibility when combined with more rigid materials. For this reason it is poor practice to support masonry or concrete with a wooden member. A brittle material will crack before the wood member has begun to carry the load. Another shortcoming of wood is its vulnerability to termites and dry rot.

Because of the inconsistent nature of wood members, there must be a close adherence to a universal grading system. In lower grades of timber, there is always a danger of excessive warping, splitting, and weakening at knot holes (Fig. 12-1).

NOMENCLATURE OF WOOD CONSTRUCTION

Lumber is commonly known by its mill size. Some of the typically used sizes are the 2 by 4 in., 4 by 6 in., 6 by 12 in., and similarly

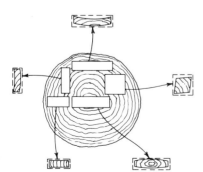

Fig. 12-1. Effect of sawing method upon lumber shrinkage.

TABLE 12-1 Properties of Common Lumber

Nominal size, in.	American standard dressed size, in.	Area of section, in.^{2}	Weight per foot, lb	Moment of inertia, in.^{4}	Section modulus, in.^{3}
2 × 4	1⅝ × 3⅝	5.89	1.64	6.45	3.56
6	5⅝	9.14	2.54	24.1	8.57
8	7½	12.2	3.39	57.1	15.3
10	9½	15.4	4.29	116	24.4
12	11½	18.7	5.19	206	35.8
14	13½	21.9	6.09	333	49.4
16	15½	25.4	6.99	504	65.1
18	17½	28.4	7.90	726	82.9
4 × 4	3⅝ × 3⅝	13.3	3.65	14.4	7.94
6	5⅝	20.4	5.66	53.8	19.1
8	7½	27.2	7.55	127	34.0
10	9½	34.4	9.57	259	54.5
12	11½	41.7	11.6	459	79.9
14	13½	48.9	13.6	743	110
16	15½	56.2	15.6	1,125	145
18	17½	63.4	17.6	1,619	185

sized members.   The finished size is somewhat less than these mill sizes, also known as nominal sizes.   The finished size, or the American standard dress size, for a 2 by 4 in. is 1⅝ by 3¾ in., for a 2 by 6 in. it is 1⅝ by 5⅝ in., and for a 2 by 8 in. it is 1⅝ by 7½ in.   Table 12-1 lists other mill and equivalent dress sizes, together with area, weight, moment of inertia, and section modulus.

LIGHT-WOOD FRAMING

A typical wood-framed building is divided into the following major subdivisions:

1. Underfloor construction, which includes pilings, mudsills, posts, bracing, and cribbing
2. Floor construction, which includes girders, floor joists, blocking, subflooring, and finish flooring
3. Wall construction, which includes bottom plate, top plates, studs, bracing, blocking, wall sheathing, and opening framing (Fig. 12-2)
4. Ceiling construction, which includes ceiling joists and blocking
5. Roof construction, which includes rafters, purlins, ties, bracing, roof sheathing, trusses, truss rafters, and ridgepole

The building codes also follow these subdivisions in their requirements. The individual wooden component members are also known
by the duty they perform. Horizontal members include beams, girders,
boards, and planks. Compression members include posts, columns,
studs, struts, and piling. Diaphragms include roof sheathing, wall
sheathing, and subflooring.

Light-wood framing is in either "platform" or "balloon" construction,
the main difference being that in platform construction the wall studs
are only as long as the height from floor to ceiling of each floor. For
multistory buildings each floor is built as a platform for the next floor.
In balloon construction, the studs are continuous on the exterior walls
extending from the first floor to the ceiling of the upper floor. Platform
construction is more popular.

A standard light-wood framing system is shown in Fig. 12-3. This
figure locates the main components and their names. Bolted to the
top of the foundation wall is the mudsill, which is of either redwood
or specially treated douglas fir. The size of the mudsill is usually 2
by 6 in., and it is bolted with $\frac{1}{2}$-in.-diameter anchor bolts spaced 6
ft on center and set 1 ft from each corner of the building and 1 ft
from the end of each individual board.

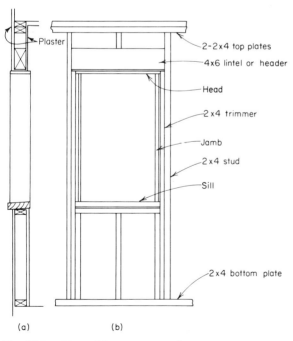

Plaster

2-2x4 top plates

4x6 lintel or header

Head

2x4 trimmer

Jamb

2x4 stud

Sill

2x4 bottom plate

(a)   (b)

Fig. 12-2. Typical framing at window opening.

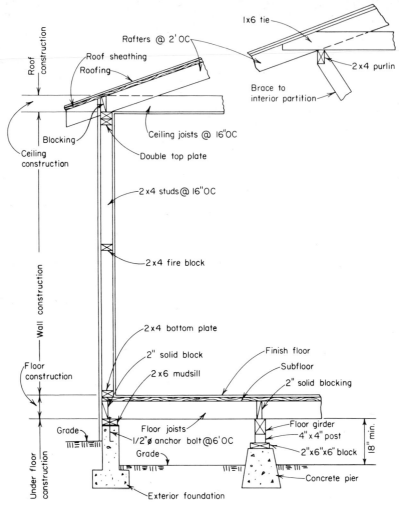

Fig. 12-3. Typical wood-framed building with wood floor system.

Resting upon the mudsill and nailed to it are the floor joists. These may be 2 by 6, 2 by 8, or in some cases 2 by 10 in. and are spaced 16 in. on center. The depth of the floor joists depends on their span. At the interior of a building, the floor joists can rest either upon foundation concrete wall or upon an interior wood girder. The wood girders are usually 4 by 6 or 4 by 8 in. The girder is supported by a 4 by 4 in. wood post which is set upon 2 by 6 by 6 in. redwood blocks. The blocks rest upon a concrete pier.

The floor joists should be blocked at all points of support and also at intervals at least 8 ft on center. This prevents the joist from twisting or warping and stabilizes the joist under load. Directly upon the floor joists and nailed securely to them is the subfloor. A subfloor can be made of 1 by 6 in. boards laid diagonally or of a sheet of plywood ⅜ to ½ in. thick. This entire system forms the platform upon which the superstructure is erected. Walls can be placed on a concrete floor as shown in Fig. 12-4.

A wood stud wall is constructed in three parts: (1) lower plate, (2) studs spaced at 16 in. on center, and (3) a double top plate. Each part of the wall is constructed of 2 by 4s. A stud wall is field-fabricated in this manner: a section of wall is measured, cut, and nailed together on the floor, raised, and then braced temporarily until finally completely stabilized by the ceiling joists.

The ceiling system is constructed of joists which may be 2 by 4s, 2 by 6s, or 2 by 8s, depending upon the span desired. It is supported by the top plates of adjacent walls. The ceiling joists are solidly blocked

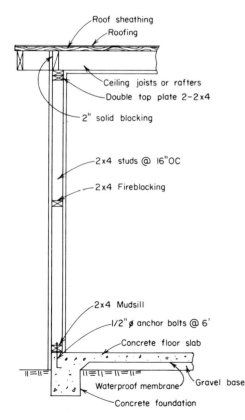

Fig. 12-4. Typical wood-framed building with concrete floor.

at all points of support and a maximum of 8 ft on center. Spacing of ceiling joists is usually at 16 in. centers.

An inclined roof is constructed of rafters, which are 2 by 4s or 2 by 6s spaced 24 in. on center. The lower part of the rafter is notched to rest upon the top plate of the exterior wall. The rafters are joined at the ridge of the roof and nailed to a ridgepole made of 1 by 6 in. lumber. The rafters are also supported at mid-height by purlins, ties, and roof braces spaced at 4 ft.

"Roof sheathing" is usually made of 1 by 4s or 1 by 6s. It is nailed at right angles to the rafters. For a composition roofing system the sheathing is as tight as possible. Where wood-shingle roofing is used, the sheathing may be spaced with 2- to 4-in. gaps between boards.

All wood stud walls 9 ft or higher are blocked at mid-height. These blocks, called "fire stops," are 2 by 4 in. and are used to prevent a fire from rising vertically between studs through the walls. They also serve to brace the studs. All walls are diagonally braced longitudinally with either 1 by 4 or 1 by 6 in. "let-in bracing." These braces are required at the ends of walls and at least 25 ft on center for long walls.

TIMBER CONNECTIONS

Most connections in a light frame system utilize nails. Nail sizes are given in "pennies," indicated by the letter d. Some common ones are listed in Table 12-2.

For connections in large beams and girders and in heavy wood construction such as mill buildings, trusses, bolts, or lag screws are necessary. The bolts are usually $\frac{1}{2}$, $\frac{5}{8}$, or $\frac{3}{4}$ in. in diameter.

BASIC CODE REQUIREMENTS

The Uniform Building Code recommends these general rules for wood construction. By following these requirements, a plant engineer can easily design a simple building.

TABLE 12-2

Nail size	Length of nail, in.
6d	2
8d	$2\frac{1}{2}$
10d	3
12d	$3\frac{1}{4}$
16d	$3\frac{1}{2}$

1. In building up to two stories in height, stud walls should have 2 by 4 in. studs.
2. The studding on the bottom of the first floor, under the second floor joists, should not be less than 3 by 4 or 2 by 6 in.
3. The maximum height of the studs is governed by the size of the stud. Unless supported laterally by adequate framing, the maximum allowable height is
   a. 10 ft for 2 by 3 in. stud framing
   b. 14 ft for 2 by 4 in. stud framing
   c. 16 ft for 3 by 4 in. stud framing and
   d. 20 ft for 2 by 6 in. stud framing
4. No studding should be spaced more than 16 in. on center unless vertical supporting members in the walls are designed as columns. Such walls may be constructed of not less than 4 by 4 in. posts spaced at not more than 5 ft 4 in. on center.
5. Wood diaphragms, of plywood or 1 by 4 or 1 by 6 in. sheathing, are used to tie the building together horizontally.

Although wood construction is one of the easiest to build, it has its shortcomings. As noted earlier a wooden member should not be used to support masonry or concrete walls. Because of the danger of dry rot and termites, the space between the bottom of floor joists and the ground of any wooden building should be provided with a sufficient number of openings through the external foundation walls to ensure ample ventilation. There should also be a minimum distance of 18 in. between the bottom of the floor joists and the ground below. The minimum distance below wood girders is 12 in.

For termite protection, all wood in contact with the concrete, such as the mudsill, should be treated with a special preservative which resists termites. For added protection, all stumps and roots should be removed from the soil to a depth of at least 12 in. in the areas to be occupied by new buildings. All wood forms which were used in placing concrete should be removed before the buildings are occupied. Before completion, loose or casual wood should be removed from direct contact with the ground, as it can provide breeding places for termites.

PANELIZED ROOF CONSTRUCTION

A very popular and economic roofing system used in large warehouses and manufacturing buildings is the panelized roof. This system consists of roof beams spaced 20 ft apart, with 4 by 12 in. purlins spaced 8 ft apart and supported by the beams. The purlins support 2 by 4 in. rafters spaced 24 in. apart, upon which are nailed 4 by 8 ft sheets of plywood. The economy of this construction lies in the fact that all members are precut on a mass-production basis.

HEAVY-TIMBER CONSTRUCTION

Heavy-timber framing is a superior structural system. The large members have high fire-resistance values and often rate higher by fire underwriters than steel structures because at 1000°F steel loses its strength while timber only chars. Floor systems for heavy-timber framing are usually a tongue-in-groove or splined planks. The main framing of the building consists of posts and girders. But to qualify as heavy-timber construction, the size of all the structural members must meet a minimum requirement, regardless of size needed to support the loads. The structure may therefore be overdesigned. The plant engineer must be certain that he is not economizing in one area only to be wasteful in another.

Wood floor beams and girders should not be less than 6 in. wide and 10 in. deep. Glued/laminated arches which spring from the floor line and support floor loads should be not less than 8 in. in any dimension.

Wood roof glued/laminated arches which spring from the floor and do not support floor loads should have members not less than 6 in. wide and not less than 8 in. deep. Walls should be provided with approved steel boxes or hangers.

Floor systems should not contain concealed spaces. They should be made of sawn or glued/laminated plank, splined, or tongue-in-groove plank. The minimum thickness of flooring is 3 in. Roof systems should be constructed similar to the floor system. The minimum thickness of a roof deck is 2 in. or a double thickness of 1-in. boards with tongue-in-groove joints or of plank not less than 3 in. wide.

Since a heavy-timber structure is classified as one constructed with 1-hr fire-resistant material, it has the same basic allowable floor area as a type III–1 hr building.

WOOD TRUSSES

For decades wood trusses have been used in industrial construction (Fig. 12-5). The most common types are the bowstring truss, the scissors truss, and the Warren truss. Long-span roof girders and arches include the tapered glued/laminated girder, the glued/laminated arch, the glued/laminated three-hinged arch or full arch, and many other similar configurations are often used in place of trusses.

In most truss designs each member of the truss is designed for either axial tension or compression. Bending stress of the members is avoided if possible except that the top chord of a truss may have a small amount of bending. Occasionally, the tension members are made of steel rods rather than of wood. There are five major parts of a wood truss. The upper member is called the "top chord," the lower member is the "bottom chord," the vertical and diagonal members between the chords are either "compressive web members" or "tensile web members."

The top chord supports the roof purlins with the roof sheathing. Each member of a truss is connected to the next member by bolted splice plates made of wood or steel or by bolted metal timber connectors such as split rings. Metal timber connectors include split rings, shear plates made of pressed steel, malleable iron, spike grids, tooth rings, and clamping plates.

The most popular of all the truss fasteners are split rings, which are available in 2½- and 4-in. diameters. These fasteners are installed in precut grooves in the contact face of the lumber being joined. The depth of the groove in the face of each piece is equal to one-half the width of the split ring. In this manner the connector is equally embedded in each face of the two joined pieces. When steel splice plates are used for wood-to-wood connections, they are installed in the same manner as the gusset plates used in steel construction.

The strength of any connection depends on the condition of the lumber at the time of fabrication, the condition and type of service, the thickness of the members connected, the angle of the load to the grain, the duration of the load, the number of bolts, the spacing of the bolts, the end distance, the edge distance, and the net section of the wood. All these factors have a direct effect on the strength of a timber connection. Neglect of any one of these factors could cause a failure in an otherwise properly designed and constructed connection.

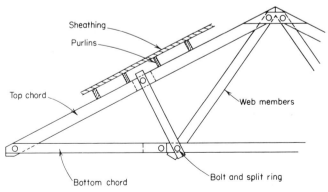

Sheathing
Purlins
Top chord
Web members
Bottom chord
Bolt and split ring

Fig. 12-5. Typical wood truss.

CONNECTIONS IN WOOD

Connections between various wood members are by timber connectors, bolts, driftbolts, pins, screws, lag screws, nails, spikes, or glue (Fig. 12-6). The value of the various types of connectors depends on the direction, type of stress, and the direction of the stress relative to the grain of the wood.

Next to nails and bolts, joist hangers are the most popular type of timber construction connectors (Fig. 12-7). Joist hangers are made from straps of steel ⅛ in. thick and 2 to 2½ in. wide and are bent to receive timbers 3 in. wide or more. They are used for connection to tops of girders, steel beams, or to the top of a wall. Other types of connectors are joist anchors.

SIMPLE STRUCTURAL DESIGN IN TIMBER

Wood members in structural systems are used in four basic categories: axial-loaded compression members, axial-loaded tension members, bending members, and shearing members. When they are used as horizontal bending members, they can be called planks, beams, rafters, joists, girders, or purlins. When these structural members are used to carry axial loads, they are called posts, columns, studs, or ties. When the wooden members are installed in large sheets, they are called sheathing, flooring, diaphragms, shear walls, subflooring, or finish flooring.

In each of the above systems, the wood is under different types of stress. Wooden beams develop flexural compressive and tensile stresses and horizontal shear. Posts develop compressive stresses parallel to the grain and bearing stress at the ends. Sheathing develops shearing stress.

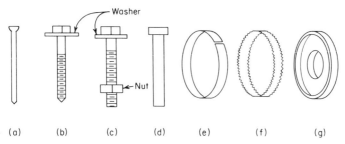

Fig. 12-6. Typical fasteners for wood construction: (*a*) nail; (*b*) lag screw and washer; (*c*) bolt, nut, and washer; (*d*) driftpin; and (*e*) to (*g*) ring connectors.

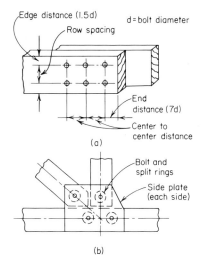

(a)

(b)

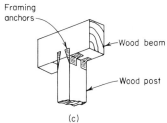

(c)

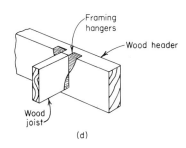

(d)

Fig. 12-7. Typical wood connections: (*a*) bolting, (*b*) split rings, (*c*) framing anchors, and (*d*) framing hangers.

The formulas set by the codes of various agencies for design of wood construction use the following symbols and notations:

a = area of net cross section of member, sq in.
b = width of beam, in.
c = compression stress parallel to grain or allowable unit stress, lb/sq in.
d = least dimension of a column, in.
E = modulus of elasticity
f = extreme fiber stress in bending or allowable unit stress, lb/sq in.
h = depth of beam section, in.

H = horizontal shear stress or allowable unit stress, lb/sq in.

I = moment of inertia of member, in.[4]

l = span, in., or laterally unsupported length of column, in.

M = bending moment, in.-lb or ft-lb

N = allowable unit stress on incline surface, lb/sq in.

P = total weight, lb

q = compression stress perpendicular to grain or allowable unit stress, lb/sq in.

R = reaction, lb

r = least radius of gyration of a section, in.[3]

t = tension stress parallel to grain or allowable unit stress, lb/sq in.

V = vertical shear at section under consideration, lb

$\dfrac{l}{d}$ = ratio of length of column to its least dimension

$\dfrac{P}{A}$ = compressive unit stress or maximum axial stress, lb/sq in.

ϕ = angle between direction of load and direction of grain, degrees

STRUCTURAL DESIGN

For columns, the safe load is given in pounds per square inch of the net cross-sectional area and is equal to

$$\frac{P}{A} = 3.619 \frac{E}{(l/r)^2}$$

For square columns or rectangular section columns. the formula can be reduced to

$$\frac{P}{A} = 0.30 \frac{E}{(l/d)^2}$$

In columns, the unsupported length l should be limited in maximum length to $50d$.

To find the flexural stress for members in bending, the formula is

$$f = \frac{Mc}{I}$$

The formula for determining the unit stress in horizontal shearing members of a rectangular section is

$$H = 3 \frac{V}{2bh}$$

The working stress for most wood members can be calculated from these three basic formulas. The strength of connections made of nails, bolts, or other devices can be determined from the building codes. These values are based upon the size of the device, type of wood, and direction of stress. The values are usually given for stresses parallel or perpendicular to the grain of the wood; for stresses in between, a resultant of the two directions should be utilized.

The recommended working stresses for stress-grade lumber depend on the duration of the normal condition of loading. The loading is an estimate based on the engineering experience and judgment of the designer. For loading due to snow, wind, earthquake, and certain temporary working conditions, the allowable working stresses for normal conditions are to be increased 15 percent for a 2-month duration (as for snow), 25 percent for 7-day duration, $33\frac{1}{3}$ percent for wind or earthquake, and 100 percent for impact condition.

DEFLECTION

Another important factor to consider in design is the tolerable deflection of the member under load. In many cases it is the most important factor to be considered. In addition to its aesthetic importance, it is also necessary in keeping crane rails, shafting, and machinery mounting in true alignment. Deflection due to permanent loads or live loads should be minimized in the design of trusses or long girders by providing sufficient cambers to offset the anticipated deflection. Where plaster ceilings are to be supported by wood members, the dead load is usually in place before the plaster hardens. Therefore, in limiting the deflection to avoid cracking the plaster, only the live load and the increase in dead load under a long-continued load need be considered. It is generally good practice to limit deflection to a proportion of the span. For live loads the deflection should be limited to $\frac{1}{360}$ of the span for plastered ceilings, $\frac{1}{240}$ of the span for ceilings of other material, and $\frac{1}{180}$ of the span for roofs having a slope of 3 in 12 or greater.

GENERAL NOTES

The following notes should appear, when applicable, on wood construction drawings and can also serve as a punch list for the plant engineer:

1. Structural lumber is to be grade marked douglas fir, S4S, construction grade, except as noted on the plans.
2. All wood studs shall be 2 by 4 at 16 in. on center except as otherwise shown.

3. 2-in. fire blocking shall be provided at mid-height of stud partitions over 8 ft high unless noted on the drawings.
4. Sills and plates in contact with concrete within 48 in. of the ground are to be pressure-treated douglas fir.
5. Where stud partitions are in contact with cement, ½-in. diameter bolts at 6 ft on center to floor shall be used, except as noted, and ½-in. diameter bolts at 4 ft on center to walls.
6. Approved-type power-actuated bolts may be used at 3 ft on center for attaching interior nonbearing partitions to floors and walls. Other connections shall be as shown on the drawings or as required by the building code.
7. All wood stud walls shall be braced near each end and at 25 ft maximum on center with 1 by 6 in. diagonal braces let into the stud and nailed to each stud and to the top and bottom plates with two 8d nails.
8. 4 by 4 in. wood headers shall be provided above openings in stud walls except as otherwise shown.
9. 2-in. solid blocking shall be provided at all supports and at 8 ft on center for rafters and floor joists except where supported by joist hangers.
10. The roof diaphragm shall be inspected by the building department prior to covering.
11. All bolts bearing on wood shall have washers.
12. Edge distance for nailing shall not be less than one-half the penetration of the nail into the joining member.

NAILING SCHEDULE

Joist to sill, toenail	2 16d
Bridge to joist	2 8d
Plate to joist or blocking	16d at 16 in. o.c.
Stud to plate, end nail	2 16d
Top plate, spike together	16d at 24 in. o.c.
Laps at intersection	2 16d
Corner studs and angles	16d at 30 in. o.c.

EXAMPLE

A uranium mill required a long launder, or sluice, to carry the plant's waste material, or tailings, several thousand feet to a pond. Since the waste water was corrosive and the structure was exposed to extreme weather conditions, wood construction was selected throughout.

Trestles were designed of 6 by 6 in. posts braced together with 2 by 6 in. boards. The posts were set on concrete footings and anchored with steel straps. The trough and walkway were built upon two 2 by 14 in. stringers spanning from trestle to trestle. The walkway deck was made of 2 by 4 in. planks placed perpendicular to the stringers with a ½-in. gap between boards to provide drainage and friction for walking.

The trough itself was constructed of 2 by 12 in. planks fitting tightly together and caulked to be watertight. The walkway was provided with a handrail made of 2 by 4 in. posts and top and middle rail. A 2 by 6 in. toeplate was also provided between posts.

All connections were made with galvanized steel bolts, washers, and nuts.

SUMMARY

Wooden construction is the simplest and most flexible of all types of industrial construction. It can be completely fabricated and erected on site without the use of special heavy equipment. Practically all work done at the job site requires only hand tools.

The disadvantages of wood construction are its combustibility, its vulnerability to dry rot and termites, its tendency to warp because of shrinkage, and the possible inconsistency of the wood. Wood must therefore be properly graded before it is used in the critical structural elements of buildings.

The most important parts of a wooden structure are the connections. Great care should be taken in selecting the type of connection of each of the critical elements as the direction of stress is more critical in wood than in steel. The bolts or other mechanical connecting devices should be placed with consideration given to the direction of stress and of the grain. Heavy-timber construction has the advantage of being as fireproof as a steel building with 1-hr protection. Glued/laminated construction for girders and arches is one of the cleanest and most attractive ways of handling large spans. For simple construction of plant offices, control rooms, laboratories, and similar types of buildings, light-wood frame construction is the most economical and easiest to build.

CHECKLIST FOR WOOD CONSTRUCTION

1. Type of wood used
2. Floor girders, size and spacing
3. Floor joists, size and spacing
4. Subfloor, size
5. Wall bottom plates
6. Studs, size and spacing
7. Top plates, size
8. Ceiling joists, size and spacing
9. Blocking, floors, walls and ceiling
10. Roof rafters, size and spacing
11. Columns and posts, sizes and spans
12. Trusses

13. Roof sheathing
14. Openings, sills, jambs, and headers
15. Rough hardware
16. Fasteners, nails, bolts, screws, and connectors

MAJOR SUBDIVISION OF A WOOD-FRAME BUILDING

In a typical wood-framed building the major subdivisions of construction can be classified as:

1. Underfloor construction
2. Floor construction
3. Ceiling construction
4. Wall construction
5. Roof construction

The individual components of a timber building include:

1. Horizontal members
   a. Beams
   b. Girders
   c. Planks
   d. Joints, floor and ceiling
   e. Boards
   f. Rafters
   g. Purlins
   h. Trusses
2. Compression members
   a. Posts
   b. Columns
   c. Studs
   d. Struts
   e. Pilings
3. Diaphragm
   a. Sheathing
   b. Subflooring
   c. Shear walls
4. Other parts of a building
   a. Bracing
   b. Ties
   c. Finish flooring
   d. Wall panels

The various wood shapes are sawed rectangular or square members, glue/laminated members, and composite members which are made from wood and steel.

BIBLIOGRAPHY

American Institute of Architects and Charles George Ramsey, and Harold Reeve Sleeper: *Architectural Graphic Standards,* 6th ed., John Wiley & Sons, Inc., New York, 1970.

American Institute of Timber Construction: *Timber Construction Standards* AITC 100-65, Washington, 1965.

Building Codes Bureau: *State Building Construction Code Applicable to One- and Two-family Dwellings,* New York, 1964.

City of Los Angeles: *Building Code,* Building News, Inc., Los Angeles, 1970.

County of Los Angeles: *County of Los Angeles Uniform Building Laws,* Building News, Inc., Los Angeles, 1968.

County of Los Angeles Uniform Building Laws: *Building Code, Plumbing Code, Mechanical Code, County Electrical Code,* Building News, Inc., Los Angeles, 1968.

Editors of Plant Engineering: *Plant Engineering Practice,* F. W. Dodge Corporation, Los Angeles, 1958.

Housing and Building Codes Bureau: *State Building Construction Code Applicable to General Building Construction,* New York, 1964.

————: *State Building Construction Code Applicable to Multiple Dwellings,* New York, 1964.

International Conference of Building Officials: *Uniform Building Code,* Pasadena, Calif., 1967.

————: *Uniform Building Code,* vol. 3, Los Angeles, 1961.

Laurson, Philip Gustave, and William Junkin Cox: *Mechanics of Materials,* 3d ed., John Wiley & Sons, Inc., New York, 1954.

Merriman, Thaddeus, and T. H. Wiggin: *American Civil Engineers' Handbook,* John Wiley & Sons, Inc., New York, 1947.

Merritt, Frederick S.: *Standard Handbook for Civil Engineers,* McGraw-Hill Book Company, New York, 1968.

Parker, Harry: *Simplified Engineering for Architects and Builders,* 4th ed., John Wiley & Sons, Inc., New York, 1967.

Southern California Chapters, American Public Work Association, Associated General Contractors of America: *Standard Specifications for Public Works Construction,* Building News, Inc., Los Angeles, 1967.

Urquhart, Leonard Church: *Civil Engineering Handbook,* 4th ed., McGraw-Hill Book Company, New York, 1959.

Wallin, R. E.: *Construction Specifications,* Plant Engineering, Barrington, Ill., 1970.

West Coast Lumbermen's Association: *Douglas Fir Use Book: Structural Data and Design Tables,* Portland, Ore., 1958.

CHAPTER THIRTEEN

Industrial Roof
Construction

THE INDUSTRIAL ROOF SYSTEM serves many purposes. The primary one, of course, is to provide a structural, load-bearing, framing system to cover a building. It must withstand expected roof loads, consisting of the dead weight of the roof itself, snow loading, live load caused by workmen and their materials, and equipment loads such as roof ventilators, cooling towers, air conditioners, storage tanks, piping, and other mechanical items. The roof structure must also withstand the dynamic forces from wind and earthquake by tying the walls of the building together, thus preventing them from collapsing.

ROOF LOADINGS

Live loads are governed by local building codes and by the judgment of the designer. According to the Uniform Building Code, the minimum live load is given in pounds per square foot and is based upon both the roof slope and a tributary loaded area for the structural member considered. For example, on a flat roof, the minimum live load for a member supporting an area of up to 200 sq ft is 20 lb/sq ft; for an area from 201 to 600 sq ft the minimum unit live load is 16 lb; and for an area over 600 sq ft the minimum live load is 12 lb/sq ft.

Where snow loads occur, the roof structure should be designed for such loads as are determined by the local building department.

All roofs should be constructed with sufficient slope to assure adequate drainage with consideration of the deflection caused by the dead load. The roof should be designed to support the weight of water on a dead-level roof due to ponding of the water. The maximum recommended deflection for structural members of a dead-level roof system is not more than $\frac{1}{360}$ of the span due to live loads only or $\frac{1}{240}$ of the span due to both live load and dead load.

For steeper roofs exposed to the direct effect of the wind, the unit pressure is based upon the height of the roof above the ground. This can vary from 15 lb/sq ft to as high as 40 lb/sq ft.

The leeward side of roofs of lightweight industrial buildings should be designed and constructed to withstand negative pressure acting upward normal to the surface of the roof. This upward force is equal to three-fourths the value of the wind pressure on the windward side of the roof. There should also be adequate anchorage of the roof to all the walls so that the walls and roof form an integral system to resist overturning, uplift, and sliding caused by wind or earthquake forces.

ROOF ASSEMBLY AS AN INSULATION SYSTEM

The second major purpose of the roof is to provide thermal insulation for the building. The insulation is to keep the interior of the building at comfortable temperatures when the exterior is at extreme low or high temperatures. This is done by slowing down the passage of heat through the roof. In metal-clad buildings insulation can save up to 90 percent of direct heat loss other than what is lost through air changes and uninsulated openings.

The choice of insulation thickness and method of application depend upon the building occupancy and the desired comfort level. The high thermal conductance of metal roof sheeting increases the demand for insulation, which must be thick enough to do the entire insulating job. Using adequate thickness not only cuts fuel bills but adds immeasurably to the comfort of the occupants.

Proper insulation of the roof system also prevents condensation. Condensation of moisture in uninsulated buildings occurs when the moisture vapor in the air within the building reaches a cold roof surface which is below the dewpoint temperature of the air, resulting in moisture accumulation of the underside of the roof. This condensation can be controlled in metal buildings by covering their interior surfaces with adequate insulation and also by proper ventilation.

The four considerations for condensation control are (1) a continuous and effective vapor barrier on the warm side of the building shell during the winter; (2) insulation of sufficient thickness to keep the surface of the vapor barrier warm to prevent condensation; (3) maintaining indoor moisture at the lowest practical level; and (4) venting of moisture-producing surfaces to the outside. Ventilation should be provided at the highest point of the roof and also along the perimeter. Prevention of condensation and damp diffusion will also eliminate the possible corrosion of sheet-iron roofing and siding.

ROOF ASSEMBLY AS A WATERPROOFING SYSTEM

The third major purpose of the roof system is for waterproofing the enclosure of the building and providing a drainage surface. Waterproofing is mainly to prevent the entrance of moisture due to rain or snow from entering the building through structural joints and around roof openings.

MAJOR COMPONENTS OF A ROOF

The major components of a roof system include the following:

1. Roof structure, consisting of beams, girders, rafters, and purlins
2. Roof deck, also known as the roof diaphragm or roof sheathing
3. Insulation, for thermal or sound attenuation
4. Roofing, or a waterproofing membrane
5. Expansion joints, for structural and thermal movements
6. Gutters, or horizontal conductors of rainwater
7. Downspouts, or vertical conductors of rainwater or leaders
8. Roof drains, or roof inlets for collection of rainwater and overflow scuppers
9. Protective granular aggregate, covering to protect the roofing

Some of the minor components of a roof that are also critical for its success and performance include:

1. Flashing, for eaves, rakes, openings, piping, and ducts
2. Counterflashing, used as a component to flashing
3. Nailer strips
4. Cant strips
5. Roof tape
6. Metal coping
7. Crickets
8. Gravel stops

9. Edging
10. Pitch pockets, vapor barriers

This should serve as a checklist for the plant engineer in reviewing plans and specifications of a new building or addition.

STRUCTURAL COMPONENTS

Roof structures consist of a system of trusses, roof beams, rafters, purlins, and subpurlins.

A rafter is a member that is in the same plane and slopes in the same direction as the roof surface. A purlin is a horizontal roof member that tilts to conform to the roof slope. A subpurlin is a relatively small member supported by a purlin or a rafter.

Rafters and purlins can be built of wood, steel, or concrete. When constructed of wood, they are usually of douglas fir construction-grade lumber. When made of steel, they are normally rolled sections made of the ASTM A36 steel. In many lightweight prefabricated buildings, the purlins are made of the high-strength cold-formed steel shapes which weigh much less than the hot-rolled members. Subpurlins are made of special shapes such as bulb-tees and are designed to carry a rigid panel forming the roof deck.

TYPES OF ROOF DECKS

Roof decks are made of wood, metal, concrete, gypsum, Zonolite, vermiculite, and many types of inorganic materials similar to fiber glass and urethane. The wood deck can be of 4 by 8 ft plywood sheets that are $3/8$ or $1/2$ in. thick. Roof decks can also be of 1 by 6 or 2 by 6 in. wood planks laid solid diagonally to the rafters. The sequence for installing an insulated built-up roof over a wood deck is shown in Fig. 13-1.

Metal roof decks are available in a variety of rectangular and corrugated cold-form shapes and are supported by purlins or roof beams (Fig. 13-2). Poured-in-place concrete roof decks are either cast on temporary forms or upon permanent metal corrugated forms which remain bonded with the slab (Figs. 13-3 and 13-4). Concrete roof decks are also made from lightweight aggregate. Other lightweight mineral decks include the gypsum deck, which is either poured in place over a gypsum form board or precast as planks and supported by bulb-tee subpurlins. Fiber-glass panels and pressed-wood fiber panels are also used as decks and are supported by subpurlins. One of the most popular types of organic roof deck is made from select chemically treated long wood fibers that are coated and pressure-bonded with a fire-retardant moisture-resistant portland cement binder and formed into panels. These panels are lightweight, insulating, acoustical, noncombustible, and resistant to termites, fungus, and rot. They also provide an attractive interior surface.

Roof-deck systems provide not only a structural shell for the roof but a significant amount of its insulating value. An exception to this is the metal deck. For this reason all metal decks must always be covered with at least a layer of ½-in.-thick insulation before the roofing is applied. Few of the prefabricated deck systems are waterproof as they have joints which are difficult to make watertight (Fig. 13-2).

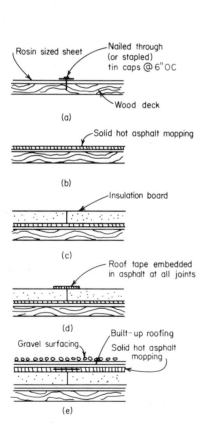

Fig. 13-1. Sequence for installing insulation and built-up roofing on a wood deck.

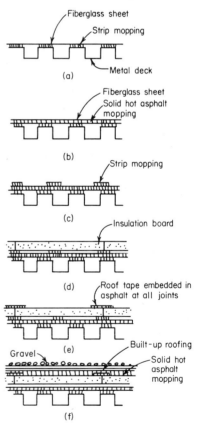

Fig. 13-2. Sequence for installing insulation and built-up roofing on a metal deck.

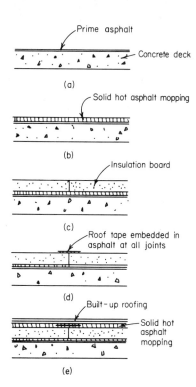

Fig. 13-3. Sequence for installing insulation and built-up roofing on a concrete deck.

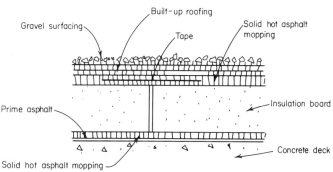

Fig. 13-4. Detail of insulated built-up roof on a concrete deck.

ROOF INSULATION

Roof insulation is available in many forms:

1. Rigid boards or panels
2. Blanket or rolls
3. Bats

4. Froth
5. Spray on
6. Blow on

The insulation material includes

1. Fiber glass
2. Urethane
3. Rock wool
4. Styrofoam
5. Foam glass
6. Gypsum
7. Various organic materials which constitute the fiberboard group

Unfortunately roof insulation in itself does not provide the waterproofing requirements, and many types do not have the structural strength required as a deck.

TYPES OF ROOFING

A typical roofing can be built up of layers of asphalt-saturated felt or consist of a sprayed-on coating of an elastomeric material. The built-up roofing may have three to five layers of felt which are mopped on with hot liquid asphalt. To protect asphalt felt, the roofing is usually covered with a thin bed or surfacing made of granulated or crushed rock or slag. This granular material is sprinkled on the top layer of asphalt and provides protection against deterioration from sun radiation and from wear.

There are five conditions to be determined for proper preparation of a specification for roofing:

1. The slope of the roof, usually given in inch rise per foot
2. The surfacing material
3. The surface upon which the roofing is to be applied, which may be the deck or insulation
4. The life expectancy of the roof
5. The number of plys of roofing material desired

TYPES OF FLASHING

Flashing, which is a system of providing flexibility and watertightness to all joints, is made of galvanized-iron sheets, copper sheets, strips of asphalt-saturated felt, or fiber-glass asphalt-saturated material.

All metal flashing should be allowed to expand and contract without rupturing the roof. This is done by isolating the roofing membrane from the metal flashing, which is vulnerable to thermal expansion. A temperature differential of 185°F can cause approximately ³⁄₁₆ in. linear expansion in a 10-ft length of galvanized steel flashing or gutter. This amount of movement would tear any attached roofing.

INSULATION PROPERTIES OF ROOF DECKS

The thermal conductivity of insulation is known as the K value, which is given in Btu per hour per square foot per degree Fahrenheit per inch of thickness. The U factor is the heat-transmission factor, given as Btu per hour per square foot. The C factor is the value of conductance and is equal to K/T, where T is the thickness of the insulation material given in inches.

Other properties of insulation are the noise-reduction coefficient, water-vapor transmission, and the mechanical properties.

Insulation should be rigid enough for foot traffic and thick enough so that the dewpoint is within the body of the insulation. When it is not thick enough, the bottom surface of the insulation could be at dewpoint temperature, thus permitting beads of water from condensation to form under the decking. Sometimes these beads of water are misread as leaks in the roof.

Insulation boards are available from ½ to 2 in. thick and are of standard 24-in. width. Some are manufactured as a sandwich and are laminated with foils, chipboard, kraft paper, and other sheetlike paper on the surfaces. They are also manufactured with tongue-and-groove or shiplap joints, which provide better seals. Some boards have an aluminum-foil facing over the surface, which provides a built-in vapor- and water-resistant layer to the insulation by protecting it against condensation; the facing also makes the board easy to install. The tongue-and-groove edges eliminate taping and reduce the amount of leakage through the joints.

One popular type of insulation board is made of polystyrene. The noninterconnecting cells of expanded polystyrene provide an exceptionally low K factor. It is a rigid, extra-light, and easily applied board weighing only 1 lb/cu ft. Polystyrene is also self-extinguishing in case of fire. It has no capillarity, and its water-absorption factor is less than 2 percent by volume.

Another common type of roof insulation board is the fiber-glass insulation, which is not only a thermal insulator but a good sound absorber. It provides a fire-safe interior finish when used as insulation boards exposed to the interior of the building. Fiber-glass boards are also used as form boards on which lightweight concrete or gypsum can be cast, forming the roof deck. Fiber-glass insulation is well suited for metal-clad buildings, as it can be applied directly over the purlins or girts and under the corrugated panels.

Rigid urethane-foam insulation is a cellular plastic material formed by the reaction of two liquid components containing a blowing agent. As the chemical reaction proceeds, heat is generated and the blowing agent forms minute bubbles in the thickening plastic. The reaction is virtually instantaneous upon mixture of the components, and the plastic foam rises and sets within a very short time. The most important aspect of urethane foam is its monolithic structure. There are no seams to seal, no voids to be concerned with, compared to precut hand-fitted insulation. This means that the total insulation value of this product can be fully realized. Application of urethane-foam components is accomplished by spraying, pouring in place, or frothing.

INSTALLATION AND MAINTENANCE OF ROOFING

Almost all premature roofing failures are traceable to:

1. Expansion and contraction
2. Shrinkage due to temperature
3. Blisters (Fig. 13-5)
4. Wet decks and condensation due to moisture and aging
5. Wind and slippage due to time

Prior to the installation of the roofing material, precautions should be taken to keep the products clean and dry. Coated sheets should not be stored in the open in humid conditions, as moisture may be collected and stick in the rolls. Even small amounts of moisture in the rolls can cause the coated sheets to blister. Rolls should be stored on end. The contractor should take precautions to prevent other construction trades from damaging the roof during and after construction. Periodic visual inspection should be conducted to assure that the deck surfaces are clean, smooth, dry, and firm with all damaged areas repaired. Roofing must be properly anchored against wind uplift and lateral movement. The asphalt type and softening point must be proper for the roof slope. Clean, dry, undamaged built-up roofing material should be applied without voids, skips, dry spots, untrapped moisture, or wrinkles. Roof-insulation and vapor-barrier materials must be embedded with the proper quantities of adhesive for application of roofing.

If roofing is bonded, manufacture requirements must be complied with and the proper number of plys and materials must be applied and nailed as specified. Roofing should not be applied before correct asphalt-application temperature can be maintained or when the roof-

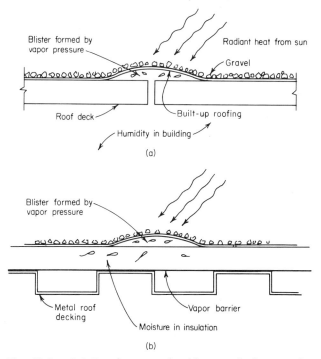

Blister formed by vapor pressure

Radiant heat from sun

Gravel

Roof deck

Built-up roofing

Humidity in building

(a)

Blister formed by vapor pressure

Metal roof decking

Vapor barrier

Moisture in insulation

(b)

Fig. 13-5. (*a*) Development of a blister in built-up roofing caused by vapor pressure. (*b*) Roofing blister caused by moisture in insulation.

deck surface temperature is less than 40°F. Roofing operations should not be conducted when water in any form is present on the deck or the materials are wet. This includes rain, water, dew, ice, frost, or snow. For maximum roof life it is recommended that the gravel be of moderate particle size ($\frac{3}{8}$ to $\frac{5}{8}$ in. in diameter), opaque, clean, dry, and sufficiently hard but without razor-sharp edges to ensure adequate embedding in, and protection of, the asphalt.

EXPANSION JOINTS

In large structures, or where otherwise structurally necessary, expansion joints should be provided in the roof deck. Insulation and/or roofing must never bridge over an expansion joint. Expansion joints should be located so that the flow of water is away or parallel to them but never against them. Flashing over expansion joints should always project above the roof surface. Any crack or movement in a structural concrete deck may be transferred to the built-up roof. Once the membrane is ruptured, water can enter and be absorbed by the insulation and then vaporize as temperature increases; this will result in roof blistering.

PROTECTION OF WORK

It is recommended that the application of roof insulation and built-up roofing be delayed until after all other trades have completed work which would require them or their equipment to cross the deck. A membrane-type vapor barrier with a light glaze coat or asphalt may be applied to protect the interior of the building during the interim. It is also necessary prior to applying the roof insulation. Installed insulation should not be left exposed to the weather but should be covered and waterproofed at once. All exposed edges left at the end of a day's work should be sealed by lapping roofing material or an extra stop of roofing over the exposed edge of the installation and mopping it in place. Installed insulation which has become wet should be removed and replaced with dry material. Applied insulation and completed built-up roofing should be protected at all times against damage by roof traffic.

Treated wood blocks with the same thickness as the insulation and approximately 6 in. wide should be installed to act as a stop for the insulation around all roof openings, vents, stacks, and drains and at open eaves and edges. Vapor barriers and insulation should not be so installed that they bridge across expansion joints.

REROOFING

For reroofing or recovering an existing roof, the following recommendations are made. All loose gravel, dust, and debris should be swept off the old roof. Blisters, buckles, and other irregularities should be cut and nailed down to provide a smooth roof surface. Wet or deteriorated roof insulation should be removed and replaced with new materials. The surface of the old roof should be primed with an asphalt primer applied at the rate of 1 gal per 100 sq ft and allowed to dry thoroughly. If the existing roof is not salvageable, it should be removed completely and the new roof deck should be applied in conformance to new construction. Old flashing metal and composition should be entirely removed from walls and curbs, which should then be reconditioned to meet the requirements for the construction. Rusted, bent, or deteriorated metal should be replaced with new. In general, all old roofing and flashing should be completely removed and the deck reconditioned to conform with requirements of new construction if a roof has been recovered one or more times or if the original roof is badly deteriorated or if the original roofing is not securely attached to the deck or if the underlying insulation has become water-soaked or otherwise deteriorated or if the roof decking has deteriorated or become otherwise damaged.

If the original roofing is securely attached to the deck and not badly deteriorated, and if the underlying insulation and the roof decking are in good condition, it may be advisable to repair the existing roof by recovering with a new built-up assembly. Where weather conditions or other extenuating circumstances prohibit a complete tear-off, it may be necessary to repair and recover the existing roofing with a new built-up assembly.

The decision to reroof or recover should be based in part on a complete survey of the roofing assembly and insofar as possible the underlying decking. The finding of this survey combined with all other pertinent factors—such as the nature and the use of the building, anticipated building life, causes of failure or deterioration of existing roofing, and funds available—should be used as a basis for deciding whether to reroof or recover. As a precautionary note, chemical compatibility of coatings or finishes should be established prior to the application of new liquid products.

Coal-tar pitch is incompatible with asphalt. When planning to reroof or recover an old coal-tar pitch built-up roof with an asphalt built-up roof, special precautions are necessary. The coal-tar roof should be removed completely and replaced with a new asphalt built-up roof, or, after removing all loose gravel and debris, the coal-tar pitch built-up roof should be covered with a new roof insulation laid in coal-tar pitch. Roof insulation must be firmly adhered to the old coal-tar surface, and then an asphalt built-up roof can be installed according to specifications for new insulated deck. Unless these precautions are observed, a totally unsatisfactory roof may result.

BONDED ROOFS

A typical roofing manufacturer's bonded roof agreement is a promise of the manufacturer to maintain a built-up roof in a watertight condition, without roof failure from ordinary wear and tear of the elements or defective built-up roofing material. The bond is usually limited to a specific number of years and a maximum aggregate monetary liability. A roofing manufacturer's bonded roof agreement is not, for example, an insurance policy guaranteeing that the roof will not leak, split, crack, tear, wrinkle, or buckle due to any cause. It is not an obligation to make any repairs to the roof where the cause of the roof failure is due to settlement, distortion, failure or cracking of the roof deck, walls, or foundation of the building or any defect or failure of material used as a roofing base over which the built-up roofing materials are applied. It does not guarantee damage resulting from traffic of any nature over the roof, damage to the roof where water is ponded or allowed to stand without freely draining to outlets, use of the roof as storage area, walking or recreational surface, or any similar purpose. The bond does not protect the owner from damage caused by lightning, hurricane, tornado, hailstorm, or any other unusual action of the elements. It is not an obligation making the manufacturer responsible for any roof failure related to workmanship or manner of application or for damage resulting from the failure of the building owner to follow normal maintenance procedures.

The manufacturer's bonded roof agreement requires two things of the building owner: (1) he must notify the manufacturer promptly in writing of any defect of the built-up roof and (2) he must notify the manufacturer of any proposed alterations, additions, or changes of any kind in the roof structure. The manufacturer's bonded roof agreement expires when the term of the bond expires or when any alteration, addition, or repair is made to the roof structure without prior written approval of the manufacturer or when the bond holder and the manufacturer mutually agree to cancellation.

COST SAVINGS FROM INSULATION

By the use of insulation, there is a definite reduction of cooling load on the air-conditioning equipment. A saving of 12,000 Btu/hr through insulation permits a reduction of approximately 1 ton in the capacity of the cooling equipment. There is likewise a reduction of the heating-plant capacity. Heat loss through roof construction is figured by multiplying the U factor of the roof by the difference between the outside and inside temperatures.

The following is an example of the annual savings in winter fuel costs assuming a 2-in. lightweight aggregate concrete deck with 1 in. of fiber-glass form board. Assuming the C value is 0.25, the U value in winter is 0.14, and the U value in summer is 0.13, the reduction in summer cooling load in Btu/hr per 1,000 sq ft of roof is 7,560. The reduction in heating-plant capacity is between 9,000 to 14,000 Btu/hr per 1,000 sq ft of roof. The annual saving in winter fuel costs in dollars per 1,000 sq ft of roof surface per season is from $8 to $27. This is based on a fuel cost of 10 cents per 100,000 Btu of heat delivered to the heated space. The reduction in the size of heating and cooling plants will also help defray the initial costs of the installation of the equipment.

As it is fundamental to good air-conditioning practice to control heating gain wherever possible, the solar heat which flows down through a roof should be kept from the air-conditioned space by applying a reflective coating to all types of roof surfaces. The primary function of the coating is to reflect radiation from the sun, thus cooling the surfaces to which it is applied and adding years of life to the roof.

During a test by the federal government, 20 different built-up roof-construction specimens covered with five surfacing materials were subjected to natural solar heating and nighttime cooling during winter and summer exposure. The data show that the roofings placed over insulation may be heated to a temperature of 80°F above the ambient due to solar heating and may be subcooled to as much as 20° below ambient due to radiative cooling. Solar heating appears to be the most important factor, causing slippage of roof membranes and chemical degration of asphalt. Therefore, it goes without saying that white roofs on buildings produce a heat-reflecting coating over the asphalt, gravel, and metal, eliminating excessive inside temperatures and protecting the roofing materials.

SUMMARY

The roof of a building is the part of the structure most vulnerable to deteriation by the elements, and therefore it requires the most maintenance. It behooves the plant engineer to be very selective in the type of roof he specifies.

The roof assembly is made up of structure, decking, insulation, and roofing. Each part has its own particular requirements and should be considered separately. The structure is for strength, the decking provides a base for the roof surfacing, the insulation is to retain heat or retard its transfer, and the roofing is for waterproofing and resistance to wear.

Close attention must be given to the details of roof construction, as carelessly designed or constructed joints can cause leaks, bubbles, and split roofing.

CHECKLIST FOR ROOF CONSTRUCTION

1. Type of main roof girders or trusses
2. Type and spacing of rafters or purlins
3. Slope of roof in inches per foot
4. Parapets, height and material
5. Eaves
6. Corrugated roofing
    a. Corrugated galvanized-steel sheets
    b. Corrugated galvanized-steel sheets, prepainted
    c. Corrugated aluminum sheets

  d. Corrugated asbestos-cement sheets
  e. Corrugated protected metal
 7. Decking
  a. Metal decking
  b. Gypsum decking, cast in place or precast
  c. Perlite decking, cast in place
  d. Zonolite decking, cast in place
  e. Lightweight concrete decking, cast in place or precast and prestressed
  f. Wood, plywood or wood planking
  g. Vermiculite
 8. Insulation
  a. Fiber glass
  b. Urethane
  c. Styrofoam
  d. Wood fiber
  e. Foam glass
  f. Rock wool
 9. Type of insulation
  a. Boards
  b. Blankets
  c. Batts
  d. Blown on
  e. Poured in place
 10. Roofing
  a. Built-up roofing
  b. Elastomeric
  c. Surfacing, type and weight per 100 sq ft
  d. Number of plies
  e. Weight of asphalt coatings per 100 sq ft
  f. Weight of each ply per 100 sq ft
 11. Flashing
  a. Galvanized sheet metal
  b. Copper
  c. Asphalt-saturated felt
  d. Counterflashing
 12. Gutters
  a. Galvanized sheet metal
  b. Aluminum sheet
  c. Galvanized steel pipe
  d. Asbestos-cement pipe
 13. Downspouts
  a. Galvanized sheet metal
  b. Galvanized steel pipe
  c. Cast-iron pipe
  d. Asbestos-cement pipe
 14. Roof penetrations

15. Roof-supported equipment
     a. Ventilators, air-conditioning equipment, tanks
16. Access to roof
     a. Ladders, stairway, elevator
17. Roof loading
     a. Dead load
     b. Live load
     c. Snow load
     d. Wind load, positive and negative
18. Roof deflection
19. Cants and crickets
20. Expansion joints
21. Roof drainage
22. Bonded roofs, number of years
23. Reroofing
24. Heat loss through roof
25. Heat gain through roof
26. Elastomeric roof coating

BIBLIOGRAPHY

American Institute of Architects and Charles George Ramsey, and Harold Reeve Sleeper: *Architectural Graphic Standards,* 6th ed., John Wiley & Sons, Inc., New York, 1970.

Building Codes Bureau: *State Building Construction Code Applicable to One- and Two-family Dwellings,* New York, 1964.

City of Los Angeles: *Building Code,* Building News, Inc., Los Angeles, 1970.

County of Los Angeles: *County of Los Angeles Uniform Building Laws,* Building News, Inc., Los Angeles, 1968.

County of Los Angeles Uniform Building Laws: *Building Code, Plumbing Code, Mechanical Code, County Electrical Code,* Building News, Inc., Los Angeles, 1968.

Editors of Plant Engineering: *Plant Engineering Practice,* F. W. Dodge Corporation, 1958.

Grinter, Linton E.: *Theory of Modern Steel Structures,* The Macmillan Company, New York, 1947.

Housing and Building Codes Bureau: *State Building Construction Code Applicable to General Building Construction,* New York, 1964.

———: *State Building Construction Code Applicable to Multiple Dwellings,* New York, 1964.

International Conference of Building Officials, *Uniform Building Code,* Pasadena, Calif., 1967.

International Conference of Building Officials, *Uniform Building Code,* vol. 3, Los Angeles, 1961.

CHAPTER FOURTEEN

Industrial Walls
And Partitions

UNFORTUNATELY, too little attention has been given to the design and selection of walls and partitions in many industrial facilities. Most of the effort has been directed to the exterior walls of the building. Many industrial plants contain tens of thousands of square feet of floor area but with no interior partitions provided in the original building design. This may be due to economy or neglect. It is only after the plant has been in operation that a need for shipping offices, foreman rooms, toolrooms, and other special rooms becomes apparent. Small areas are then hurriedly partitioned off with little thought given to the best type of wall materials to use.

Also, during operation of the plant it becomes apparent that other enclosures are necessary. A grinder is so noisy it disturbs operations in the adjacent areas. A crusher spreads dust into the balance of the plant. Instrument repair in the machine shop requires an isolated area with constant temperature and humidity and dustfree atmosphere. Storage of welding rods must also be in a controlled atmosphere. Certain operations must be isolated because they generate noxious fumes, dust, or flammable or other undesirable atmospheric pollution. These areas are often "temporarily" separated by partitions and walls with little design but a great deal of "field expedience."

The exterior walls of the building are usually controlled by building codes which require specific types of wall material in order to comply with the type of construction and the occupancy group. The proximity of the building to property lines and adjacent buildings also governs construction of exterior walls.

Most modern industrial facilities require many types of walls and partitions. The difference between a wall and a partition is that a "wall" serves as an enclosure while a "partition" divides one part of an area from another. These terms are often used interchangeably. Walls can vary from the highly aesthetic and decorative types found in executive offices, conference rooms, and entrance lobbies to the simple temporary type of wall used for the foreman and shipping offices. Special types of walls are used for locker and toilet rooms, where sanitary maintenance and resistance to humidity are critical. There are also the highly impervious and airtight walls required for quality control and clean rooms. Walls that are acidproof are used in laboratories and other rooms where chemicals are stored or frequently used. There are soundproof walls within the production area of the plant which provide a quiet environment for supervisory personnel or isolation of noise. There are also partitions and walls for administration, engineering, sales, and purchasing offices which offer the occupants full or partial privacy. Each type of room requires a different choice of wall construction and finish as determined by the needs of the occupant and the relative costs.

PURPOSES OF WALLS

Before selecting the type of wall, there should be a careful analysis of the purpose the wall is to serve. It may be to provide visual privacy to the occupants, where they are not to be seen from the outside, or inversely they are not to see out from their area. This type of room would be for personnel who must have relative silence and visual privacy to avoid distraction by outside activity. There are also walls that provide physical separation from operational areas but where visual contact between the two areas must be maintained, which is done by providing glazed areas in the walls.

An important purpose of a wall is to provide sound insulation. Soundproofing is achieved both by sound absorption and sound attenuation. Sound absorption is obtained by using absorbant, porous materials into which sound energy is dissipated. Sound attenuation is the result of stopping radiating sound energy with a system of dense rigid walls and dead air spaces. Some absorbing materials are fiber-glass bats, acoustic tile, acoustic plaster, fiber insulation boards, vermiculite, perlite, and cork. The better sound-attenuating materials are concrete, masonry, lead, gypsum, and any dense material.

The planning and design for acoustic insulation involves the consideration of three basic elements of sound:

1. The source which generates sound (grinders, compressors, machines)
2. The path the sound travels (corridors, ducts, air, and walls)
3. The receiver who perceives the sound

Each of these elements must be contended with to control sound successfully.

All acoustic materials are either sound barriers or sound absorbers, and each type must be used properly. When sound energy passes through a wall, the sound waves acting against the wall set it into a vibrating motion. This vibrating wall then reradiates sound energy into the adjacent room.

Certain building materials can absorb sound energy by converting it to heat, which dissipates the acoustic energy, thus reducing the sound.

A heavy concrete wall may be a good barrier, but by reflecting sound into the source room it is a poor absorber.

Sound insulation is used to keep the sound out of a particular room from adjoining noisy work areas. Sound conditioning is used to limit reverberations, muffle noises, or even add pleasing sounds to an all too quiet area. Piped music is a typical example.

Visibility through soundproof walls can be achieved by providing acoustic glass panels, which are made from twin panes installed in rubber frames.

THERMAL INSULATION

Walls are also selected for their thermal insulating value to prevent heat from entering or leaving an area. Insulated walls are necessary for any air-conditioned room. The selection of a thermally insulated wall must be made with the consideration of radiant, conductive, and convective heat movement.

OTHER PURPOSES OF WALLS

Walls are also selected for their properties of resistance to chemical attack and excessive moisture from rain, high humidity, spraying operations, open tanks, and similar conditions. These walls may also resist the effects of corrosive fumes. Some walls are selected for their resistance to extremely high radiant heat, destruction caused by impact from flying objects, or vehicular traffic.

In areas with high occupancy loads, the building and safety laws require that all exit corridors be constructed of fireproof walls and ceilings. The fireproof rating of these walls is classified as 1-, 2-, 3-, or 4-hr fire resistance, depending on the number of occupants. The accepted method throughout the country by which fire-resistant walls are rated is based upon a length of time the material will resist combustion when exposed to a standard high temperature. Normally, walls in escape corridors leading to the building exits are classified as 1-hr walls.

Wall construction is also defined as "combustible" or "incombustible." An incombustible wall is one which will not ignite or burn when subjected to fire. This does not necessarily apply to surface finish materials under $\frac{1}{8}$ in. thick. Any other type of material is combustible.

Exterior walls of a building which are adjacent to property lines or nearby buildings are controlled by the building codes, and the allowable area of the building is governed by the fire resistance of the exterior walls.

Another purpose of a wall is its aesthetic appearance, especially in presenting a favorable image of the company to the public. For this reason professional architectural and interior decorators are retained by management to design lobbies, conference rooms, and executive offices. These sensitive areas must be carefully planned by experts trained in color, texture, and pattern to give pleasant surroundings to the plant personnel and the public.

MATERIALS AND CONSTRUCTION

A typical wall or partition is made up of several important components: the structural frame, which provides the strength; the surfacing, which provide the ability to separate the environment between the two areas; the finish; the trim; and the accessories. Each of these components must be carefully considered when selecting the wall as a whole. Some may be highly impervious to moisture while others are very soluble. Gypsum plaster is an example of a soluble wall material, while cement plaster is insoluble. The wall surfacing may be hard and smooth or soft and porous. These two characteristics affect its sound-absorption properties as well as ease of maintenance. Hard, impervious, and smooth surfaces are important when designing walls in rest rooms.

Walls may be combustible or incombustible. Therefore, in selection of each of the components of a wall, the designer must consider the ultimate purpose of the wall and the characteristics of the material making up the wall.

Walls are also defined as "bearing" or "nonbearing." A bearing wall is one that supports any load other than its own weight.

MASONRY AND CONCRETE WALLS

The three major types of massive wall construction are brick, concrete block, and reinforced concrete.   Each provides a permanent, highly fire-resistant, noncorroding wall with relatively high structural strength. Because of their density and thickness, these walls are also very good for thermal and sound insulation.   Since concrete block is more pervious to moisture than cast-in-place concrete, concrete-block walls exposed to constant moisture should be made waterproof by sealing with waterproof finish or a coat of cement plaster.

LIGHTWEIGHT WALLS

Among the lightweight, permanent walls is a wide selection of materials. The most common and inexpensive type of construction is the wood-frame wall made from 2 by 4 in. studs spaced 16 in. on center or constructed of 4 by 4 in. posts spaced at 4 ft on center.   A similar framing system is with metal studs with the approximate dimensions of 2 by 4 in. which are spaced 24 in. on center.   Metal studs are made from closed or open channels formed from 16- and 18-gage cold-rolled steel. These are classified as bearing and nonbearing studs.

The surfacing of both the wood- and metal-frame walls can be of gypsum plaster, which is applied over gypsum or metal laths.   The laths in both cases are attached to the framing by nails or self-taping screws.   Other important accessories for a plastered wall are the corner and casing beads, expansion joints, and metal door and window frames. Although gypsum is an ideal fireproof and acoustical material, its one shortcoming is solubility in water.   Therefore, for locations exposed to moisture a portland cement plaster is recommended.   Portland cement plaster is applied only upon a metal lath and never directly over a gypsum lath surface because the wet cement plaster would soften the gypsum lath.   Metal lath is available as diamond-mesh or flat-rib type, and its gage is determined by the spacing of the studs.

Gypsum Plaster

Gypsum plaster is manufactured as "sanded gypsum," "neat gypsum," "wood-fibered gypsum," and "gypsum perlite."   Each has specific fire-resistant characteristics and finish.   The most popular types of wall surfacing used in plant offices are the gypsum boards which are manufactured as two layers of kraft paper sandwiched over a $\frac{1}{2}$- to $\frac{3}{4}$-in.-thick gypsum core.   These boards are nailed to the wall studs, and after the joints between panels are covered with tape, the entire surface is painted. Another popular method of finishing gypsum boards is a thin coat of gypsum plaster, which covers not only the joints but the entire board surface.

Paneling

For areas requiring aesthetic treatment, prefinished paneling of many types is used as wall surfacing. Wood paneling can be applied directly to the wood or metal framing or cemented over the gypsum boards. Wood paneling is usually made of plywood with the outer layer made of a thin veneer of selected hardwood. Also available as finished paneling are many types of composition boards with the exposed surface finished with a vinyl film embossed and textured to simulate hardwood veneer, tile, cork, and other attractive materials. In rest rooms, walls adjacent to showers, urinals, lavatories, or other areas exposed to moisture, ceramic tile is recommended for the protection of the wall. Ceramic tiles are embedded in a layer of grout made of cement and sand or applied with an epoxylike adhesive.

Industrial walls made of metal include flat, ribbed, and corrugated sheets of galvanized steel, aluminum, and asbestos cement. These panels are available as prepainted sheets and are made in a wide range of colors. For added resistance to the elements, the steel sheets can be galvanized and protected with layers of asbestos felt and asphalt saturants. Asbestos-cement siding is made in standard and lightweight sheets, which are $3/8$ or $3/16$ in. thick. These are finished in natural grey and many acrylic colors. Also available for cold climates are asbestos-cement insulating boards made with two $1/8$-in.-thick layers over an insulative core. Aluminum battens and mullions are used to seal the joints in these insulated panels.

The plant engineer should not neglect the many accessories required for each type of industrial wall, including fasteners, closure strips, flashing, trim, and door and window frames.

Walls should also be insulated when necessary. Insulation can be a filler between the two surfacing materials and may be fiber glass, glass foam, or other lightweight expanded materials. Insulation may also be in rigid panel form such as absorbant insulation boards attached directly to the studs.

Also important for sound insulation is to provide discontinuity of the wall framing by staggered studs, double studs, resilient spring clips and channels, and isolation from the floor with rubber pads (Fig. 14-1).

The construction of the walls should provide for installing electric conduits to the various receptacle boxes and switches. A wall without facilities for conduit installation is very limited. In addition to conduit placement, the wall should provide space for piping, plumbing, and vents.

Another important component of the wall is the treatment around openings. Doors are installed in a wood or metal frame. Doors are normally made of metal or wood, either hollow-core or solid-core construction. The normal door size for the use of personnel is 3 ft wide

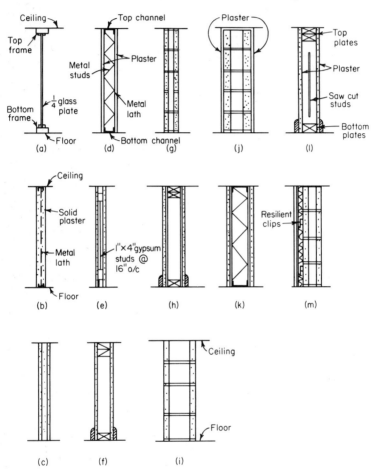

Fig. 14-1. Relative soundproofed wall construction: (*a*) ¼-in. glass partition (least effective); (*b*) 2-in. solid plaster; (*c*) laminated gypsum plaster; (*d*) wire stud, metal lath, and plaster; (*e*) special gypsum; (*f*) 2 by 4 in. wood stud, ½-in. gypsum board; (*g*) 4-in. cinder block; (*h*) 2 by 4 in. wood studs, gypsum lath and plaster; (*i*) 6-in. cinder block; (*j*) 6-in. cinder block and plaster; (*k*) wire studs, mineral lath, and plaster; (*l*) split studs and gypsum board; and (*m*) cinder block, wood furring, resilient clips, mineral lath, and plaster (most effective). (*Bolt, Beranek and Newman, Inc.*)

and 6 ft 8 in. high. Door hardware should also be carefully selected for initial cost, maintenance, and durability. Finish hardware includes lock and latch sets, hinges, push and pull plates, stops, and automatic closers. These items will probably attract more attention from management than many hidden structural parts of a building.

Windows are either openable or fixed. If openable, they may be sliding, casement, pivoted, or projected. Most windows are constructed of wood, steel, or aluminum. Fixed windows are set in wood or metal stops and occasionally in integral aluminum frames. All openings are provided with trims, which can be of milled wood, cold-formed steel, or extruded aluminum shapes.

Also important for every industrial plant are the toilet partitions, which are usually constructed of galvanized bonderized steel with baked enamel finish and supported from the floor, walls, or ceiling.

For toolrooms and part-storage rooms, wire-mesh partitions are common. They are usually made from 10-gage steel wire woven into 1½-in. diamond mesh and attached to frames of cold-rolled steel channels. These partitions are available in heights from 7 to 20 ft. Components include standard panels, sliding and swinging doors, and service windows.

Before making the final selection of any wall or partition, the plant engineer should review the following checklist:

1. The initial cost of the wall
2. Permanence
3. Maintenance cost
4. Appearance
5. Sound insulation
6. Sound absorption
7. Thermal insulation
8. Incombustibility
9. Fire resistance
10. Surface durability

MOVABLE PARTITIONS

Movable partitions are also known as "portable" and "dismountable" partitions. The main components of this type of wall are posts and the filler panels. The posts are made of wood, extruded aluminum, or cold-rolled steel and the filler panels of plywood, tongue and grooved wood, asbestos cement, tempered hardboard, gypsum board, steel, or glass. Movable walls are manufactured in standard heights ranging from 44 to 84 in. Normally they do not extend to the ceiling but provide only visual insulation and a small amount of sound insulation while not obstructing room lighting or the air-conditioning system. The panels of movable walls are sometimes insulated with a core made from fiber honeycomb, rigid rockwool, glass wool, or solid gypsum. The surfacing is finished with hardwood veneer, high-pressure laminates, low-pressure laminates, vinyl film, conversion coating, lacquer, or baked enamel paint.

The plant engineer should look for the following properties in a movable partition:

1. Strength
2. Easy erection
3. Flexibility, interchangeability, rearrangement
4. Durable finish; resistance to abrasion, scratches, and stains
5. Light and air transmission
6. Accessories, windows, counters, shelves, and utilities
7. Panel choice, clear or fluted glass

WALL TRIM AND GLAZED PANELS

In the design and construction of a wall or partition, equal care must be taken in the selection of the minor architectural components of the wall. The "baseboard," which is used to seal the wall to the floor, can be of preformed rubber, vinyl, or milled wood trim. For high-moisture areas, a raised concrete curb will serve as a good base. If the wall goes to the ceiling, there should be a "closure strip" sealing the joint between the wall and the ceiling surface. Glazing in the wall affords a wide range of glass to be selected. Glass may be clear plate glass or tinted to reduce glare, double plated for sound insulation, ribbed and pebbled to provide privacy, and reinforced with wire to provide safety. The glass could be ordinary window glass or plate glass. Care must be taken in selecting the best glass for the purpose with due regard to initial cost and replacement costs.

EXAMPLE

A newly installed grinder made to shred aluminum cans was installed adjacent to a bottling company's parking lot. This was to be a reclamation station for aluminum cans returned by the public.

The resulting noise from this machine was so excessive that the plant engineer was requested to determine the best method of reducing the grinding noise radiating toward the public area. He first made sound-intensity readings with a dB A meter to establish the existing noise

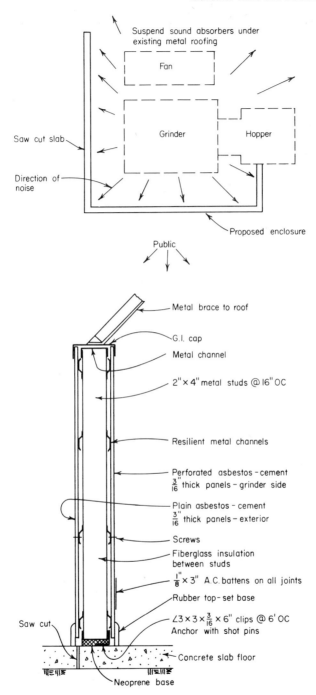

Suspend sound absorbers under existing metal roofing

Fan

Saw cut slab

Grinder

Hopper

Direction of noise

Proposed enclosure

Public

Metal brace to roof

G.I. cap

Metal channel

$2'' \times 4''$ metal studs @ 16" OC

Resilient metal channels

Perforated asbestos-cement $\frac{3}{16}''$ thick panels — grinder side

Plain asbestos-cement $\frac{3}{16}''$ thick panels — exterior

Screws

Fiberglass insulation between studs

$\frac{1}{8}'' \times 3''$ A.C. battens on all joints

Rubber top-set base

$\angle 3 \times 3 \times \frac{3}{16} \times 6''$ clips @ 6' OC Anchor with shot pins

Saw cut

Concrete slab floor

Neoprene base

Incombustible construction

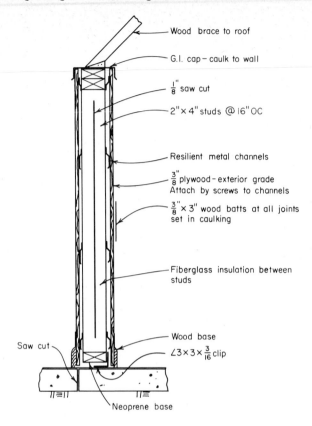

Wood brace to roof

G.I. cap-caulk to wall

$\frac{1}{8}''$ saw cut

2"× 4" studs @ 16" OC

Resilient metal channels

$\frac{3}{8}''$ plywood-exterior grade
Attach by screws to channels

$\frac{3}{8}'' \times 3''$ wood batts at all joints
set in caulking

Fiberglass insulation between studs

Wood base

$L3 \times 3 \times \frac{3}{16}$ clip

Saw cut

Neoprene base

Combustible construction

situation. His findings were as follows:

With grinder operating............................ 105–107 dB(A)
Without grinder operating (background sound)....... 72– 75

A preliminary solution was a three-sided enclosure and acoustical material suspended from the ceiling. Two types of wall construction were considered, one combustible and the other incombustible. In each type the plant engineer designed structural components to block the various ways that sound travels.

Noise from conduction through material was reduced by:

1. Saw cutting the concrete slab around the enclosure, thus isolating the slab from adjoining areas.
2. Isolating wall panels from the wall studs so that vibration could not pass through the wall.
3. Saw cutting through the center of each wood stud to improve isolation of one face of the wall from the other.

Noise conduction through air was reduced by:

1. Sealing all joints in wall panels
2. Sealing the joint of the wall at the floor

Noise by absorption was reduced by:

1. Placing fiber-glass insulation in the space between wall panels
2. Using perforated paneling on inside wall paneling
3. Suspending absorption panels from the ceiling

The resulting sound intensity was 15 to 20 dB lower.   The accompanying sketches illustrate these methods of sound insulation.

SUMMARY

Walls and partitions make a building out of a shell.   They provide privacy and thermal and sound insulation, keep out dust or keep in pollution, separate different types of plant operation, and provide beauty to interior spaces.

The plant engineer should clearly define the purpose of each wall and partition and select its material of construction accordingly.   Unlike the steel beam or concrete foundation, walls can be made on a wide range of materials and construction to serve each purpose.   For this reason costs vary widely.   To have a true comparison, each element must be judged with its alternatives on the basis of insulative value, fire resistance, water resistance, etc.

CHECKLIST FOR WALLS AND PARTITIONS

1. Purpose of wall
   a. Visual screen
   b. Soundproofing
   c. Thermal insulation
   d. Fire protection
   e. Dustproofing
   f. Acidproofing
2. Type of construction
   a. Incombustible
      (1) Steel
      (2) Aluminum
      (3) Concrete
      (4) Masonry
      (5) Tile
      (6) Glass
      (7) Asbestos cement
   b. Combustible
      (1) Wood
      (2) Masonite

3. Type of wall surface
   a. Gypsum plaster
   b. Cement plaster
   c. Gypsum board
   d. Asbestos-cement board
   e. Masonite
   f. Fiberboard
   g. Ceramic tile
   h. Composition board
4. Type of finish
   a. Paint
   b. Natural finish
   c. Acidproof
   d. Waterproof
5. Insulation
   a. Fiber glass
   b. Acoustic plaster
   c. Fiberboard
   d. Vermiculite
   e. Perlite
   f. Lead sheet
6. Types of accessories
   a. Baseboards
   b. Electric receptacles
   c. Wainscots
   d. Expansion joints
   e. Doors
   f. Windows
   g. Louver vents
   h. Flashing
   i. Closure strips
   j. Trim

BIBLIOGRAPHY

American Institute of Architects and Charles George Ramsey, and Harold Reeve Sleeper: *Architectural Graphic Standards,* 6th ed., John Wiley & Sons, Inc., New York, 1970.

Building Codes Bureau: *State Building Construction Code Applicable to One- and Two-family Dwelling Building Codes Bureau,* New York, 1964.

City of Los Angeles: *Building Code,* Building News, Inc., Los Angeles, 1970.

County of Los Angeles: *County of Los Angeles Uniform Building Laws,* Building News, Inc., Los Angeles, 1968.

County of Los Angeles Uniform Building Laws: *Building Code, Plumbing Code, Mechanical Code, County Electrical Code,* Building News, Inc., Los Angeles, 1968.

Editors of Plant Engineering: *Plant Engineering Practice,* F. W. Dodge Corporation, 1958.

Housing and Building Codes Bureau: *State Building Construction Code Applicable to General Building Construction,* New York, 1964.

———: *State Building Construction Code Applicable to Multiple Dwellings,* New York, 1964.

International Conference of Building Officials: *Uniform Building Code,* Pasadena, Calif., 1967.

———: *Uniform Building Code,* vol. 3, Los Angeles, 1961.

Knudsen, Vern O., and Cyril M. Harris: *Acoustical Designing in Architecture,* John Wiley & Sons, Inc., New York, 1965.

Glossary

AASHO: American Association of State Highway Officials.

Abstract of title: A summary of facts establishing evidence of title to a piece of property, including any records that may impair the title.

Accessory building: A detached subordinate building the use of which is customarily incidental to that of the main building or main use of the land although it is located on the same lot.

ACI: American Concrete Institute.

Acquisition: The process by which property is acquired.

Acre: (1) A unit of land containing 160 sq rods, 4,840 sq yd, or 43,560 sq ft.   (2) A tract of land about 208.71 ft square (208.71 is the approximate square root of 43,560).

Addition to a building: The result of any work that increases the volume of an existing building or replaces a demolished portion.

Admixture: Any material used in concrete other than water, aggregate, or portland cement.   Popular substances are calcium chloride, natural resins, sodium lauryl sulfate, aluminum powder, and calcium lignosulfonate.

Adobe: A sandy, calcinous clay occurring in the southwestern part of the United States and used to make sun-dried bricks.

Adverse possession: An unrecorded acquisition of property based on continued use and payment of taxes rather than direct purchase or easement.

A490 bolts: See A325 bolts.

Aggregate: The inert material mixed with portland cement and water to produce concrete. It includes sand, gravel, and crushed rock.

AIPE: American Institute of Plant Engineers.

AISC: American Institute of Steel Construction.

Alignment: The location of the centerline of a street, pipe, or railroad.

Alluvium: The fine, deep deposit of earth, sand, gravel, and other transported material which has been left by rivers, floods, or other sources on land not permanently submerged.

Alteration to a building: Work on a building or structure that does not result in any addition to it.

Aluminum: A white, malleable, very light metal that is almost noncorrodible.

Anchor bolt: Bolt used to fasten the baseplate of a column to the foundation; usually it has an L- or J-shaped hook.

Anchor-bolt plan: A drawing locating all the embedded anchor bolts that hold the steel frame to the foundation.

Angles: Structural-steel shapes consisting of two legs set at right angles to each other.

Approved plans: Plans approved and stamped by the department of building and safety.

Arc welding: A nonpressure (fusion) welding process in which the welding heat is obtained from an electric arc between the base metal and an electrode or between two electrodes.

Arch: A curved girder or truss which develops inclined reactions even under vertical loads.

AREA: American Railroad Engineering Association.

ASCE: American Society of Civil Engineers.

Asphalt: A solid or semisolid bitumen, either native or obtained by refining petroleum, which melts on the application of heat.

Asphalt primer: A coat of asphalt applied to a concrete deck or insulation board to seal the surface and provide a bond for built-up roofing.

Asphaltic concrete: A mixture of bitumen, sand, and gravel used for pavements.

Assembly room: A room appropriate for gatherings for such purposes as instruction, entertainment, dining, or awaiting transportation.

Assessment: A tax or specific sum charged on persons or property for the purpose of land improvement beneficial to the neighborhood.

A307 bolts: Often called unfinished machine, plain, common, or rough bolts, these are employed for shop and field connections where loading is not highly critical.

A325 bolts: High-strength structural bolts used in field connections where loads are highly critical.

Azimuth: The angular distance measured eastward from the north point of the horizon.

Backing strip: Material (metal, asbestos, or carbon) used for backing up the root of a weld.

Back sight (BS): In topographic surveying, a procedure in which the telescope of the instrument is aimed toward the previously sighted bench mark.

Balcony: Partial floor in an assembly room.

Ballast: Granular material below railroad tracks to hold the track in line and grade, provide drainage, and distribute the load uniformly to the subgrade.

Base flashing: Flashing at the junction of the roof plane and the interior surface of the parapet wall; usually built of overlapping layers of composition roofing sheets and metal sheet flashing.

Base lines: Imaginary east-west lines which intersect meridians to form a starting point for the measurement of land.

Basement: Any story below the first story of a building in which the surface of the floor above is less than 6 ft above the adjacent ground elevation at all points.

Base metal: The metal to be welded or cut.

Bat: Portion of a brick, usually a half or less, found in a bond pattern.

Bead weld: Weld made by one passage of an electrode or rod.

Beam: A horizontal load-carrying member usually framed between girders or columns.

Beams, roof: Structural members which support rafters or purlins.

Bearing-type connection bolt: A bolt in which the shank bears against the sides of the holes in the connected material.

Bearing wall: A wall which (1) supports more than 100 lb per foot of ceiling load, or (2) supports any other vertical load except its own weight, or (3) is self-supporting for more than 20 ft, or (4) is more than one story in height.

Bedrock: Relatively solid, undisturbed rock, either at the ground surface or beneath a surface deposit of gravel, sand, or soil.

Bench mark: (1) A durable marker used by surveyors. (2) A permanent mark placed at intervals along a survey line, noting differences in elevation.

Bill of material: A list usually found on the structural-steel shop-drawing sheet that tabulates the number of pieces, shape, description, length, and weight with remarks for every structural member detailed on that sheet.

Bitumen: A mixture of hydrocarbons such as asphalt that are more or less adhesive.

Bituminous: Containing or compounded with bitumen.

Blanket insulation: Flexible pads or rolls of insulation which have practically no structural strength and usually are stapled to the studs or rafters.

Blisters: Defects in roofing caused by vaporized moisture bubbles between layers of roofing sheets.   Expansion of these bubbles forms large blisters which weaken the sheets.

Block: A city section or square whether vacant or built upon.

Blown-on insulation: Loose insulation particles pneumatically applied to the space between joists.

Board insulation: Rigid insulation which has a relatively high density, strength, and weight and can support its own weight between structural members.

Boards: Lumber less than 2 in. thick and 1 in. or more wide.   Boards less than 6 in. wide are classified as strips.

Boiler room: A room containing a steam boiler or water heater using fuel gas having a maximum gas input of 440,000 Btu/hr or using liquid fuel in any quantity.   Maximum fuel-gas input may be 880,000 Btu/hr provided the equipment is equipped with an approved low-water cutoff and is enclosed in an approved insulated cabinet.

Bonded roof: A high-quality roofing guaranteed watertight for a specified period of time.   This warranty is usually made by the manufacturer of the roofing materials and covers work done by an authorized roofing contractor.

Bonder: A header or other masonry unit overlapping and bearing upon two or more leaves, piers, or wythes.

Brick: A solid masonry unit made from clay or shale, dried or burned, and fired at about 185°F without special attention to color.

Brick grades: SW (severe weather) is brick used where high resistance to frost action is required.   MW (moderate weather) is brick intended for use in temperatures below freezing but unlikely to be permeated by water.   NW (no weather) is brick intended for use as backup or interior masonry.

British thermal unit (Btu): The quantity of heat required to raise the temperature of one pound of water one degree Fahrenheit at some specified temperature.

Building: Any structure having a roof supported by columns or walls, used for the housing, shelter, or enclosure of persons, animals, chattels, or property of any kind.

Building area: The ground area in square feet under the floor of the exterior walls of a building and bounded by their inside surfaces.   This includes the areas under projections from the building.

Building line: Commonly called the setback line, it is established by law to indicate the minimum distance from a street line that an owner may build his structure.

Built-up roofing: Roofing composed of layers of asphalt-saturated felt bonded together by asphalt mopping.

Butt weld: Also known as a groove weld, it is used to attach two adjacent plates in the same plane at their common edges. The butt weld is subdivided into the square, bevel, U, J, flare V, and flare bevel weld.

Camber: A predetermined concave curve set into a beam during fabrication to compensate for the sag that will occur from the dead and live loads of the beam.

Cant: Also known as cricket, it is a built-up plane adjacent to parapets to provide slope and direct water flow to roof drains.

Cantilever beam: A member with one end projecting beyond the point of support, free to move in a vertical plane under the influence of a vertical load placed between the free end and the support.

Cap sheet: Roofing felt, used as the top sheet, made of organic or asbestos fibers, saturated and coated on both sides with bituminous compound, and surfaced with mineral granules.

Carbon steels: ASTM A7: steel for bridges and buildings (discontinued 1967); ASTM A373: structural steel for welding (discontinued 1965); ASTM A36: structural steel.

Cast-in-place pile: In an excavation a concrete column cast in place without forms.

Cast iron: A saturated solution of carbon in iron, the amount of carbon varying from 1.7 to 4 percent.

Catch basins: Concrete vaults with sumps below the outlet pipe to retain debris and trash from the storm water.

Cesspool: A lined excavation in the ground which receives the discharge of a drainage system. It is designed to retain the organic matter and solids but permit the liquids to seep through the bottom and sides.

Chain of title: A chronological list of recorded documents relating to the ownership of some specific property.

Channel: Name given to the structural steel shape called the American standard channel. It has a profile similar to a square capital letter C. The new designation for a channel is C12 × 20.7 which replaces 12⌷20.7.

Chase: A continuous recess built into a wall to receive pipes.

Chezy formula: A basic hydraulic formula developed by Chezy for determining a flow of water, particularly in open channels. The formula is as follows:

$$V = cRS \qquad Q = AV \qquad Q = AcRS$$

where V is the velocity in ft/sec, Q is the flow in cu ft/sec, A is the cross-sectional area of water in sq ft, R is the hydraulic ratio or cross-sectional area/wetted perimeter, and S is the slope or inclination in ft/ft.

Chord: The structural member on the top or bottom of a truss, normally known as either a top chord or a bottom chord.

Civil engineering: The branch of engineering encompassing fixed works for irrigation, drainage, water power, water supply, railroads, highways, airfields, buildings, and bridges.

Clay: A fine-grained inorganic soil possessing sufficient cohesion (1) when dry to form hard lumps which cannot readily be pulverized under finger pressure and (2) when moist to be rolled into threads ⅛ in. in diameter and 3 in. long which will support their own weight when suspended.

Clip angle: Usually a short length of a steel angle used for connecting two steel members together.

Coal-tar pitch: A thick, black, viscous liquid used in roofing. It is formed during the distillation of coal.

Column: A major vertical compression member used as a post to support a vertical load.

Composition roofing: Roofing made from asphalt-saturated sheets or shingles.

Compression: The stress which tends to keep two adjoining planes of a body from being pushed together under the influence of two forces acting toward each other.

Compression steel: Reinforcing bars used to help concrete carry a portion of compressive forces.

Concrete batch plant: Central plant where ready-mixed concrete is prepared.

Construction joint: (1) A specially designed joint between two adjacent concrete slabs which is reinforced and keyed to prevent differential settlement. (2) A line where the first concrete pour is stopped and a succeeding pour is made.

Construction shed: A temporary building incidental to the construction of another building which is removed within 30 days after the completion of the construction.

Continuous beam: A beam having more than two points of support.

Contraction joint: A designed crack cast in a concrete slab to control cracking due to shrinkage or contraction stress during curing. The joint is made by marking the green concrete, placing a thin strip in the concrete, or saw cutting the concrete after it is cured.

Conveyance: (1) The act of conveying; transference; the means, instrument, or vehicle in which anything is conveyed. (2) The assignment of property by deed or otherwise; the instrument of such transfer, specifically a deed; the transfer of the title of land from one party to another.

Coping: (1) Capping at the top surface of a roof parapet usually applied to seal and drain the top surface. (2) The masonry or concrete units used for forming a cap or finish at the top of a wall, pier, or pilaster.

Corbel: (1) Shelf or ledge formed by projecting successive courses of masonry out from the face of a wall. (2) An offset in the vertical alignment of a masonry wall.

Couple: Two equal, parallel, and opposite forces. The perpendicular distance between the forces is the "arm" of the couple.

Course: One of the continuous horizontal layers of masonry bonded together to form a masonry structure.

Court: An unoccupied space on a lot bounded on three or more sides by a building.

Covenant: Agreement (contained in deeds and other documents) which restricts the use of property.

Creep: The deformation which increases with the length of time as the stress is maintained.

Crown of the road: The rise in the center of a paved roadway which directs the surface water toward the edges of the road.

Culvert: A drain or conduit for carrying surface water beneath a roadway.

Curb: The raised edge of a road; used to restrain traffic.

Cut sides or faces: The sides or faces of a building brick cut by the wires which divide the clay extruded from the brickmaking machine. The other surfaces of a brick are either smooth or textured.

Dedication: A setting aside (by the owner) of land for public use.

Deformation: The amount of change in the shape of a body caused by the action of an internal force.

Deformed bars: Reinforcing steel bars used to develop tensile strength of concrete; their surface is irregular to improve bonding to the concrete.

Differential settlement: A condition in which a foundation does not settle equally, causing distortion in the superstructure and leading to failure, cracking, and misalignment of machinery.

Downspout: A metal conductor connected to a roof drain. It is usually made from galvanized sheet metal on the exterior of a building and galvanized steel pipe on the interior of a building.

Drainage structures: Structures including catch basins, channels, pipelines, and culverts to direct storm waters.

Dry rot: Deterioration of wood caused by its fermentation and chemical breakdown when attacked by a fungus.

Dry standpipe: A pipe with a fire department connection on the exterior of a building.

Durability: The ability of a material to continue to function properly, resisting destruction from all causes during the life of the structure in which it is used.

Dwelling: Any residential building other than an apartment house, hotel, or apartment hotel.

Easement: The right, privilege, or interest that one party has in the property of another. Easements are granted to companies and individuals. They are heritable and remain in effect after the grantor sells his property.

Efflorescence: A white deposit on the surface of a masonry wall caused by the crystallization of soluble salts brought to the surface by moisture in the masonry.

Elastic action: An action said to occur when a strain which accompanied a stress vanishes upon the removal of that stress. (Plastic or inelastic action occurs if there is a residual strain after the stress has been removed.)

Elastomeric roofing: An elastic rubberlike substance produced synthetically and used for roofing; it can be made of urethane or polyvinyl chloride.

Encroachment: (1) The illegal diminution of another's possessions; taking more than one's right or due. (2) Building on someone else's land.

Encumbrance: A lien on the land.

Endurance limit: The maximum reverse unit stress to which a material can be subjected many times without failing.

Engineer's chain: A measuring device containing 100 links, each link 1 ft long. Gunter's chain, formerly used for land surveys, is 66 ft long and also contains 100 links.

Equivalent fluid pressure: The horizontal pressure of soil upon the vertical surface of a retaining wall, usually assumed to be 30 lb/sq ft per foot of depth.

Erection plan: A drawing showing all separate pieces of a structure, including subassembly pieces, with assigned shipping or erection numbers in their correct position in the finished framework. Commonly, the design framing plans and elevations are used as the basis of the erection plans.

Erosion: The gradual wearing away of the soil by wind, rain, or tides.

Excavation: (1) Any act by which earth, sand, gravel, rock, or any other similar material is cut into, dug, quarried, uncovered, removed, displaced, relocated, or bulldozed. (2) The conditions resulting from such an act.

Exit: A passageway from a portion of a building to the exterior ground surface including every intervening doorway, passageway, stairway, or ramp.

Exit court: A yard, court, or inner court providing access to a public way for one or more required exits.

Expansion joint: Designed and constructed joint in concrete work to allow horizontal but not vertical movement of a slab or beam. This type of joint usually includes steel bars or interlocking keys to maintain the plane of the slab.

Expansion soil: A fine-grained cohesive soil undergoing large volume changes with changes in moisture content.   When dry, the soil cracks into wide, deep blocks.   The laboratory criterion for expansive soil is that a laterally confined undisturbed sample of soil or a sample compacted to 90 percent of the maximum density expand at least 5 percent from air dry at 100°F to saturation while under a normal load equivalent to 400 lb/sq ft.

Export: Surplus earth to be carried away from a road-construction job or similar major earthwork project.

Exterior wall: A wall located on the perimeter of the area under the roof of a building.   Open spaces under the perimeter of the roof are presumed to be openings in the exterior wall of the building.

Facing: A structural material applied to, and bonded with, a wall of a different material.

Factor of safety: The number of times by which the ultimate stress must be divided to be equal to the working stress.

Factory and shop lumber: Lumber that is produced or selected primarily for remanufacturing purposes.

Faying surface: That surface of the base metal which comes in contact with another part of the base metal to which it is fastened.

Felt, asphalt: Roofing felt made from organic, asbestos, or glass fibers and saturated with a bituminous compound.

Fiber-glass insulation: Boards, batts, or blankets of fiber glass of various densities.   Some are covered with kraft paper or foil.

Field-bolted connection: A connection in which the final bolting is done on the site.

Fill: (1) Any act by which earth, sand, gravel, rock, or similar material is deposited, placed, pushed, pulled, or transported to a place other than that from which it was excavated.   (2) The conditions resulting from such movement.

Filler metal: Material to be added in making a weld.

Fine sand: Sand consisting chiefly of grain sufficiently large to be retained upon a 270-mesh sieve but passing through a 60-mesh sieve.

Fire-resistive wall: One which will resist combustion for a definite length of time when exposed to a standard high temperature.

Flame cutting or gas cutting: A method of cutting steel that uses an excess of oxygen with acetylene gas.   The gases are fed through a blowpipe and ignited at the tip.   The heated steel burns in the presence of oxygen, and a narrow gash in the steel is produced.

Flood hazard: Overflow water having sufficient velocity to transport or deposit debris, scour the surface soil, dislodge or damage buildings, and/or erode the banks of watercourses.

Floodplain: A relatively flat area or lowland adjoining the channel of a river, stream, watercourse, ocean, lake, or other body of standing water which has been or may be covered by flood water.

Floor: Any structure which divides a building horizontally. This includes the horizontal members, floor coverings, and ceiling.

Floor area: The area in square feet within the exterior walls of a building, excluding the area of inner courts, shaft enclosures, or exterior walls.

Fly sheet: A lightweight asphalt sheet nailed to a roof deck to serve as a waterproof membrane and base for built-up roofing.

Footing: That portion of a structure which rests upon the foundation. Piles, caissons, and piers are considered a portion of a footing.

Foresight (FS): In topographical surveying, a sighting taken in the forward direction at the leveling rod set upon a new point.

Foundation: (1) The ground upon which a structure is supported. (2) The lowest part of a structure, designed to distribute the weight of the structure and superimposed loads onto the soil.

Foundation settlement, permissible: The amount of differential settlement of a foundation which will not have detrimental effect on a building or structure.

Fracture: A sudden separation of the material with complete destruction of cohesion. It may occur suddenly without warning if the material is brittle or more slowly after a large amount of inelastic deformation in ductile materials.

Frequent storm: A storm which can occur at intervals of 10 years or less when averaged over a long period of time. As an example, over a 100-year period, a "frequent" storm may be expected to occur at least 10 times. Several of these storms may occur in a single decade, or there may be no such occurrence for a period of time much greater than 10 years.

Friction-type bolt: A bolt which clamps the connected parts together with an extremely high pressure so that the shearing force is resisted by the friction between the connected parts. This is one type of high-strength bolt.

Frost line: The depth at which groundwater freezes. This freezing can damage foundations and pipelines.

FS: See foresight.

Gage: In railroad design, the distance between the inside heads of rails, measured $\frac{5}{8}$ in. below the top of the rail. Standard gage is 4 ft $8\frac{1}{2}$ in.

Gas-metal arc welding: This method is similar to the submerged arc welding except that a stream of inert gas shields the arc.

Gas service: A pipe conveying gas to a building from the distribution system of a public service corporation.

General plan restrictions: Restrictions on the use of property, usually a tract, imposed for the benefit of adjacent parcels of property.

Girder: A major horizontal member used to carry a series of beams or a large load.

Glass, annealed: Glass that is subjected to a slow cooling process under factory-controlled conditions to relieve internal stresses.

Glass, tempered: Glass that is subjected to a rapid air-cooling process under factory-controlled conditions to increase its strength and control the pattern of breakage.

Glass, wired: A single sheet of glass made with a layer of wire mesh completely embedded in it.

Glued/laminated lumber: Lumber composed of an assembly of wood laminations bonded with adhesive in which the laminations are too thick to be classified as veneers.

Grade: (1) The slope or pitch of a street, pipeline, railroad, or channel with reference to the horizontal plane.   (2) The top surface of soil, paving, or concrete slab.

Grade stress: A lumber grade defined in such terms that a definite working stress may be assigned to it.

Grades of lumber: The classification of lumber according to its strength and utility as specified by the West Coast Lumbermen's Association.

Grading: All excavations, embankments, ditching, and diversion of roads and streams; usually classified as solid-rock, loose-rock, and common excavation.

Grain: Fibers in wood and their direction, size, and arrangement in appearance and quality.

Gravel: An uncemented mixture of mineral grains ¼ in. or more in diameter.

Gravel stop: Galvanized sheet-metal edging installed to keep roof gravel from being blown or washed off the edge of the roof.

Gravel-surfaced roof: Roofing on top of which gravel is applied to serve as a wearing surface and insulation against sun-ray damage of the roofing.

Groundwater: Subsurface water in a zone of saturation.

Grout: Mortar to which sufficient water is added to give a pouring consistency without segregating the constituents.

Gumbo: A dark-colored, very sticky, highly plastic clay occurring abundantly in the central and southern parts of the United States.

Gusset: A piece of plate steel used for connecting two structural-steel members.

Gutter: (1) Channel or passage for water at the side of a road or a street. (2) Horizontal metal conductor used to collect rainfall from the roof and drain it to a downspout.

Gypsum deck: Precast or cast-in-place roof deck made from gypsum cement. Precast gypsum planks are supported on steel subpurlins. Joints between the planks are filled with gypsum mortar. Cast-in-place gypsum deck is constructed by pumping a gypsum slurry upon gypsum form boards supported by steel subpurlins.

Hardpan: (1) A very dense heterogeneous mass of clay, sand, and gravel of glacial drift origin. (2) The hard stratum of consolidated soil underlying the surface soil.

Hardwood: Lumber which has been manufactured from one of the broad-leafed deciduous trees. It is heavy and close-grained, as distinguished from wood of coniferous trees. Primary construction use is flooring.

Header: (1) A masonry unit laid lengthwise across a wall. (2) A wood or steel member over an opening.

Heat-treated constructal alloy steel: ASTM A514: High-yield-strength quenched and tempered alloy steel plates, suitable for welding.

Height of instrument (HI): In topographic surveying it indicates the elevation of the center of the telescope above the bench mark.

High-strength low-alloy steels: ASTM A242: high-strength low-alloy structural steel; ASTM A440: high-strength structural steel; ASTM A441: high-strength low-alloy structural manganese-vanadium steel; ASTM A572: high-strength low-alloy columbium-vanadium steels of structural quality.

Hollow-unit masonry: Masonry consisting wholly or in part of hollow units laid continuously in mortar or grout.

I beam: The common name given to the American standard beam. It is called the I beam because of its resemblance to the capital letter I. The old designation for this beam was 24I100. The new notation is S24 $\times$ 100.

Impact loads: Forces that require a structure or its components to absorb energy in a short interval of time.

Import material: Earth which must be carried into a road-construction job to make up a shortage of earth for fill.

Incombustible material: Any material having an ignition temperature higher than 1000°F.

Incombustible wall: A wall that will not ignite or burn when subjected to fire.

Industrial waste: Any liquid waste from a plant that is neither storm water nor human waste.

Inelastic action: See Creep; Fracture; Slip.

Infrequent storm: A storm which occurs at an average of once in more than 10 years.

Inlets: Openings in the curb or street surface for admitting storm water.

Inorganic loam: A mixture of sand and silt in nearly equal proportions with a small amount of clay.

Inorganic silt: A fine-grained inorganic soil consisting chiefly of grains passing a 270-mesh sieve. When dry, it forms lumps which can be pulverized by the fingers. When wet, it cannot be rolled into thin threads capable of supporting their own weight when suspended.

Intercepting ditches: Drainage channels built along slopes to prevent erosion of the surface of the slopes.

Intermittent weld: A weld whose continuity is broken by unwelded spaces.

Inundation: Ponded water or water in motion of sufficient depth to damage property due to the mere presence of water or deposition of silt.

Junior beams and junior channels: Lightweight steel shapes similar to the standard I beam and channels but fabricated with thinner webs and flanges; also called M shapes and miscellaneous channels. The old designation for these shapes was 8M18.5, 10JR9.0, 8 × 8M34.3, and 12JR10.6. The new designations for the same shapes are M8 × 18.5, M10 × 9, M8 × 34.3, and MC12 × 10.6.

Kiln-dried wood: Wood seasoned in a special chamber by artificial heat.

Knee brace: A diagonal member connected between a column and a lower chord of a truss to provide stiffening to the column.

Legal description: A description that locates a piece of property definitely by reference to government surveys or recorded maps.

Leveling rod: A narrow pole or board used by surveyors. It is graduated in feet and decimals of a foot and is used for determining elevations. It is usually highly visible with red and black markings on a white background.

License: A permit to use another's property; a license is not heritable and usually may be canceled on notice.

Lien: A claim upon property for the payment of a debt or obligation.

Light beams and miscellaneous shapes: Lightweight steel shapes similar in cross-sectional profile to the I-beam or the wide-flange shapes.

Lintel: A horizontal structural member placed over an opening in a wall to carry the superimposed weight above; sometimes called a header.

Loose gravel, loose sand, and loose silt: Deposits easily removable by hand shoveling.

Lot: A piece, parcel, portion, or division of land.

Lot line: A line dividing premises from each other or from a street or other public space.

Low-heat portland cement, type IV: A special cement for use where the rate of heat generated must be kept at a minimum. Used where very large masses of concrete are to be poured and the heat generated would be critical. This type of concrete is commonly used in dam construction.

Lumber: The product of the manufacture of logs into boards; divided into two main classes, softwood and hardwood.

Manning's formula: Published in 1890, it gives the value of c in the Chezy formula as $c = (1.486/n)R^{1/6}$. The complete formula is

$$V = (1.486/n)R^{2/3}S^{1/2} \qquad Q = A(1.486/n)R^{2/3}S^{1/2}$$

See Chezy formula for explanation of variables.

Manual shield-metal arc welding: Also referred to as manual, hand, or stick welding. An electric arc is produced between the coated metal electrode and the steel components to be welded. The arc heats the base metal and the electrode to the point where they melt together and form a molten pool on the surface of the work.

Masonry unit: Any brick, tile, or block.

Mechanic's lien: A lien in favor of laborers and materialmen who have contributed to the work of the land improvement. Architects and engineers can also be included when they provide services on the work.

Meridians: Imaginary north-south lines which intersect base lines to form a starting point for the measurement of land in land subdivision.

Metal-cased pile: Concrete pile in a driven metal casing.

Metes and bounds: A surveying procedure whereby the perimeter of a parcel of land is completely specified. The segments of the perimeter are taken in consecutive sequence and specified by length and direction. The surveying procedure is checked by the geometric principle that the interior angles of an n-sided polygon total $(n-2)180°$.

Mezzanine floor: A partial floor within a room which has an area under one-third that of the main floor.

Mill-order steel: Steel usually purchased from the rolling mill from lists prepared by the order department of the fabricator; often required for large orders not normally stocked in warehouses.

Mixed occupancy: Occupancy of a building in part for one use and in part for another not accessory to the first.

Modified portland cement, type II: A cement having a lower heat of hydration than type I. It is also more resistant to sulfate attack.

Modulus of toughness: Maximum amount of energy which a unit volume of material will absorb without fracture.

Moment (or moment of a force): The product of the magnitude of a force and the perpendicular distance between the force and the point considered.

Moment of inertia I: A geometric property of the area of a structural shape which is an indication of its strength. The mathematical quantity is the sum of the products obtained by multiplying the area of each element of a surface by the square of its distance from a line. A moment of inertia is always given with respect to a particular line, i.e., at neutral axis or base of an area. $I = \int r^2 \, dA$.

Monuments: Objects or marks such as pipes, concrete posts, or nails set by surveyors and used to fix or establish a boundary.

Mortar: A mixture of portland cement, fine aggregate, and water.

Motor vehicle: A self-propelled vehicle powered by an internal-combustion engine.

Natural drainage course: A swale, wash, ditch, or gully that is well defined, unimproved, or partially improved.   With a natural watercourse there is no doubt where the water runs or the extent of the watershed.

Negative steel: Reinforcing used for negative tension or tension at the upper portion of a concrete beam.   When a beam is continuous over several supports, tension occurs at the top of the beam at the point of support.

Normal loading: A design load that stresses a member or a fastening to a full allowable stress.   This loading may be applied for approximately 10 years, continuously or cumulatively.

Normal portland cement, type I: General-purpose cement suitable for all uses where the special properties of other types of cement are not required.   It is used in pavement, sidewalk construction, bridges, reinforced-concrete buildings, railroad structures, tanks, reservoirs, and all installations not subject to special sulfate hazards or damaged by high heat of hydration.

Normal size: The commercial size designation in widths and depths of standard lumber.   This size is somewhat larger than the standard net-size stress lumber.

Occupancy: The purpose for which a building or portion of a building is used or intended to be used.

Overlap: Protrusion of weld material at the toe of a weld beyond the limits of fusion.   This is considered an imperfect weld.

Parkway: The space adjacent to a roadway between the curb and the right-of-way line.

Partition: An interior wall.

Partition, nonrated: Any partition (1) which is not higher than three-fourths of the ceiling height of the room in which it is located, or (2) which has one-fourth of its height in plane glass of openings, or (3) which is constructed entirely of combustible materials.

Partition, permanent: Any partition not classed as a temporary partition.

Peat: Highly organic humus and swamp soils, generally containing fibrous vegetable matter.

Pedestal: An upright compression member whose height does not exceed three times its least lateral dimension.

Penthouse: A shelter over any shaft or exit way passing through the roof.   It may include the area for equipment necessary to the operation of the building.

Perlite deck: A cast-in-place lightweight mineral roof deck made by casting perlite concrete on corrugated-steel forms.

Percent compaction: The dry density as determined in accordance with ASTM Designation D698, modified to use a 10-lb rammer falling free from an 18-in. height above the soil layer.

Photogrammetry: The science of measurement by photographs.

PI: See Point of intersection.

Pier: A vertical isolated structural compression member with a ratio of unsupported length to least width of 4 or more.

Pilaster: A portion of a wall which projects on one or both sides of a wall and acts as a vertical beam, column, or both.

Pile: A load-carrying column inserted into the soil to carry the weight of the structure; constructed of wood, steel, or concrete.

Pipe drains: Also called storm sewers, pipe drains are used for removing surface water and carrying it along a roadway when sufficient width of right-of-way is not available for suitable ditch construction. Pipe drains are constructed of vitrified-clay pipe, concrete pipes, corrugated-metal pipe, and asbestos-cement pipe.

Pitch pocket: An enclosure encircling a roof vent or other object penetrating a roof which is filled with pitch to make a watertight seal.

Plans and specifications: One or more drawings or documents indicating and describing the amount, arrangement, kind, and quality of the materials to be used for the construction of a building or structure.

Plat: A map or plan of a certain parcel of land prepared by a surveyor or civil engineer.

Plates and flat bars: Rectangular steel cross sections that come in many widths and thicknesses under 8 in.

Ply: A single layer of felt in a built-up roof.

Plywood: Built-up wood panels of laminated veneers.

Point of intersection (PI): The location where the centerlines meet in road and railroad surveying.

Portland cement: Cement made by crushing limestone and clay and then calcining this mixture in kilns to a temperature of 2700°F. The calcined product of the kiln is pulverized with gypsum to a powder.

Positive reinforcement: Reinforcing bars used in concrete construction to resist tensile stresses due to positive moment. The bending moment at midspan of a simply supported beam is a positive movement, with the lower portion of the beam in tension.

Precast concrete: Construction whereby concrete members are cast before being moved to their final position.

Premises: A lot, plot, or parcel of land including the buildings or structures.

Prescription: The right to use another's property (easement) by using the property openly and continuously, without permission or opposition, for a period of time as specified by the civil code. An example of this is found in existing power poles and lines over a portion of property. No previous permission was given by the owner for use of his land but because of the length of time that has passed, the power company now has the right to use that area.

Prestressed concrete: A method of concrete construction in which the steel reinforcement has been stretched, causing compressive forces in the concrete. This increases the carrying capacity of the beam.

Property line: A line separating parcels of real property having separate legal descriptions, not including a building line.

Public way: Any parcel of land more than 12 ft wide appropriated to the free passage of the general public.

Purlins: Wood or steel beams extending horizontally from truss to truss which carry the roof load to the trusses.

Quit-claim deed: Deed of release, an instrument by which all claims to an estate are relinquished to another without any covenant or warranty expressed or implied.

Radius of gyration r: The r given by $r = I/A$, where I is the moment of inertia and A the area of a surface.

Range: In land subdivision, a strip of land running in a north-south direction.

Reglet: A slot or recess in a parapet wall that anchors the top edge of the metal flashing. The slot is usually packed with lead wool.

Reinforced concrete: Concrete in which steel reinforcement other than that provided for shrinkage or temperature change is embedded in such a manner that the two materials act together to resist forces.

Reinforced grouted brick masonry: Masonry in which the continuous vertical joint is filled with grout and reinforcing steel. No masonry headers are used in this system.

Reinforced masonry: Masonry in which reinforcement is embedded in such a manner that the two materials act together to resist forces. Structural-steel shapes, bars, and rods, wire mesh, or expanded metal are embedded or encased in the masonry to increase its resistance to internal stresses.

Reinforcing steel: Deformed steel reinforcing bars used to develop tension or compressive strength in reinforced-concrete structures.

Resistance welding: Also called heat or fusion welding, it is effected by generating a resistance to electric current flow as the current passes from the work of the contact area where the weld is to be made. When the metal reaches a suitable temperature, pressure is applied, which causes the two components to unite in a joint area. This method is used mainly for light construction, such as open-web joists and light-gage material. The process is also known as spot, seam, projection, and flash welding.

Resurvey: A survey of an area already surveyed, usually for the purpose of restoring the original surveyor's monuments or verifying the original survey.

Retaining wall: Any wall resisting the lateral pressure of any retained liquid or granular material such as soil, ore, or similar material.

Right of eminent domain: The right which a government possesses to take the property of its subjects, at a fair evaluation, for necessary public use.

Right-of-way: A privilege which an individual or particular group of persons may have of going over another's ground, subject to certain conditions.

Roadway: That portion of a public way appropriated to vehicular traffic. It is the paved portion between curbs or shoulders.

Rock: Any consolidated or coherent and relatively hard naturally formed mass of mineral material.

Rolling mill: Machine in which steel billets are formed into plates and structural shapes by successive rolling, for use in steel structures.

Roof: The cover of any building including the structure necessary to carry the roof load to the upright supporting members. Exterior surfaces of roofs which slope more than 2 vertical to 1 horizontal are classed as exterior walls.

Roof slope: The pitch of the roof is measured in inches of rise per 12 in. of horizontal distance.

Roof structure: Any structure extending from and above the roof, including a shelter for the protection of equipment necessary only to the operation of the building but excluding a penthouse, roof sign, or space for the purpose of providing additional floor area.

Roof tape: An adhesive tape used to seal joints between insulation boards, prevent asphalt mopping from leaking into the building, and provide a continuous insulation.

Root of a weld: The most remote point of the gap to be filled with weld material.

Sand: An uncemented mixture of mineral grains less than ¼ in. in diameter and retained on a 270-mesh sieve.

Sapwood: The outer layers of growth on trees, exclusive of bark, which contain the living elements; usually lighter in color than heartwood.

Scupper: An opening in a parapet wall above each low point of the roof, used to provide drainage should the roof drain become plugged.

Section: A portion of land equal to $\frac{1}{36}$ township, containing 640 acres and measuring 1 mile square.

Section modulus: A measure of the resisting moment or strength of a beam of a given cross section. It is largely used as a basis of computation in the design and investigation of beams. $S = I/C$, where I is the moment of inertia of the cross-sectional area about its neutral axis and c is the maximum distance from the neutral axis to its outer fiber.

Separation wall: Any wall forming a separation between occupancies in a building. It normally requires a special fire-resistive rating.

Shear: The stress which tends to keep two adjoining planes of a body from sliding on each other under the influence of two equal and parallel forces acting in opposite directions.

Sheet overflow: An overflow of water of minor depth either quiescent or flowing at velocities less than those necessary to produce serious scour. This type of flow is considered a nuisance rather than a menace to property.

Shipping or erection mark: A system of marking various fabricated structural-steel pieces which identifies the type of member and its location on the detail sheets.

Shipping piece: A steel beam or column with its connection attachment or a complete assembly of members, such as a truss or cross frame.

Shop-bolted connection: A connection with the bolting completed in the fabricating shop.

Simple beam: A horizontal member simply supported at the ends so that all parts have free movement in a vertical plane under the influence of vertical loads.

Site: A parcel of land upon which one or more buildings are proposed or erected.

Skylight: A glazed structure over or within an opening through a roof, used to admit light or to provide ventilation to the interior of the building.

Slip: An inelastic action which proceeds a fracture when the deformation of the material under constant stress is independent of the length of time.

Soft clay: A clay which when freshly sampled can readily be molded by light finger pressure.

Softwood: Lumber manufactured from a group of trees which have a needle-like or scalelike leaf. The term has no specific reference to the softness of the wood. Softwood lumber is divided into three classes, yard lumber, structural lumber, and shop lumber.

Soil: All the relatively loose incoherent earth material of whatever origin which overlies the bedrock.

Soil bearing pressure, allowable: The maximum unit load which can be placed on the soil without causing excessive deformation, shear, rupture, or consolidation of the soil.

Solid masonry: Masonry consisting wholly of solid masonry units laid continuously in mortar or grout and without steel reinforcement or voids.

Spandrel wall: That part of a multistory building wall above the top of a window of one story and below the sill of the window in the story above. This band constitutes an important horizontal structural member of the building.

Spot mopping: Spaced quantities of asphalt applied to the roof deck for the purpose of bonding the insulation boards to the roof deck.

Stadia rod or board: A highly visible calibrated board used in topographic surveying. By reading the interval on the rod between the horizontal cross hairs in the telescope, the distance between the instrument and the rod can be determined.

Static loads: Forces which are applied slowly and then remain nearly constant.

This term usually refers to forces that affect the roof structure such as equipment and roofing materials.

Steel: (1) Iron produced by fusion in the electric-furnace process, the crucible process, the Bessemer process, or the open-hearth process.   (2) Chemically, a compound of iron and carbon, generally intermediate in composition between cast and wrought iron but having a higher specific gravity than either.   See also Carbon steels; High-strength low-alloy steels; Heat-treated constructional alloy steel.

Stiff clay, stiff silt: A clay or silt which can be removed by picking or hand shoveling but which is difficult to mold by light finger pressure.

Stiffener: A piece of steel plate solidly welded to the web and flange of a beam to stiffen both against buckling.

Stock steel: Steel that is usually stored at the fabricator's plant or warehouse.

Story: A portion of a building which is between the first floor level and the next higher floor level or roof.   If a mezzanine floor area exceeds one-third of the area of the floor immediately below, it is deemed a story.   A basement is classified as a story when its ceiling is 6 ft or more above the finished grade.   An attic is not deemed a story if it is unfinished and without human occupancy.

Street line: Line dividing a lot, plot, or parcel from the street.   The street line is the line which divides the premises from the street regardless of any required setback.   When a building is built to the street line, the building line and street line may coincide.

Stress: The internal force which when a body is subjected for external forces tends to hold the molecules in their original relationship and preserve the integrity of the body.

Stress-grade timber: Pieces of lumber segregated into groups having assured minimum strength.   They may be assigned working-stress values for structural design such as select structural construction, standard, utility, and industrial grades.

Stress-strain diagram: Chart in which unit stresses and the corresponding unit strains are plotted.

Stretcher: A masonry unit laid with its length horizontal to, and parallel with, the face of the wall or other masonry member.

Structural lumber: Lumber which is more than 2 in. thick used where working stresses are required.

Structural T: Shapes made by splitting standard I beams, wide-flange shapes, light beams, and others, by gas cutting at the center of their web.

Subdivision: Improved or unimproved land divided or proposed to be divided into five or more parcels.

Submerged arc welding: Similar to the manual shield arc welding.   A bare-wire electrode is used instead of a coated-wire electrode.   The flux is supplied separately in a granular form. Loose flux is placed over the joint to be welded, and the electrode wire is pushed through the flux. As the arc is established, part of the flux melts to form a slag shield which coats the molten metal.

Subpurlin: Secondary structural-steel member framing between roof purlins; usually used to support insulation board.

Subsoil: The bed or stratum of earth lying below the surface of the soil.

Sulfate-resistant portland cement, type V: A special cement intended for use only in structures exposed to severe sulfate action, as in a chemical plant exposed to seawater.

Sump: A low-lying area having an inadequate outlet or no outlet at all.

Surfaced lumber: Lumber dressed by running through a planer.

Surfacing, roof: Gravel or crushed-slag surfacing applied to protect the built-up roofing from radiant heat and to provide a durable wearing surface.

Surveyor's authority: The surveyor has no judicial authority. Landowners can accept or reject the surveyor's monuments, but only a court of law can decide whether the property survey is binding and truly represents the legal description of the land.

Talbot formula: An empirical formula for determining the required culvert area based on a large number of observations in the Middle West. Maximum rainfall is assumed to be 4 in./hr with a velocity of flow under 10 ft/sec.

$$A = C \sqrt[4]{M^3}$$

where A is the required waterway in sq ft, M is the area drained in acres, and C is a coefficient that, depending upon the contour of the land drained, varies from 1 for steep rocky slopes to 1/5 for level districts.

Temperature steel: Reinforced steel used to prevent cracking due to thermal expansion and contraction in a concrete structure. Welded wire mesh used in slabs is a common example.

Tension: The stress which tends to keep two adjoining planes of a body from being pulled apart under the influence of two forces acting away from each other.

Terra cotta: A burned-clay produce made in the same way as brick, which may be dense, semiporous, or porous.

Tier: Each vertical 4-in. or single-unit section or thickness of masonry; called a withe or wythe.

Tilt-up concrete construction: Method of concrete construction whereby precast concrete walls are lifted or tilted up from the floor to their final wall position.

Timbers: Lumber 5 in. or more in the least dimension and all lumber classified as beams, stringers, posts, caps, sills, girders, and purlins.

Title: (1) A claim or right. (2) In law, property or right of ownership or the sources of such right, or the facts and events which are evidence of a right. (3) The evidence that a party is the legal owner of a certain land; the instrument that proves such ownership.

Title insurance: Insurance written by a title company to protect the property owner against loss if there is a flaw in the title.

Topography: Description of the condition of the surface of the land. Land can be classified as level, rolling, or mountainous.

Toughness: The capacity of the material for resisting fracture under dynamic loading.

Township: A unit of land division 6 miles square with an area of 36 sq miles. It is bounded by range line (east and west) and contains 23,040 acres.

Tract: A region or quantity of land of definite extent which has been surveyed, monumented, and recorded.

Transit: An instrument used by surveyors for measuring horizontal and vertical angles, consisting of a telescope, a compass, and graduated horizontal and vertical scales; also known as a theodolite.

Truss: A primary structural framework used to span great distances between walls or columns. It consists of an assemblage of bars or members which form a structure.

Turnout: A railroad track arrangement of a switch and frog with closure rails, by means of which rolling stock can be diverted from one track to another.

Ultimate strength: The maximum unit stress which a material can develop before fracture occurs.

Uniform Building Code (UBC): A building code recognized as law by many communities in the United States.

Underpinning: Footing introduced beneath an existing footing to provide additional support to the foundation.

Unit stress: The measurement of intensity of stress over a square inch or square foot.

Vapor barrier: A membrane or coating used to prevent passage of moisture into a building; usually used in conjunction with roof and wall insulation.

Veneer: Exposed masonry attached to a backing but not structurally bonded to the backing to sustain loads.

Vernier: A device for determining the subdivision of the smallest division of a scale more accurately than can be done by simply estimating by the fractional part. The transit has such a device.

Vitrifying: Fusing all the grains and closing the pores in clay products by the high temperature in the kiln. When products become vitrified, they are impervious to liquid.

Warehouse steel: Steel that is purchased from an established warehouse or steel service center, usually at a premium price.

Water/cement ratio: The ratio of gallons of water per sack of cement in a concrete mix. The normal ratio is between 4 and 8, with maximum strength at 4.

Water table: The depth below the ground surface at which natural water is found.

Web members: The diagonal and vertical members which constitute the framing between a top and bottom chord of a truss.

Web reinforcement: The steel reinforcing in a concrete beam so placed that it is resistant to shear.

Wide-flange shapes: A term used for both beams and columns but often covering the H, B, and CB shapes, depending upon the producer. The flange is wider than in the I beam.

Workability: The ease with which a material can be converted into useful shapes for structures.

Working stress: The unit stress which experiment has shown to be safe in that material while maintaining a proper degree of security against structural failure.

Wrought iron: A product of the reverberatory furnace, composed principally of ferrite (pure iron) and slag (iron silicate).

Wythe: A tier.

Yard lumber: Lumber of grades, sizes, and patterns generally intended for ordinary construction and general building purposes.

Yield point: The unit stress less than the ultimate stress at which a specimen of material first exhibits an appreciable increase of strain with no increase in stress.

Yield strength: The unit stress at which a material exhibits a specified limiting deformation.

Zoning: Governmental classification that regulates and restricts property use.

Index